MATEI
FOR ENG

by the same author

Introduction to Jig and Tool Design

Workshop Technology for Technicians

MATERIALS FOR ENGINEERS

M. H. A. KEMPSTER

C ENG, M I MECH E, A F R AE S, M I PROD E

Senior Lecturer in Production Technology
Rolls-Royce Technical College
Bristol

HODDER AND STOUGHTON

LONDON SYDNEY AUCKLAND TORONTO

ISBN 0 340 19077 9

First printed 1964
Second edition 1965
Third edition 1975
Reprinted (with revisions) 1976, 1979, 1981, 1984

PRINTED AND BOUND IN GREAT BRITAIN
FOR HODDER AND STOUGHTON EDUCATIONAL,
A DIVISION OF HODDER AND STOUGHTON LTD, BY
BIDDLES LTD, GUILDFORD AND KING'S LYNN

PREFACE

THE engineer, whether he is engaged in research, design or manufacture, cannot hope to perform his duties effectively unless he has a sound understanding of both the service properties and the manufacturing properties of engineering materials, and the problems that have been solved, and are being solved by materials scientists.

This book, written by an engineer for engineers, includes sufficient metallurgical detail to enable the reader to appreciate the principles involved. By the selection of suitable sections by the lecturer, it can be used by the student when studying the materials topic areas in the Workshop Processes until at level I, and in the Manufacturing Technology units at levels II and III of the engineering technicians certificate programme. It is anticipated that it will also be used as a reference book at levels IV and V, and in the reader's daily work.

In an early chapter, the basic types of thermal-equilibrium diagram are described in some detail, and where necessary, the appropriate diagram is included in the chapters that follow. Although materials can be studied without the use of these diagrams, the author believes that the effort needed to understand them will be well rewarded because they make the subject easier to follow, and as a result, much more interesting.

The author wishes to thank his colleagues at the Rolls-Royce Technical Colleges and at other colleges, for their advice and encouragement, and in particular, his wife who continually assists him in his work.

M. H. A. KEMPSTER
1979

CONTENTS

CHAPTER 1

INTRODUCTION

The Selection of Material

1.10 Several requirements must always be studied when selecting the material from which to make a particular component, and the final choice usually involves a compromise. These requirements can be broadly classified as:

(*a*) service requirements
(*b*) fabrication requirements
(*c*) economic requirements.

1.11 SERVICE REQUIREMENTS

In order that a component be successful in service, it must be of suitable strength, hardness, toughness, elasticity, rigidity, etc., and it must be of a suitable weight. In addition to these basic requirements, certain other properties may also be required, such as suitable electrical, magnetic or thermal properties, heat resistance, and creep or fatigue resistance. Corrosion resistance must usually be as high as possible; alternatively, the material must respond to corrosion resistance treatment.

Even at this stage a compromise is almost always necessary, such as a suitable strength/weight ratio, an acceptable life at high temperature, or an acceptable degree of corrosion resistance.

Commercially pure metals have extreme properties; for example, excellent corrosion resistance, but with low strength. It is usual to alloy metals to obtain a suitable compromise between the properties associated with the metals before alloying, or to produce other properties.

The hardness, strength, and ductility of some metals and alloys can be modified as a result of fabrication and the component must be designed to suit the manipulation method to be used, and to give the directional properties that are required (see page 33, section 4.3).

Some alloys will respond to heat treatment so that their strength and hardness can be improved after the manipulation, and it is important that the component be designed to avoid distortion or cracking as a result of this heat treatment.

1.12 FABRICATION REQUIREMENTS

It is convenient to classify materials as (*a*) casting materials, and (*b*) wrought materials. Casting involves heating the material to make it molten and then pouring it into a mould so that it assumes the shape of the impression and retains that shape upon solidification. Wrought materials are suitable for working; working involves the manipulation of the material when it is in the solid state. Casting and working are briefly described in Chapter 4.

Few materials are equally suitable for both casting and working, and very few materials are equally amenable to all variations of casting or working. It is necessary to consider the duty and the shape of the component, and the quantity required and then to select a material with the required properties and which will be suitable for the fabrication method to be used; the component must then be designed to suit the method selected.

The ease with which a material can be machined, and the quality of the finish so obtained is usually very important, as is the suitability of the material for joining by welding, brazing, or soldering. As already stated, the properties of some alloys can be altered by heat treatment, but in some cases this treatment is involved and lengthy, and may thus make such materials unsuitable.

1.13 ECONOMIC REQUIREMENTS

Except in certain military, research, and similar applications, economical considerations are important. These economic considerations should take into account the total cost of the component, which must include the cost of the raw material, and the cost of its manipulation, machining, joining, and finishing; the overall costs of a number of materials should be compared, and the use of an expensive material must be justified. The availability of a material will influence its cost, and will in addition affect the delivery date of the components that are made from it; it must be appreciated that the completion date of the product is in itself an economic problem. A material is not necessarily inexpensive because its ore is plentiful; the material cost is often associated with the complexity of the method that must be used to extract it from its ore, or to prepare it for use.

1.20 The Materials that are Available to the Engineer (see fig. 1.2)

Engineering materials can be classified as (*a*) metallic materials, and (*b*) non-metallic materials.

Although metallic materials are the main ones used in engineering, the non-metallic materials, which include the plastics, rubber, and wood, are of special importance.

The metallic materials are sub-divided into two groups; these are the ferrous alloys, and the non-ferrous metals and alloys. The ferrous alloys contain iron and carbon, to which may be added other elements to confer special properties. The non-ferrous metals are all metals other than iron and its alloys, but the non-ferrous alloys may include small amounts of iron.

Figures 1.3, 1.4, and 1.5 indicate the occurrence, melting point, and strength/weight ratio of some representative metals.

1.30 The Study of Engineering Materials

As an introduction to materials, the principle of extraction, alloying, manipulation, and heat treatment will first be considered; the testing of materials and materials specifications will then be described, and finally the characteristics and treatment of some of the more important engineering materials will be considered in some detail.

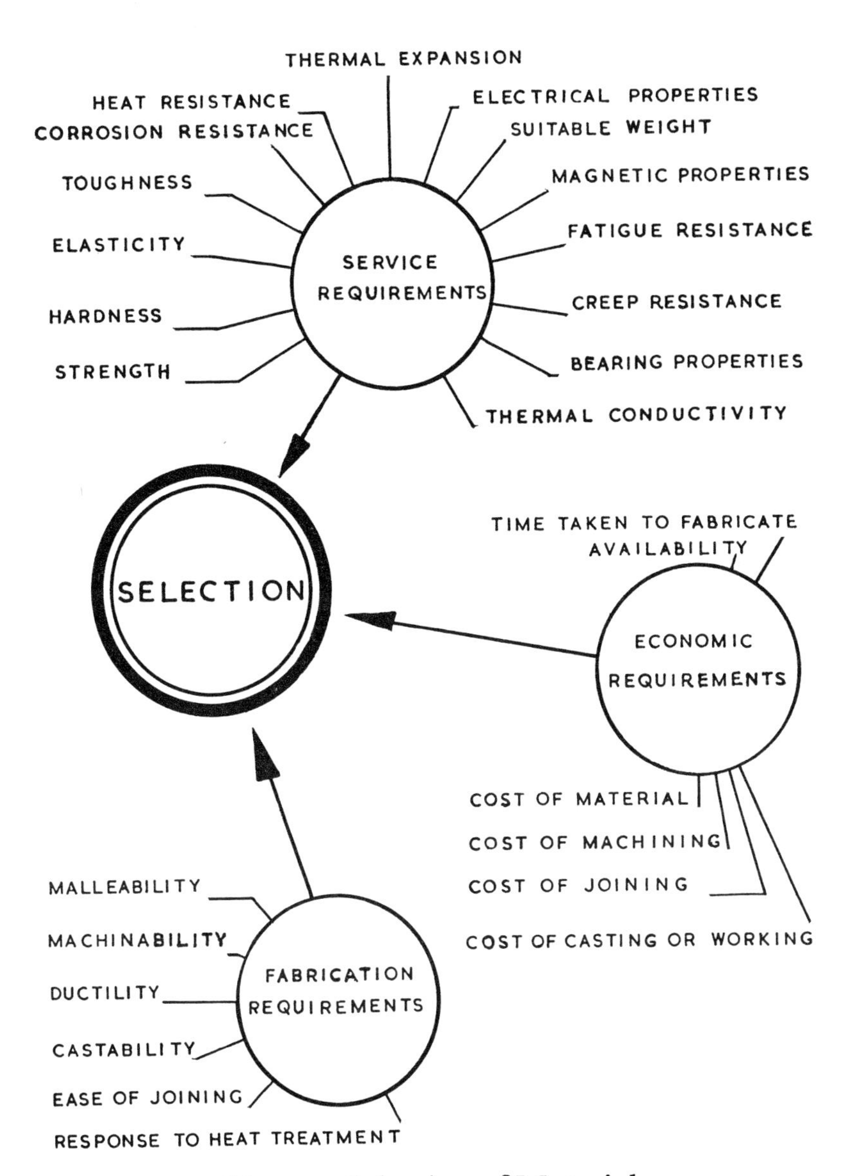

Fig. 1.1 Selection of Material

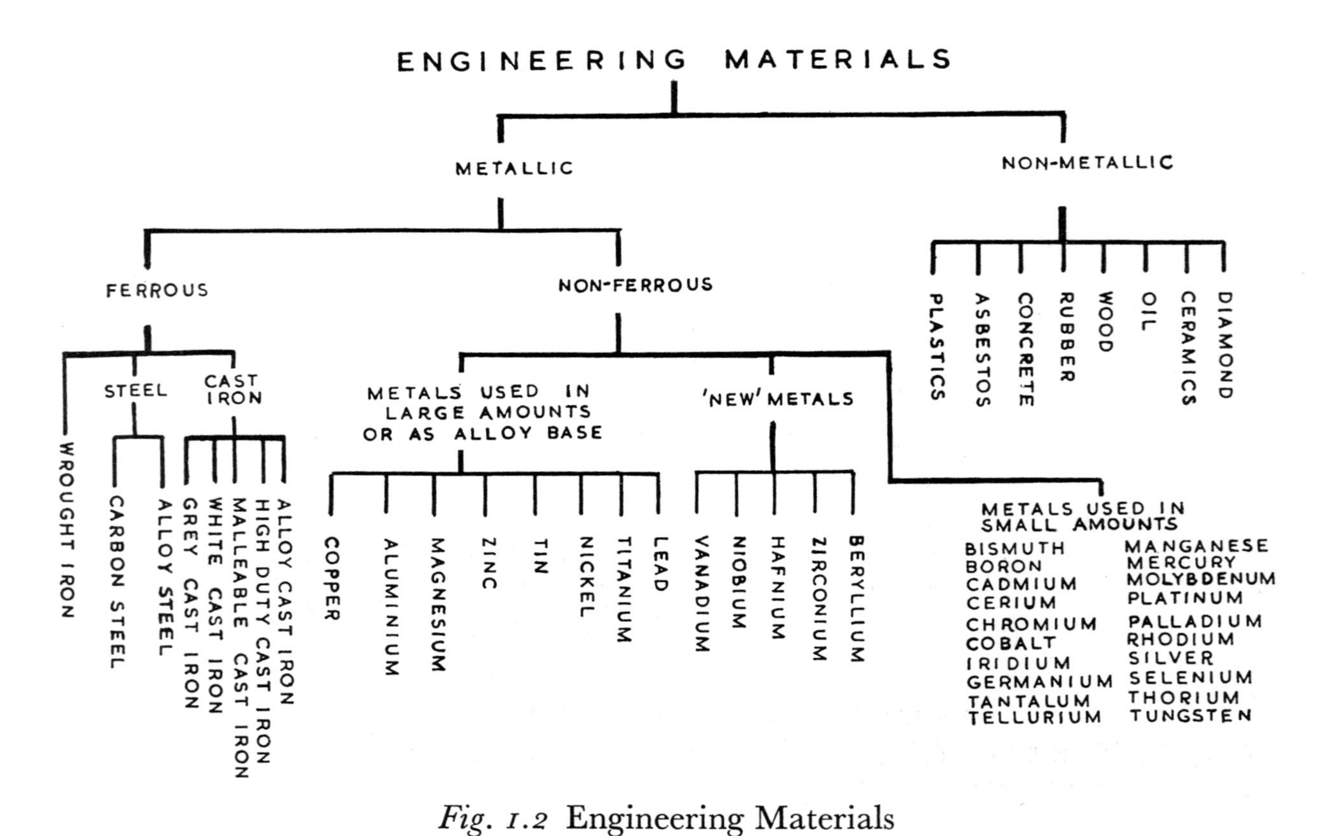

Fig. 1.2 Engineering Materials

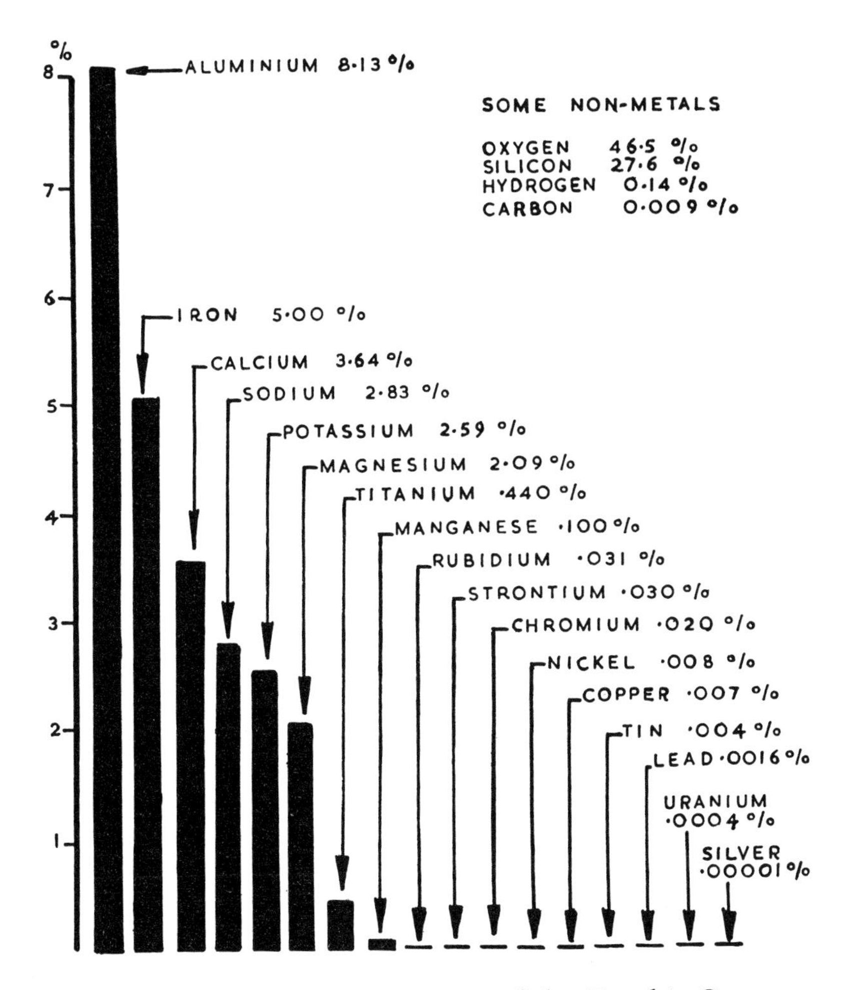

Fig. 1.3 Metallic Constituents of the Earth's Crust (Weight %)

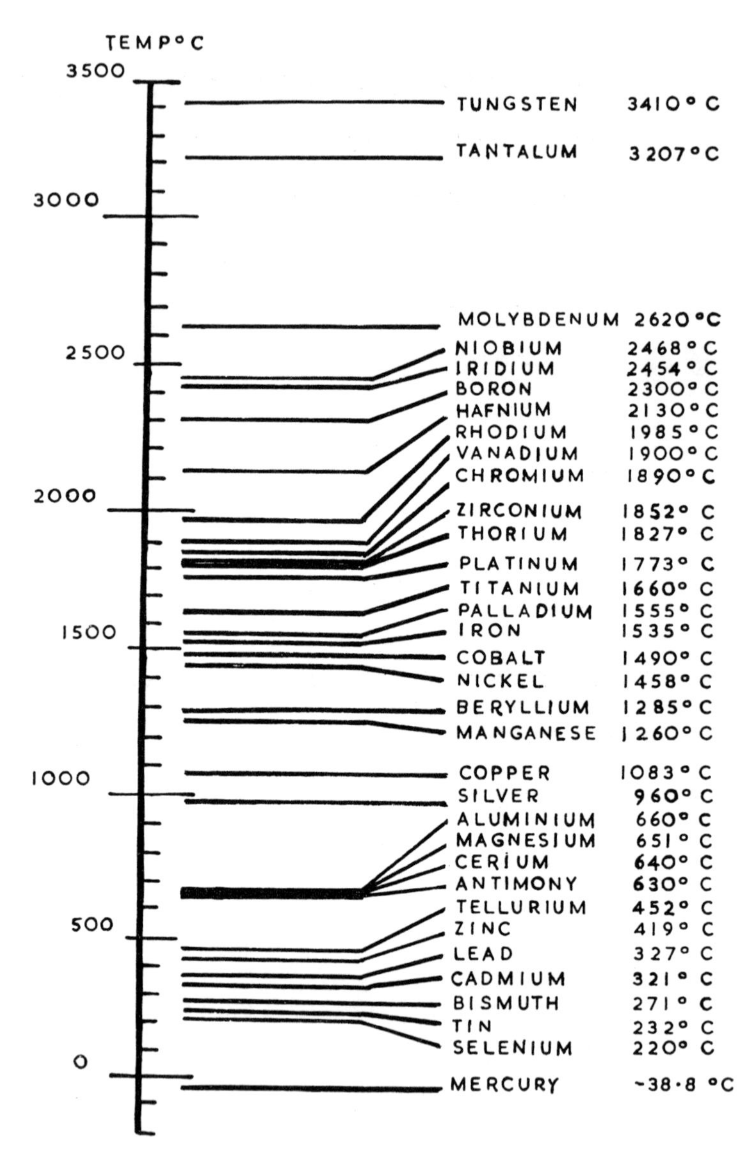

Fig. 1.4 Melting Point of Some Metals

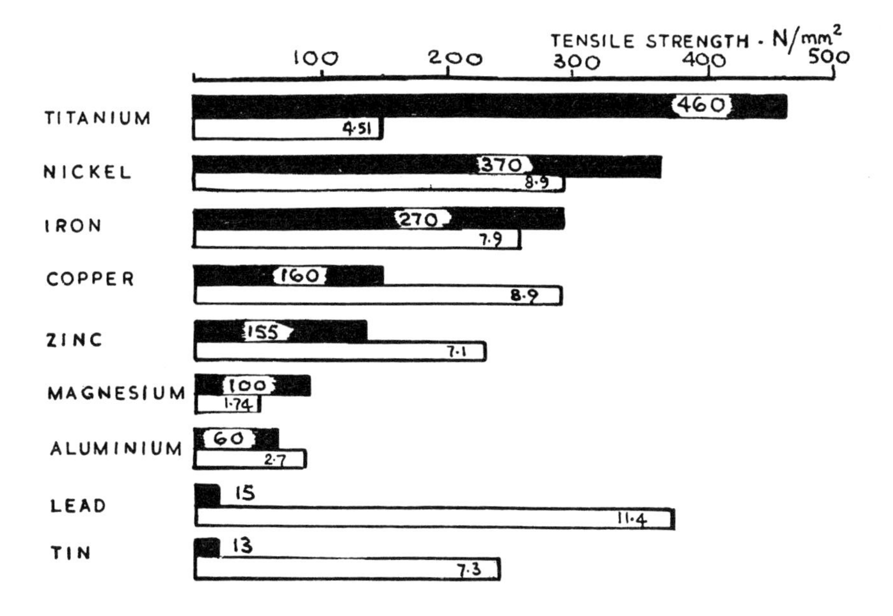

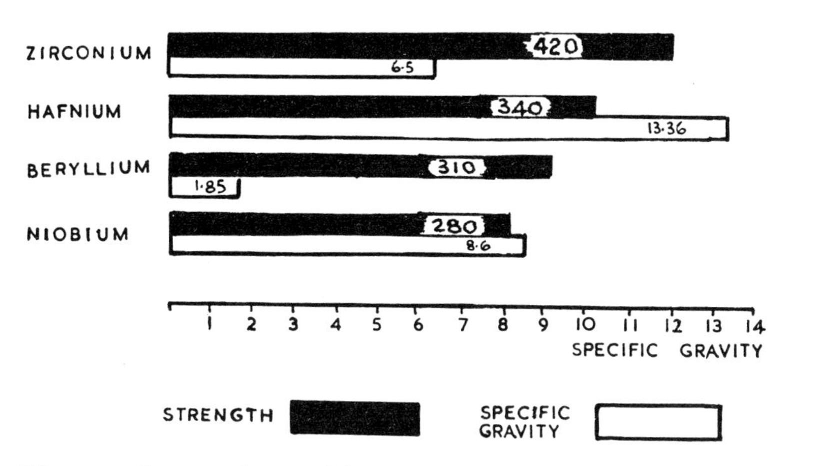

Fig. 1.5 Strength-specific gravity comparison of some Metals

The specific gravity is used to compare the weights of equal volumes of different substances—the s.g. of water is 1.

CHAPTER 2

THE EXTRACTION OF METALS FROM THEIR ORES

2.10 Although some metals, such as gold, are found in **elemental state**, and can be separated from the earthy part of their ores by washing, metals usually occur naturally as oxides, carbonates, sulphates, or sulphides. These ores are washed or heated after they are mined, to remove the earthy part and the moisture; the carbonates, sulphides, and sulphates are usually heated with air to convert them into oxides, and so, in most cases, the metal is extracted by the reduction of an oxide.

2.11 Reduction is usually done by heating the ore with carbon and air as the fuel and to produce the reduction agent, carbon monoxide; zinc, copper, lead, and iron can be extracted by this method. The production of pig iron will be described as an example of this process.

2.12 If oxygen has a greater affinity for the metal than for carbon, a reduction process cannot be employed, because this would only produce more oxide, and so special techniques, such as electrolysis, must be used. Electrolysis is also used when a particularly high purity is required. The production of aluminium will be described as an example of electrolytic refining.

2.13 Certain metals can only be extracted by special techniques; titanium, for example, requires a special process because its oxides are extremely stable; nickel requires a lengthy and complicated process because it is only found in economical deposits with copper, from which it is difficult to separate.

The Production of Pig Iron

2.20 Iron ore is refined in the **blast furnace** to produce **pig iron,** which is an impure form of **cast iron**, and which is refined to produce wrought iron and steels, and is used in the production of cast irons.

2.21 TYPES OF IRON ORE

1. Oxides (*a*) Magnetite Ores, contain the mineral **magnetite** (Fe_3O_4), which is magnetic, brown in colour, and the richest known iron ore; it contains up to about 56% iron as mined.
   (*b*) Haematite Ores, containing the mineral **haematite** (Fe_2O_3), which is reddish-brown, and contains between 40 and 65% iron.
2. Hydrated Ores containing **limonite** ($2Fe_2O_3.3H_2O$) and **goethite** ($Fe_2O_3.H_2O$), these ores contain between 20 and 55% iron.
3. Carbonates, containing the mineral **siderite** ($FeCO_3$) with about 30% iron.

In some places these ores lie within 30 metres of the surface, and can be mined by opencast working; some ores, for example haematite, require deep working.

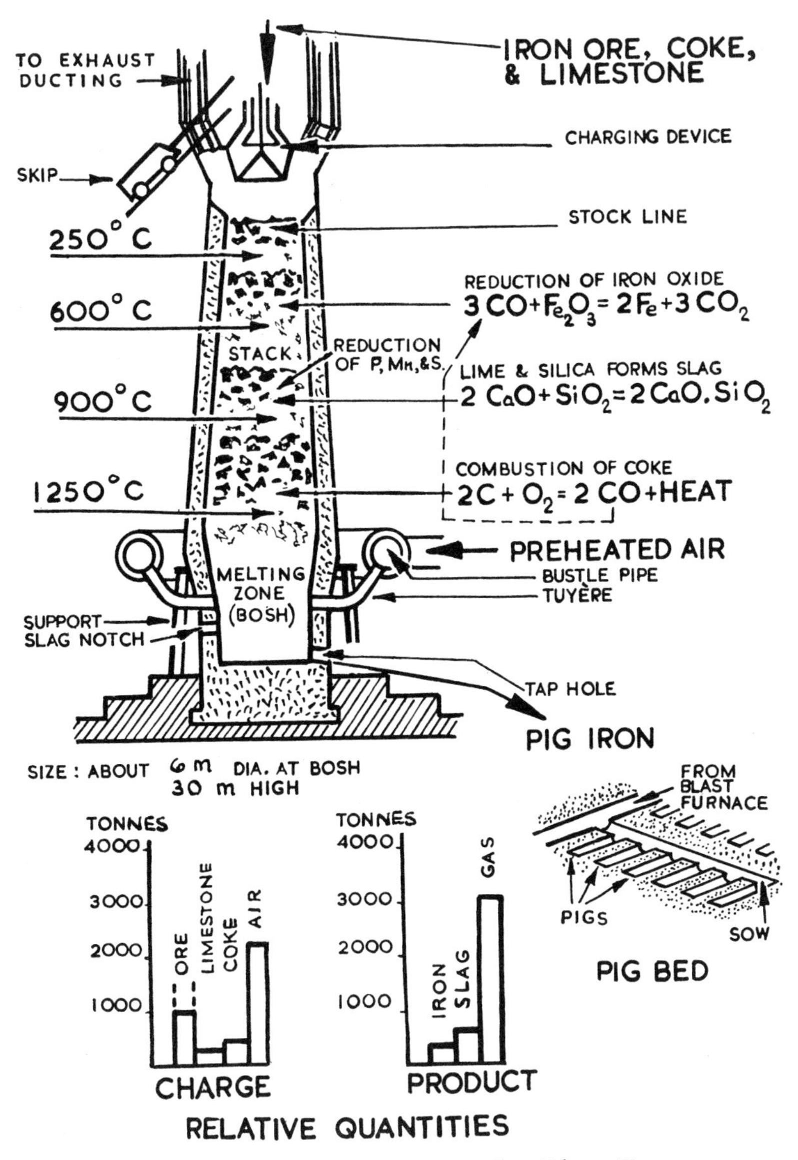

Fig. 2.1 Production of Pig-Iron—the Blast Furnace

2.22 PHOSPHORUS

Iron ores are also classified according to their phosphorus content because this impurity cannot be removed in the blast furnace, and because it has a bad effect upon the mechanical properties of irons and steels.

1. Low phosphorus ores, containing up to about 0·04% phosphorus. These ores usually have a relatively high silicon content.
2. High phosphorus (or basic) ores, with up to about 2·5% phosphorus.

British ores are mainly of the basic type, and contain a low iron content. They require a rather costly operation to remove the phosphorus, and it is usual to mix them with imported ores of the haematite group to improve their purity.

2.23 PRE-SMELTING OPERATIONS

In order that an iron ore can be acceptable, it must have a high enough grade (iron content); must have a suitable density, so that it will not crumble easily but not be too dense to allow the chemical reactions to take place; it must be of a suitable size to allow the pieces to be fully reduced in the furnace, and must not contain not more than about 0·2% sulphur and 2·5% phosphorus. The actual amount of these impurities that is allowed depends upon the type of iron or steel to be produced. The blast furnace must be fed continuously with iron ore, and it is necessary that a uniformity of supply be maintained over a number of years.

The ore is washed, and where applicable, the ore is upgraded by magnetic separation from the non iron-bearing mineral; sulphur is removed by weathering, and moisture and carbon dioxide is removed by heating. The treated ore is crushed to produce a suitable lump size, and the dust produced is rendered suitable for smelting by mixing it with coal dust or tar to produce lumps.

2.24 COKE AND LIMESTONE

Coke for use as blast furnace fuel is produced from coal in coke ovens on the site, which utilise the blast furnace waste gases; town gas is a by-product of this process, and this is often piped and used by the local gas undertaking. Other by-products include tar, crude oil, and ammonium sulphate (sold as fertiliser).

Limestone is used as a flux in the blast furnace, and is quarried near the blast furnace site if possible.

2.25 THE SITING OF THE BLAST FURNACE PLANT

The blast furnace plant is usually sited near a coal field where suitable coking coal can be mined, near limestone deposits, and near ore deposits; alternatively, the plant may be sited near the coast, particularly if imported ores are used.

2.26 THE SMELTING OPERATION

The prepared ore is charged into the blast furnace where smelting takes place. The smelting operation converts the iron ore into iron by chemical reduction, and at the same time controls the impurities that find their way into the metal so produced. In order that the smelting operation can be a practical method for quantity production, the iron must be run from the furnace from time to time, and the gangue (the unwanted minerals that cannot be readily separated from the ores during its extraction) must be liquified to form a slag that can also be run from the furnace. In addition to producing heat and the reducing agent, the coke assists in making the iron run from the furnace by combining with it to produce a lower melting point alloy; limestone produces a liquid slag that can be run from the furnace.

The blast furnace is a vertical steel shell that is roughly cylindrical in shape, and lined with a refractory material. It has a charging device at the top, and means of running off the iron and the slag at the bottom. In order to produce the necessarily high temperature, and to minimise the amount of coke that is required, hot air is blown into the bottom of the furnace through nozzles known as tuyères; there are usually about twelve tuyères, and they are connected to a main, or bustle pipe, by elbow pipes. At the point of each elbow there is a small piece of blue glass; by looking through this glass, the interior of the furnace can be inspected, and the efficiency of operation can be judged so that any adjustment of conditions can be made.

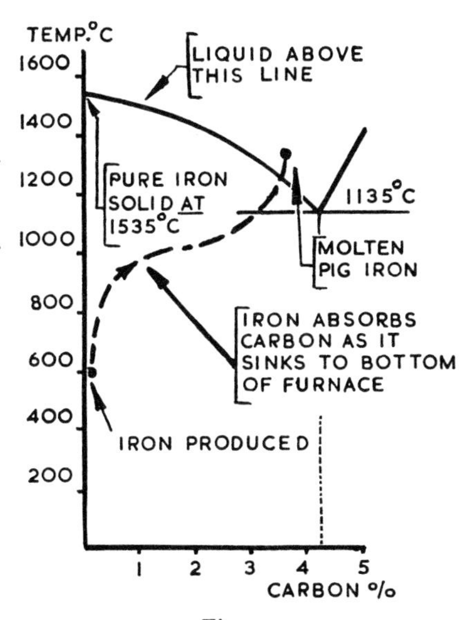

Fig. 2.2

The charge, consisting of iron ore, coke, and limestone, is carefully weighed in the stockyard, and taken to the top of the furnace in large small-wheeled containers called skips, which are automatically tipped to charge the furnace. In order that the top of the furnace is gas-tight, a system of cones, called bells, is employed. The bell system incorporates a revolving distributor so that the stock line is even all around the furnace.

The hot air produces a partial combustion of the coke at the bottom of the furnace, producing intense heat and carbon monoxide. This carbon monoxide rises to the top of the furnace, where it reduces the iron oxide to iron; the iron so produced will be solid because the temperature at this part of the furnace is only about 600°C, whereas the melting point of iron is about 1535°C. At high temperatures iron will, however, absorb carbon if surrounded by a carbonaceous atmosphere, and an iron-carbon alloy will be produced; the melting point of the alloy will fall with increase in carbon content, to reach a minimum (see fig. 2.2). As the iron sinks towards the bottom of the furnace it becomes hotter, and, at the same time, it absorbs some of the carbon that is rising towards the top of the furnace as carbon monoxide; an iron-carbon containing about 3·5% carbon is eventually produced; this alloy has a melting point of about 1200°C, and is therefore molten when at the bottom of the furnace, from where it can be tapped.

The limestone dissociates at the top of the furnace to produce quicklime, which in turn produces the slag. The slag passes to the bottom of the furnace with the iron, but on reaching the bottom it floats on the surface of the molten metal. The slag is tapped off when its level approaches that of the tuyères; the blast furnace operates continuously, and is only normally stopped when the refractory lining needs attention. The slag from the blast furnace is used for railway track ballast, or coated with tar and used for road making.

The hot furnace gases are collected in a large down-pipe and passed, after cleaning, to the coke ovens and to the Cowper Stoves. These stoves have a chequered brick lining which is heated up by the gas; when the stove has been heated up by the gas, it is used to preheat the cold air on its way to the furnace. Usually a blast furnace has three Cowper Stoves, one being 'on blast' and giving up heat, whilst the others are 'on gas' and receiving heat.

The impure iron-carbon alloy is known as **pig iron**, and is either cast into moulds of sand or metal, or run into large refractory-lined ladles, and then transferred in the molten state to the steel-making plant. Molten pig iron is usually called **blast furnace metal.**

2.27 PIG IRON

Pig iron is a complex alloy which may contain up to 10% by weight of other elements in addition to iron, can be regarded as an impure form of cast iron.

Composition by weight, of pig iron:

Total carbon 3–4% Some of this carbon will be combined with the iron to form Fe_3C (or cementite), and some may be free (graphite). The proportion of free carbon to combined carbon will depend upon the cooling rate, and upon the other elements that are present. Rapid cooling and sulphur both tend to keep the carbon combined, and silicon tends to produce free carbon. The pig iron can contain between 0·1 and 3·0% combined carbon, with up to 2·7% free carbon.

Silicon 0·4–2·5%.
Phosphorus 0·04–2·5%.
Sulphur 0·02–0·2%.
Manganese 0·4–2·7%.
Balance, iron.

With the exception of phosphorus, the relative quantities can be controlled by furnace conditions.

Pig iron is passed to the foundry, where it is refined or modified to produce cast iron, or to the steel plant, where it is refined to produce steel. Pig irons are graded according to the impurities present, because these will effect the properties of the cast iron produced from it, and will influence the choice of system used to convert the pig iron into steel.

The Production of Aluminium

2.30 Aluminium is found in economic quantities in the bauxite group of rocks. Bauxite is a mixture of oxides that are held together mechanically; one of these oxides is hydrated aluminium oxide, and which can be made to yield **alumina** (pure aluminium oxide). The hydrated aluminium oxide is removed from the bauxite by mixing finely ground bauxite in a hot solution of caustic soda and a soluble sodium-aluminate is produced that is filtered and then allowed to cool. During cooling, crystals of aluminium hydroxide

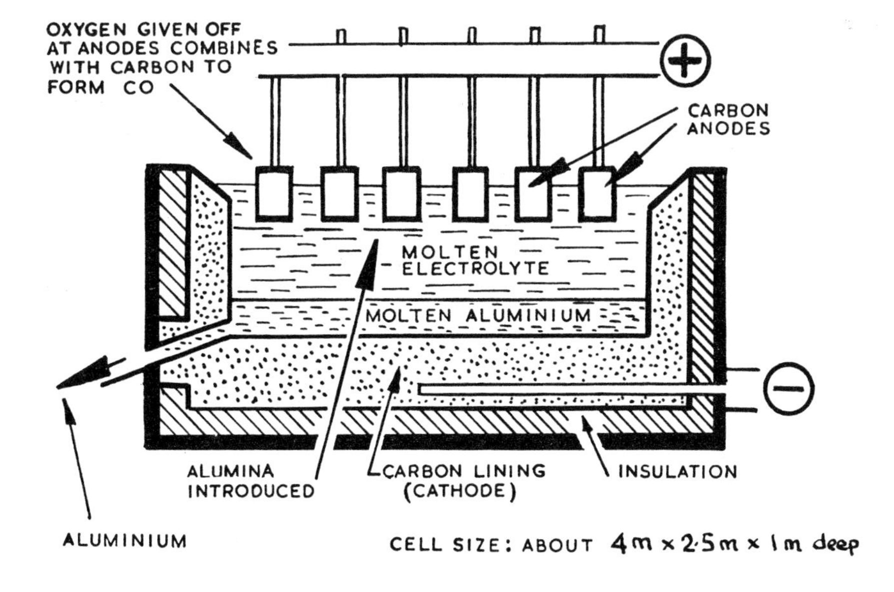

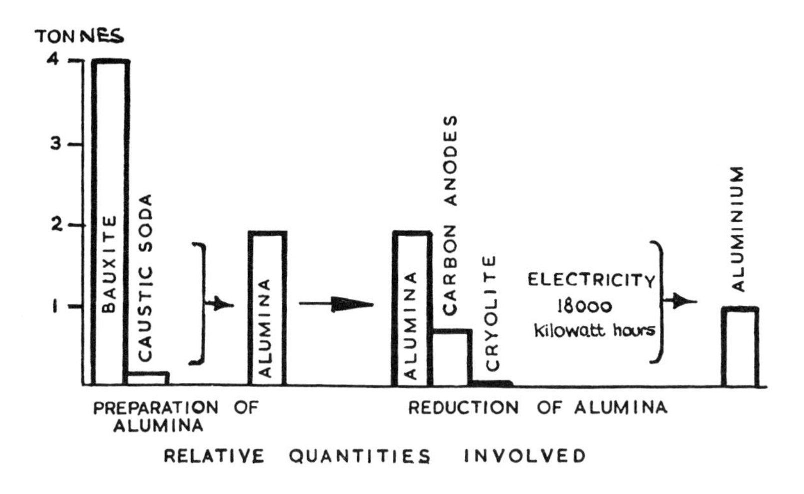

Fig. 2.3 Production of Aluminium—Electrolytic Cell

are formed, which are heated to remove the water, and so leave powdered alumina.

2.31 The alumina can be made to yield aluminium by electrolysis (see fig. 2.3). The alumina is dissolved in natural or synthetic cryolite (a double fluoride of sodium and aluminium) in the cell bath, by heating the cryolite to melt it, and then introducing the powdered alumina. As a result of the electrolytic action, aluminium is deposited at the bottom of the cell, and from time to time, the aluminium is removed by tapping, ladling, or siphoning, and then cast into 'pigs', each of which weigh about 20 kg.

2.32 Aluminium can be further treated to improve its purity by electrolytic refining in a cell with aluminium alloy at the bottom, and covered with molten cryolite, fluorides, and alumina, upon which is molten aluminium. During the electrolysis, aluminium is transferred from the alloy to the top of the cell, producing aluminium with up to 99·99% purity.

CHAPTER 3

THE FORMATION OF ALLOYS

3.10 The Reason for Alloys

Alloys are used extensively in engineering because, as stated in Chapter 1, an engineering material must usually satisfy a number of requirements. A pure metal usually has extreme properties such as high corrosion resistance but low strength; an alloy usually has properties that are a compromise between those of its constituents, and often has some properties that are superior to, or quite different from, those of its constituents. Many alloys will respond to heat treatment so that an improved hardness and strength, or other properties, can be developed; the heat treatment procedure will depend upon the structural changes produced when the alloy is heated within the solid state.

3.11 Generally, if an alloy is to be useful, its constituents must dissolve in each other to form a completely homogeneous solution when in the liquid state; if the constituents do not form a liquid solution, they will be present as laminations, or regions of pure metal when the alloy has cooled to room temperature. Sometimes an element that will not enter into the liquid solution is included in the alloy; this element will form globules in the liquid solution, and will be present as very small particles when the alloy has cooled to room temperature. These small particles will not reduce the strength of the alloy when only a small quantity of the element is included, but will produce **free cutting properties** by breaking up the chips produced during machining; lead is added to brass and to steel, and tellurium to copper to produce free cutting properties.

3.12 An alloy behaves differently from a pure metal during its cooling from the liquid state, and has a different structure from that of a pure metal when it is at room temperature.

The effects of alloying will be discussed under:

(*a*) The effect of alloying upon behaviour during solidification.

(*b*) The structural changes during cooling to room temperature when in the solid state, and the structure produced.

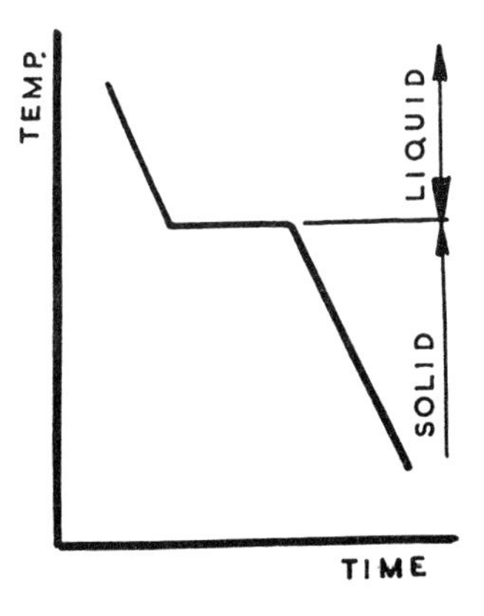

Fig. 3.1

The Effect of Alloying upon Behaviour During Solidification

3.20 When a pure metal is cooled from the liquid state the change from the liquid state to the solid state occurs at a definite temperature. This change causes a short check in the fall in temperature of the metal, as indicated by the arrest point on the temperature/time cooling curve (see fig. 3.1).

The cooling curve for an alloy indicates that solidification occurs gradually during a fall in temperature of the alloy (see fig. 3.2); the solidification of some alloys is completed at a constant temperature as shown in fig. 3.3.

3.21 If the cooling of a number of alloys that contain different proportions of the same constituents is studied, a diagram can be produced to show the effect that variation of proportions has upon the temperature at which solidi-

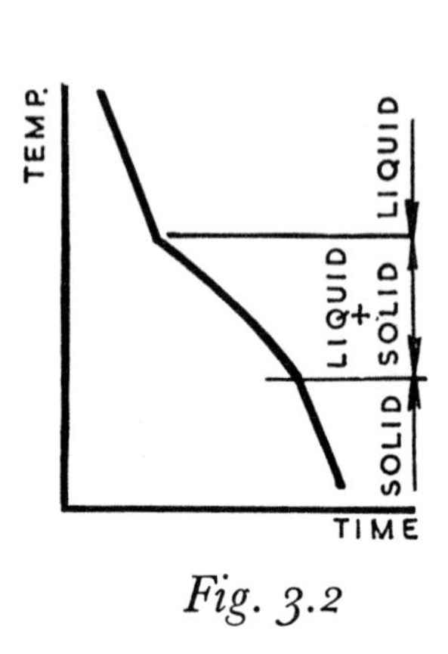

Fig. 3.2

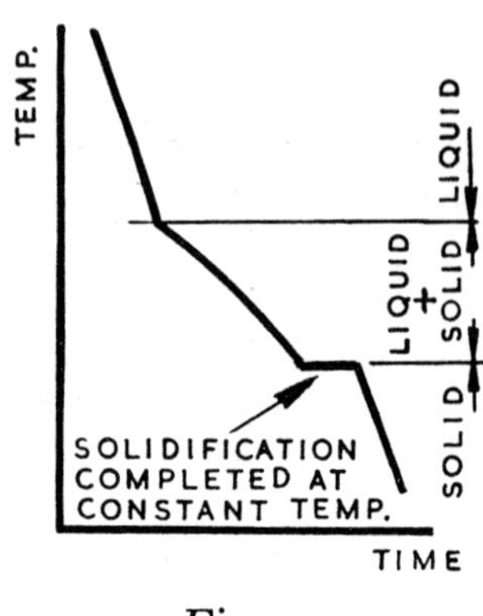

Fig. 3.3

fication commences and that at which it is completed. Figures 3.4 and 3.5 are two typical diagrams of this type; the line drawn between points at which each alloy in the system ceases to be in the liquid state is called the **liquidus line**, and that drawn between points at which each becomes completely solid is called the **solidus line.** The liquidus and solidus lines form the basis of the **thermal-equilibrium diagram** for the system; this diagram is a convenient method of indicating the changes in state and structure through which each alloy passes during slow cooling from the liquid state, and the temperature at which these changes occur.

The Structural Changes during Cooling to Room Temperature when in the Solid State and the Structure Produced

3.30 Depending upon its composition and temperature, an alloy may consist of a single phase, or a mixture of phases; a **phase** is part of a chemical system with distinctive characteristics.

The phases present during cooling and at room temperature will depend upon the behaviour of the constituents towards each other. Their behaviour when in at room temperature may be classified as: (i) complete solid solubility, (ii) no solid solubility, (iii) limited solid solubility, (iv) formation of an intermetallic compound.

3.31 Complete Solubility when in the Solid State

When an alloy is in the liquid state the atoms of the constituent metals will be distributed at random to form a **liquid solution**; when solidification takes place, the atoms assume an orderly arrangement called a **space lattice**. If the atoms of the constituents are of similar diameter, an atom of one con-

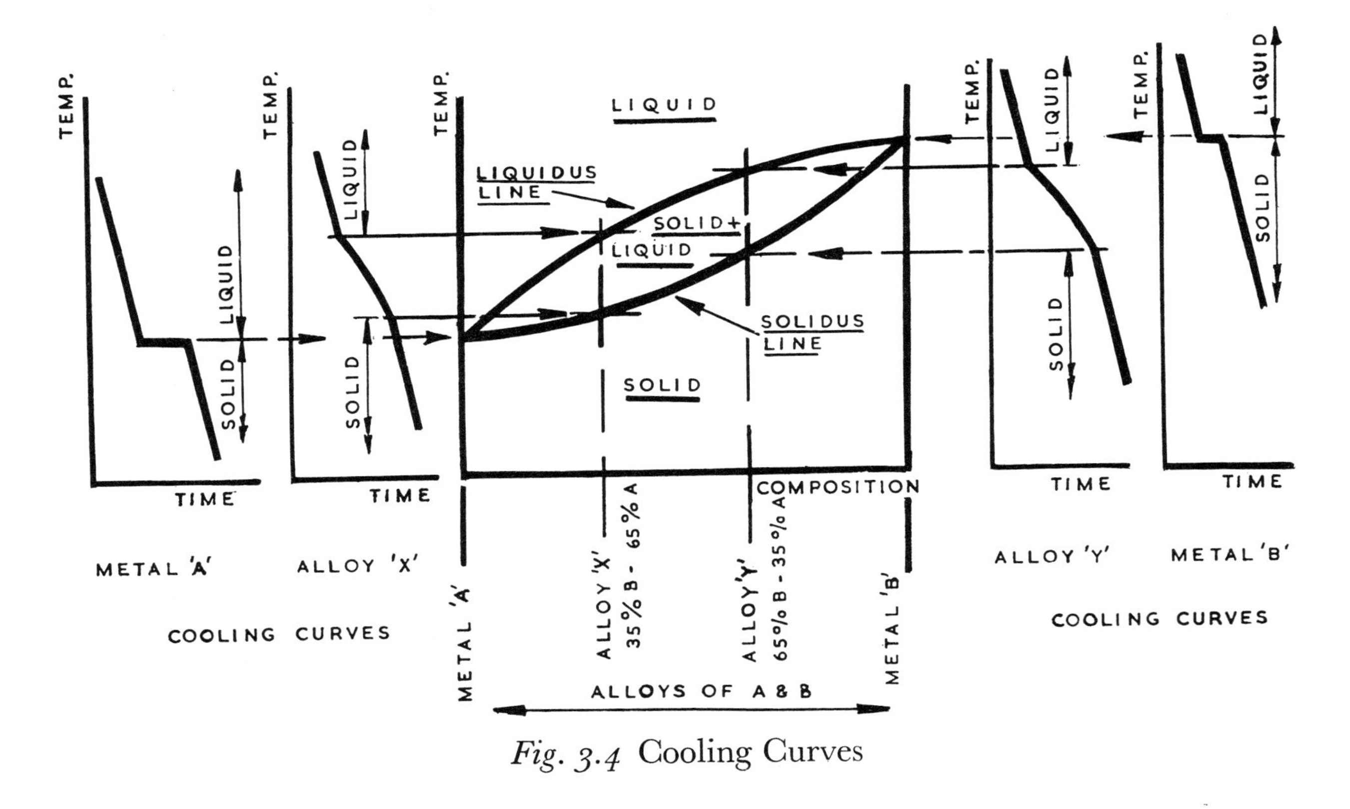

Fig. 3.4 Cooling Curves

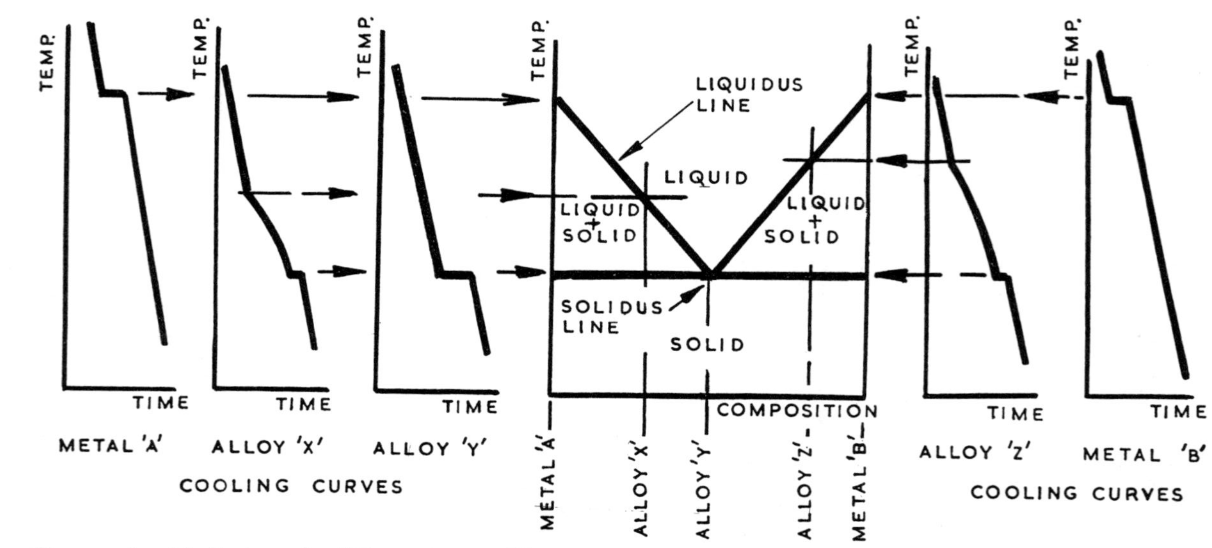

Fig. 3.5 In this System the Temperature of Start of Solidification is a Minimum at Alloy 'Y'. This Alloy is called the Eutectic and has a Cooling Curve Similar to that of a Pure Metal.
The Solidification of all other Alloys in the System is Gradual but is Completed at the Temperature at which the Eutectic Solidifies.

stituent can take the place of an atom of the other constituent in the space lattice; this will produce a single **phase**, and when viewed microscopically it will be impossible to trace the constituents, and the alloy will resemble a pure metal; when this happens, a **solid solution** is said to exist. A solid solution produced by constituents whose atoms are similar in size is called a **substitutional solid solution.**

A solid solution may also be produced if the atoms of one constituent are small compared with those of the other, so that they can take up position between them in the space lattice; this will produce an **interstitial solid solution.**

3.32 No Solubility when in the Solid State

Very occasionally the constituents will display no solubility, and each grain will consist of laminations, each of a pure metal. No engineering alloys are of this type, but it will be dealt with as an introduction to a more complicated system.

3.33 Limited Solubility when in the Solid State

Very often the metals forming the alloy have a limited solubility, one in the other. If a small quantity of one metal or the other is present, a solid solution will be formed, but alloys with intermediate proportions will have a structure that includes laminations of two solid solutions.

3.34 The Formation of an Intermetallic Compound

Certain metals will combine to form an intermetallic compound; two metals may obey normal valency laws to form such a compound, or may be present in a ratio that is associated with the total number of valencies in each molecule, and the total number of atoms in each molecule. These intermetallic compounds are hard and brittle and are unsuitable for most engineering requirements; they are, however, often present in a solid solution matrix, and in these cases the alloy combines the wear resistance of the intermetallic compound with the toughness of the solid solution.

The Thermal-equilibrium Diagram

3.40 The thermal-equilibrium diagram for an alloy system indicates the behaviour of each alloy in the system during solidification, and the structural changes that take place as a result of **slow cooling** within the solid state. The behaviour of binary alloys (those containing two metals) can be easily shown using a diagram of this type, but more complicated alloys demand three-dimensional methods; only the equilibrium diagrams for binary alloys will be described in this book.

An understanding of equilibrium diagrams will enable the student to appreciate the characteristics of the alloys used in engineering, and also to understand the principle of heat treatment of some of these alloys.

Alloys can be grouped according to the behaviour of their constituents towards each other, and the thermal-equilibrium diagrams associated with the alloys in each group are of a similar shape.

Some representative thermal-equilibrium diagrams will be described in this chapter, and specific equilibrium diagrams will be used where necessary in the chapters that follow.

Equilibrium Diagram for Two Metals that are Completely Soluble in All Proportions when in the Solid State (Fig. 3.6)

3.50 Two phases occur in this system, these are liquid solution and solid solution. The equilibrium diagram shows two single-phase fields separated by a double-phase field; the liquidus and solidus lines are the boundaries between these fields. The liquidus and solidus lines also indicate the changes in the composition of the liquid and solid solutions during solidification of each alloy in the system.

3.51 The solidification of an alloy of 60% B and 40% A will be described as an example of the interpretation of this diagram. The solidification of this alloy will be traced with the aid of the vertical line shown on fig. 3.6.

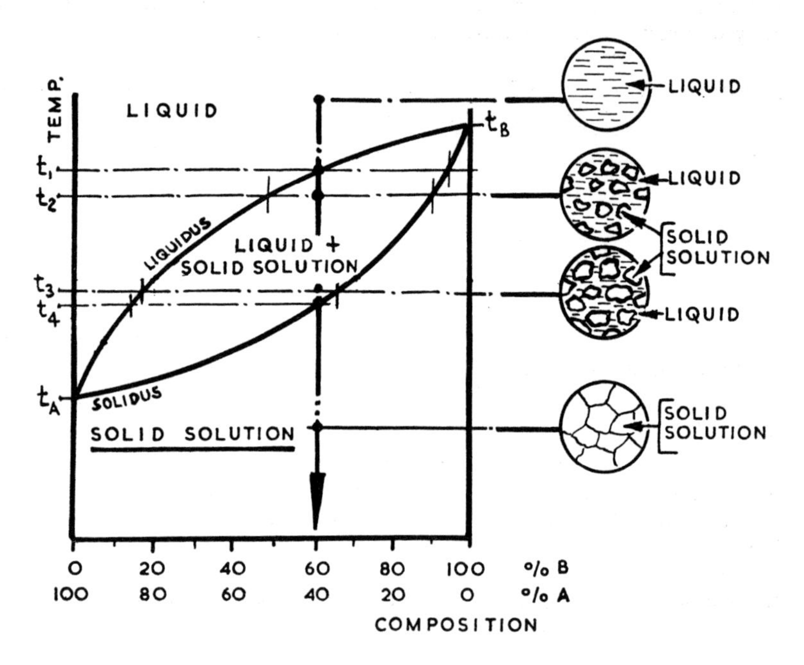

Fig. 3.6 Equilibrium Diagram for two Metals that are Completely Soluble in all Proportions when in the Solid State

When the temperature of the liquid solution has fallen to t_1 solidification will start, and the first particles of the solid solution produced will contain 93% B (this is indicated by the intersection of the horizontal line at t_1 and the solidus line).

When the temperature of the alloy has fallen to t_2, the liquid will contain 48% B, and the solid solution will contain 90% B (this is indicated by the intersection of the horizontal line at t_2 and the liquidus and solidus lines respectively).

The percentage of B that is present in the liquid and the solid solution will continue to fall during cooling, and when the temperature of the alloy has reached t_3, the liquid will contain 18% B, whilst the solid solution will contain 65% B.

At temperature t_4, when the solidification is just about to be completed, the remaining liquid will contain 15% B, and upon completion of the solidification the solid solution will contain 60% B.

3.52 The gradual change in the composition of the solid solution as indicated by the equilibrium diagram will only take place if the alloy cools slowly enough to permit the necessary diffusion. In practice, cooling is not sufficiently slow, and so the core of each grain, which is the first to solidify, will be rich in B and the outer fringes of each grain will be weak in B; this non-uniformity is known as **coring.** A uniform structure can be produced by reheating the alloy to a suitable temperature below the solidus line.

Equilibrium Diagram for Two Metals that are Completely Insoluble when in the Solid State (Fig. 3.7)

3.60 Three phases occur in this system, these are liquid solution, metal A, and metal B. The equilibrium diagram indicates that at one composition, called the **eutectic** (in this example the alloy that contains 60% A and 40% B), the temperature at which solidification starts is the lowest for the system. The eutectic solidifies at a constant temperature (t_E) like a pure metal, to form a characteristic laminated structure. The eutectic structure for this system consists of laminations of two pure metals.

The interpretation of this diagram will be explained by considering the solidification of two alloys.

3.61 THE SOLIDIFICATION OF ALLOY 1

This alloy starts to solidify at temperature t_1; the solid produced will be pure metal A, and consequently the **percentage** of metal B that is present in the remaining liquid will increase during cooling. This is indicated by the liquidus line.

When the temperature of this alloy has fallen to t_2, the remaining liquid will contain 20% B; when the temperature of the alloy has reached t_3, the remaining liquid will contain 40% B.

It will be apparent that the composition of the remaining liquid approaches the eutectic during cooling, and that this composition is reached when the temperature of the alloy has fallen to t_E. When this temperature is reached, the remaining liquid will solidify to form the eutectic. The structure of the solid alloy will be pure metal A + eutectic (A + B).

3.62 THE SOLIDIFICATION OF ALLOY 2

This alloy starts to solidify at temperature t_4; the solid produced will be pure metal B, and consequently the **percentage** of metal B that is present in the remaining liquid will decrease during cooling. This is indicated by the liquidus line. From the diagram it will be seen that the percentage of metal B that is present in the remaining liquid will reach 90% at t_5, and 75% at t_6.

Again, the composition of the liquid approaches the eutectic during cooling,

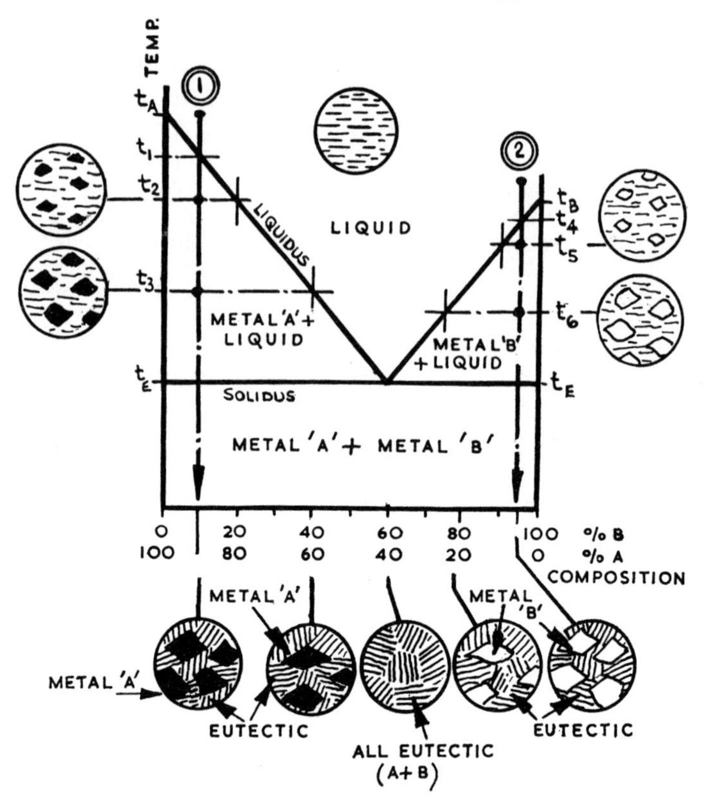

Fig. 3.7 Equilibrium Diagram for Two Metals that are Completely Insoluble when in Solid State

and the eutectic composition is reached at temperature t_E. When this temperature is reached, the remaining liquid will solidify to form the eutectic; the final structure will be pure metal B + eutectic (A + B).

Equilibrium Diagram for Two Metals that have Limited Solubility when in the Solid State (Fig. 3.8)

3.70 This diagram is similar to that described on page 21, except that since each constituent has some solubility in the other, two solid solutions are involved instead of two pure metals. These solid solutions are (1) a solid solution of B in A (indicated on the diagram by α) and (2) a solid solution of A in B (indicated on the diagram by β). The eutectic for this system consists of laminations of two solid solutions ($\alpha + \beta$).

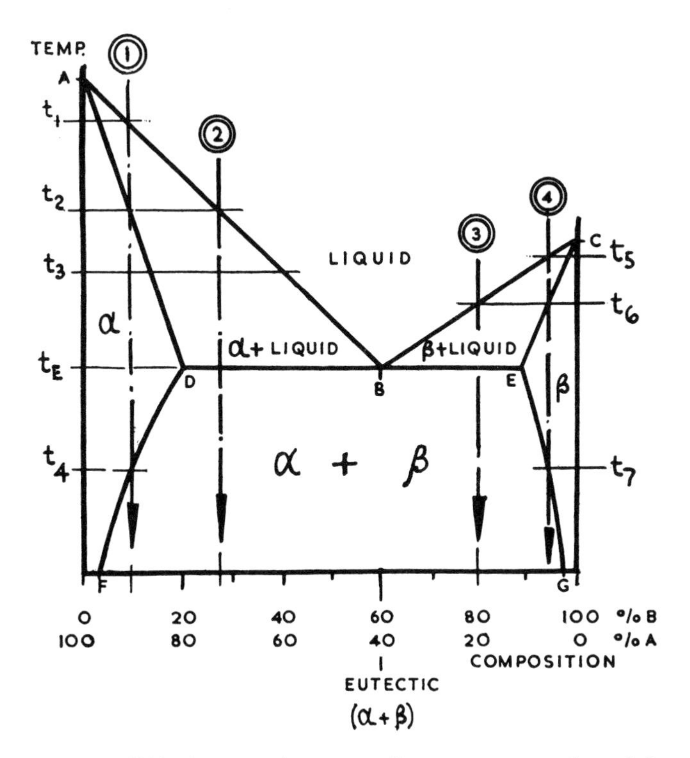

Fig. 3.8 Equilibrium Diagram for two Metals with Limited Solubility when in Solid State

Line 'A-B-C' is the Liquidus
Line 'A-D-E-C' is the Solidus
Some Metal 'B' will Dissolve in Metal 'A' to Form the Solid Solution 'α'. Solubility is indicated by Solvus Line 'D-F'.
Some Metal 'A' will Dissolve in Metal 'B' to form the Solid Solution 'β'. Solubility is indicated by Solvus Line 'E-G'.

3·71 In the system illustrated, the solid solubility of B in A is maximum at t_E, when the solid solution can contain 20% B (point D on the diagram); the solubility falls with temperature and only 3% B can be contained in the solid solution when at room temperature (this is indicated by the solvus line DF).

3·72 Similarly, the solid solubility of A in B is a maximum at t_E, when the solid solution can contain 10% A (point E on the diagram); the solubility falls with temperature, and only 2% A can be contained in solid solution when at room temperature (indicated by the solvus line EG).

The cooling of four alloys in this system will be used to illustrate the interpretation of this diagram.

3·73 THE COOLING OF ALLOY 1

This alloy will start to solidify at temperature t_1; this will occur gradually, and be completed when temperature t_2 is reached to form a complete solid solution α. No further change will occur until the temperature has reached t_4 when the solubility of B in A starts to fall; the excess metal B will be precipitated from the solid solution α to form solid solution β with some metal A. This precipitation is completed when the temperature has fallen to room temperature, and the final structure will be $\alpha + (\alpha + \beta)$.

3·74 THE COOLING OF ALLOY 2

This alloy will start to solidify at t_3, to produce solid solution α. During solidification, the percentage of B in the remaining liquid will rise, and so the remaining liquid will be of eutectic composition when its temperature has fallen to t_E. At this temperature, the remaining liquid will solidify to form eutectic $(\alpha + \beta)$. The final structure will be $\alpha + (\alpha + \beta)$.

3·75 THE COOLING OF ALLOY 3

The solidification of this alloy will start when its temperature has fallen to t_6, when the solid produced will be solid solution β. This solid solution contains a large percentage of metal B, and so the percentage of B in the remaining liquid will fall with temperature (as indicated by the liquidus line). When the temperature of the alloy has fallen to t_E, the remaining liquid will be of eutectic composition and solidify as the eutectic; the final structure will be $\beta + (\alpha + \beta)$.

3·76 THE COOLING OF ALLOY 4

When this alloy reaches the temperature t_5 solidification will start, and continue gradually until completed when the temperature has fallen to t_6. No further change will occur until the temperature has fallen to t_7, when the solubility of A in B will start to fall; the excess metal A will be precipitated from the solid solution β to form solid solution α with some metal B. This precipitation will be completed when the temperature has fallen to room temperature; the final structure will be $\beta + (\alpha + \beta)$.

3·77 If an alloy contains less than 3% B, or less than 2% A, no precipitation will take place, and the final structure will consist of a single phase.

Equilibrium Diagram for Two Metals that Form an Intermetallic Compound (Fig. 3·9)

3·80 In this example, the two metals form an **intermetallic compound**, and also have a limited solubility, one in the other.

The complicated equilibrium diagram can be simplified by considering it

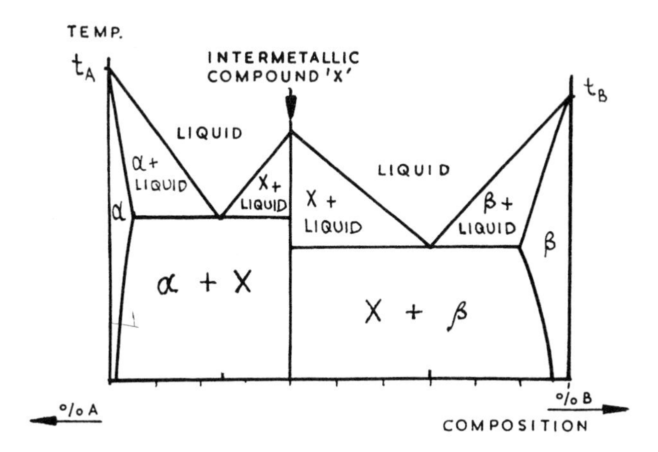

Fig. 3.9 Equilibrium Diagram for two Metals that form an Intermetallic Compound

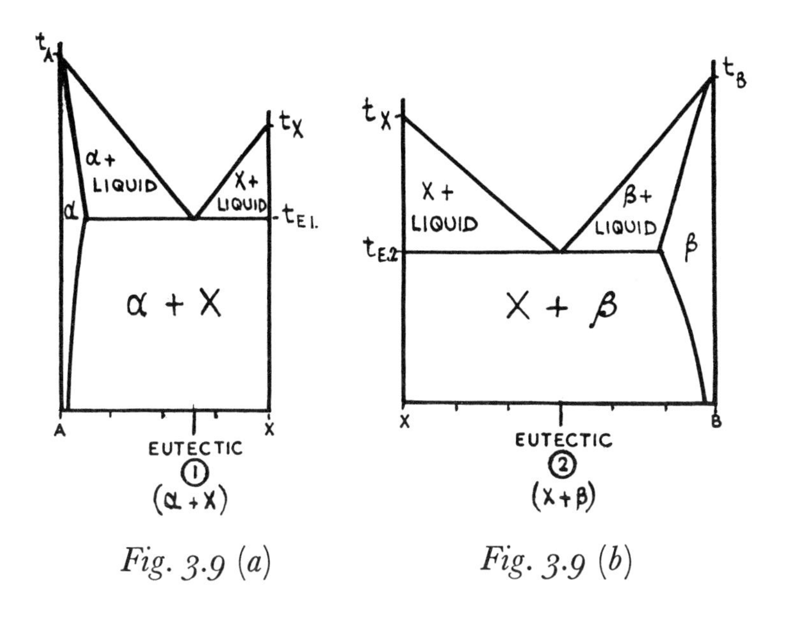

Fig. 3.9 (a)   *Fig. 3.9 (b)*

to be two equilibrium diagrams alongside each other; one diagram (see fig. 3.9(*a*)) being the diagram for metal A and intermetallic compound X, and the other diagram (see fig. 3.9(*b*)) being for intermetallic compound X and metal B.

Each of these systems has its own eutectic, and it will be seen that these eutectics do not solidify at the same temperature.

3.81 Some metals form one intermetallic compound at one composition, and another intermetallic compound at a different composition; such a system may have three eutectic compositions. The equilibrium diagram for such a system, although complicated, can be broken down into simpler diagrams as described above.

Peritectic Reaction

3.90 A peritectic reaction is said to take place when a solid that has been produced during cooling reacts with liquid that is remaining, to form another phase. This reaction is illustrated in fig. 3.10.

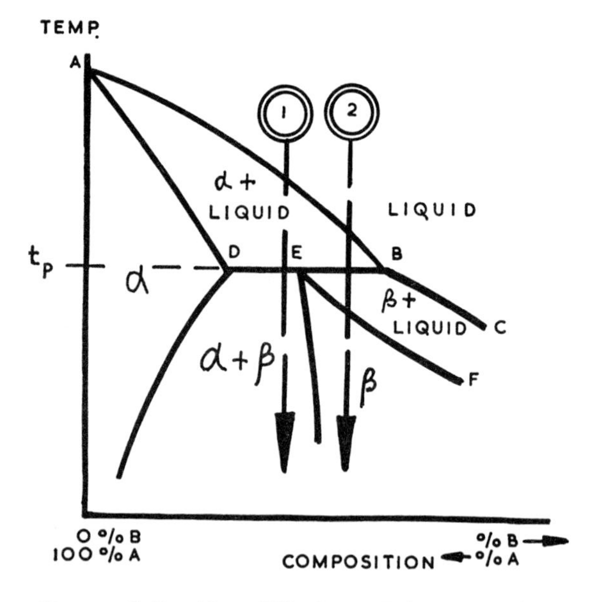

Fig. 3.10 Part of the Equilibrium Diagram for A System in which a Peritectic Reaction takes place

Line 'A-B-C' is the *Liquidus*
Line 'A-D-E-F' is the *Solidus*
A Peritectic Reaction takes place at Temp. t_p when the Alloy Composition lies between 'D' and 'B' (see fig. 3.10)

3.91 THE SOLIDIFICATION OF ALLOY 1

During cooling of this alloy the α phase is produced. The composition of this phase approaches 'D', whilst the composition of the remaining liquid approaches 'B'; this composition is reached when the temperature of the alloy has fallen to t_P, when the peritectic reaction takes place to produce the β phase. The quantity of constituent 'B' present in this alloy is insufficient to produce all β phase, and so the solid produced contains both α and β phases.

3.92 THE SOLIDIFICATION OF ALLOY 2

When the temperature of this alloy has fallen to t_P, the peritectic reaction takes place to produce the β phase; because of the higher amount of constituent 'B' that is present, the liquid is not all used up. Solidification is completed when the temperature of this alloy has fallen further and the solid produced will contain only the β phase.

3.93 A peritectic reaction takes place during the cooling of certain copper-zinc, copper-tin, and copper-aluminium alloys.

CHAPTER 4

THE MANIPULATION OF METALS

4.10 When a metal is first produced it is cast into ingot form; it can then be manipulated into a more convenient form by casting or by working. It is not the purpose of this book to describe the various casting and working methods in detail, but a survey of the principal processes and their characteristics will be made in this chapter.

Casting

4.20 Casting consists of heating the metal to make it molten, pouring it into a mould, and then removing it from the mould upon solidification. Casting materials should melt at a reasonably low temperature, be reasonably fluid when molten, and pass through a solidification range (see page 16) during cooling so that the streams of molten metal unite before solidification is completed, and so produce a sound casting; the solidification range should not extend over too great a temperature range, otherwise the material will be of a cored structure (see page 21, section 3.52).

The shape of the casting, and the casting technique must be chosen to suit the material to be cast. Cast iron, for example, can be made very fluid, and can be cast into quite intricate shapes using a sand mould; cast steel, which has a slightly lower carbon content, has a higher melting point, is not very fluid, requires special moulding and casting techniques, and cannot be cast into such intricate shapes.

4.21 Casting Methods

4.211 SAND CASTING

In this method a pattern, made of wood or metal, is used to make an impression in sand, into which the metal is poured. The casting shape must be such that the pattern can be withdrawn easily after moulding, and the mould must be split to allow the pattern to be removed. When the metal has solidified it can be removed by breaking away the sand. Hollow shapes can be produced by employing 'cores' made of a suitable sand, which restrict the space into which the molten metal can flow; the core sand can be removed from the inside of hollow castings through 'core holes' which must be incorporated into the casting design.

Sand casting can be used for most casting metals, but it does not produce very accurate castings and is unsuitable for thin-walled sections. The lack of accuracy is due to the sand not being very rigid, the slight enlargement of the impression produced when the pattern is removed, and also to the need to employ a split mould to remove the pattern.

Sand casting is not a very rapid casting method because a mould must be made for each casting, but it can be speeded up by machine moulding; it is economical for small quantities, and does not require elaborate equipment. Figure 4.1 illustrates a sand mould ready for the pouring operation.

CASTING METHODS

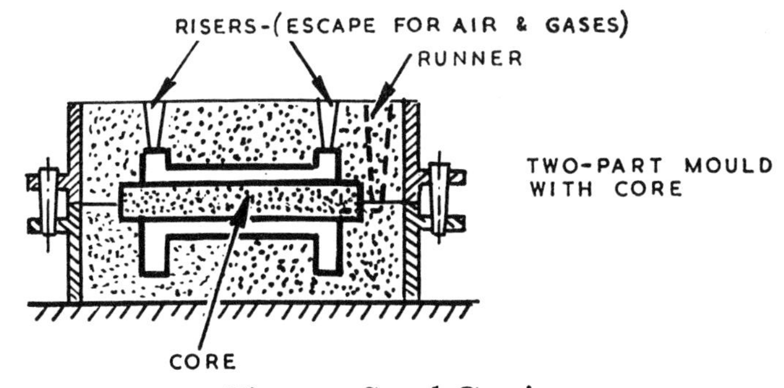

Fig. 4.1 Sand Casting

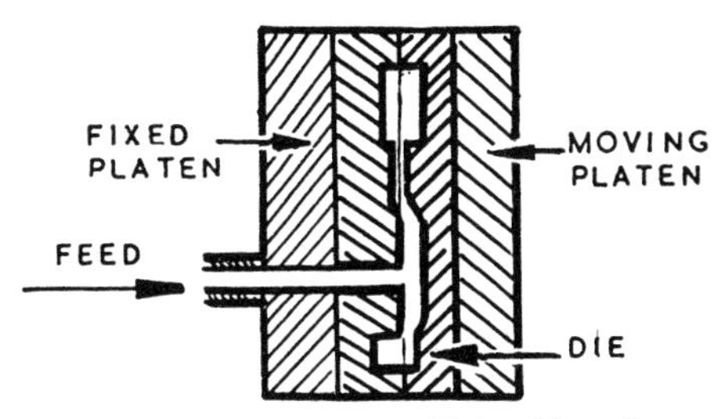

Fig. 4.2 Pressure Die Ca$ting

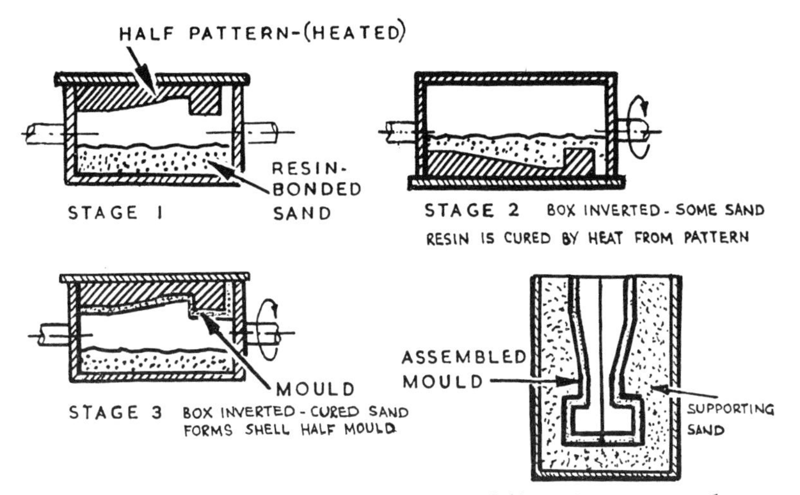

Fig. 4.3 Shell Moulding—Moulding Stages and Assembled Mould

4.212 DIE CASTING

Die casting employs a metal mould, and so a more accurate casting is obtained than by sand casting; some accuracy is lost due to the need to employ a split mould (known as the **die**) to enable the casting to be removed. Die casting is more expensive than sand casting for small quantities due to the high cost of machining the die, but it becomes economical for large quantities. These are two variations of die casting, these are **pressure die casting**, and **gravity die casting**.

(*a*) *Pressure Die Casting*. This method uses a machine to open and close the die, and to inject the metal into the die; it is the most rapid casting method, and produces castings of great accuracy. It is only suitable for small castings because the capacity of the machine is limited; it cannot be applied to all metals, but it is especially suitable for zinc base alloys. Figure 4.2 illustrates the principle of pressure die casting.

The success of this method depends to a large extent upon the casting design, which must allow the rapid ejection of the finished casting. Sand cores cannot be used to make hollow castings, and although movable metal cores can be used, they tend to wear and cause innacuracies; very often the use of cores can be avoided by careful casting design.

The accuracy of castings produced by pressure die casting is so good that little, or no machining is required.

(*b*) *Gravity Die Casting*. Gravity die casting is similar to sand casting, except that a metal mould (die) is used. It is less rapid than pressure die casting, and does not produce such accurate castings; castings produced by this method are sounder than those produced by the pressure die casting method, and they can be larger because no special equipment is required. A wider range of materials can be cast by gravity die casting, and sand cores can be used if required to produce hollow castings.

4.213 SHELL MOULDING

Thin two-part moulds can be made from a resin-bonded sand; the mould is produced using a heated pattern, and the heat 'cures' the resin (see page 193) so that an accurate, thin mould is obtained. Very accurate castings in most metals can be obtained using this technique, and although the cost of the pattern is high, semi-skilled labour can be used to make the mould. This method is illustrated in fig. 4.3.

4.214 INVESTMENT CASTING (see fig. 4.4)

In this method a pattern, made of a low melting point material, such as wax, is made for every casting; the wax pattern is covered (invested) with a suitable refractory material to produce a one-piece mould; the investment is then heated to harden the mould and to melt out the pattern. The metal is poured into the heated mould, which is broken open to extract the casting when it has solidified.

This casting method is very accurate because the mould is rigid and in one piece. It enables shapes to be cast that would be impossible by methods which demand either ease of removal of pattern (as in sand casting), or ease of removal of finished casting (as in die casting).

Investment casting is expensive but it is often the only way to produce

Fig. 4.4 Some Stages in Investment Casting

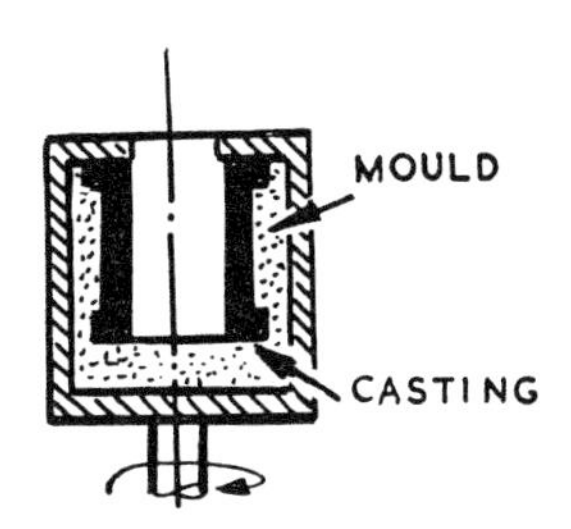

Fig. 4.5 True Centrifugal Casting (Hollow Cylinder Produced without Core)

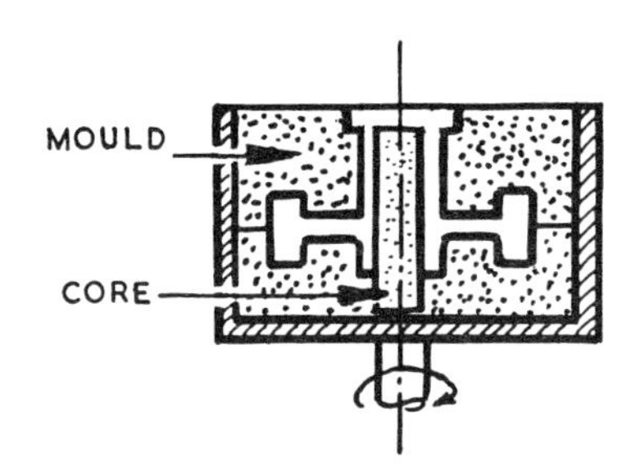

Fig. 4.6 Semi-centrifugal Casting

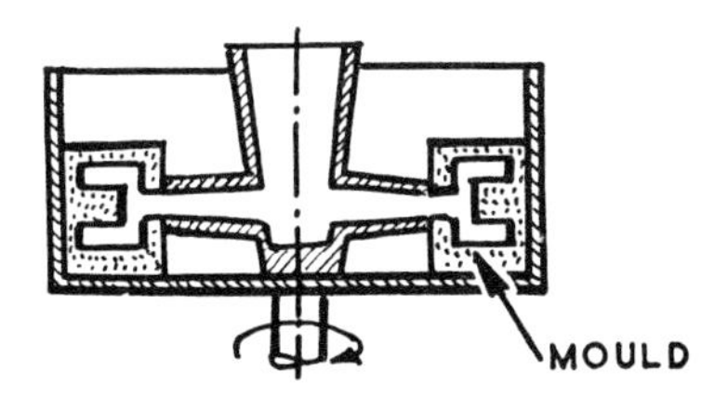

Fig. 4.7 Centrifuging

certain parts, either because the material is difficult to machine, or because the shape is difficult, or impossible, to machine.

4.215 CENTRIFUGAL CASTING

Castings that are accurate in shape and sound in structure can be produced by rotating the mould during casting. This system can be used to cast hollow cylinders, and castings that are symmetrical about one axis. A variation of this process is called centrifuging, and in this method, a pouring basin with radial runners is used, and a mould is attached to the end of each runner; the assembly is rotated about the basin axis during casting and sound, intricate castings can be obtained. Centrifuging is often used in conjunction with investment casting. Centrifugal casting is illustrated in figs. 4.5, 4.6 and 4.7.

4.216 CONTINUOUS CASTING

The more conventional technique of working consists of pouring the metal into moulds to produce ingots; these ingots are reheated and rolled to produce more convenient sizes. The billets, slabs, etc., are then heated and hot worked by rolling, forging, etc. Continuous casting aims at the rapid casting of long lengths of metal that can be cut up into suitable lengths for working.

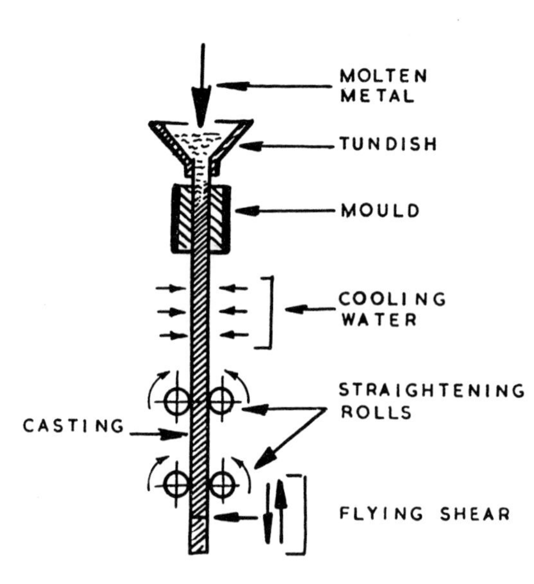

Fig. 4.8 The Principles of Continuous Casting

The continuous casting machine consists of a refractory-lined tundish, into which the molten metal is poured; the nozzle at the bottom of the tundish directs the metal into a vertical tubular mould. This mould is about 1 metre in length and is made of copper; the inside of the mould corresponds to the section required, and is usually chromium plated; the mould is water-cooled.

The casting is water-cooled as it leaves the mould and is controlled by special rollers. The speed of the machine is controlled so that a constant level of metal is maintained in the mould, and the casting is cut up into suitable lengths by flying shears.

It is claimed that continuous casting can be applied to very small sections, and produces very good quality material; the product is nearly hot enough for further hot working, and the process can be made automatic. The principle of continuous casting is illustrated in fig. 4.8.

Working

4.3 Working involves the manipulation of material when in the solid state; it usually produces mechanical properties that are better than those of a cast metal. Wrought (working) metals must be ductile or malleable, or be made so as a result of heating or heat treatment; they are often of a simple microstructure.

Working processes can be broadly classified as (*a*) hot working processes and (*b*) cold working processes. Hot working processes are done at a temperature that is higher than the recrystallisation temperature of the metal being worked, and so can produce large deformation without causing residual stresses. Cold working processes are done at a temperature below that of recrystallisation of the metal, and do not permit large deformation without frequent heat treatment to soften the metal; cold working causes residual stresses and so increase the hardness and strength of the metal.

The grain structure produced by working is different from that of a casting. Figure 4.9 illustrates the grain structure of a casting; the grains at the outside are small due to the rapid cooling and those just below the surface are columnar because they grow towards the core, which is the last to solidify; the grains at the core are coarse and equiaxed because the core will cool very slowly. Wrought parts usually display **grain flow** or **grain fibre**; when tested along the grain they show a greater strength than across the grain, and by arranging the grain fibre, the required directional strength can be obtained. Figure 9.1 on page 70 shows the grain flow of a typical forging.

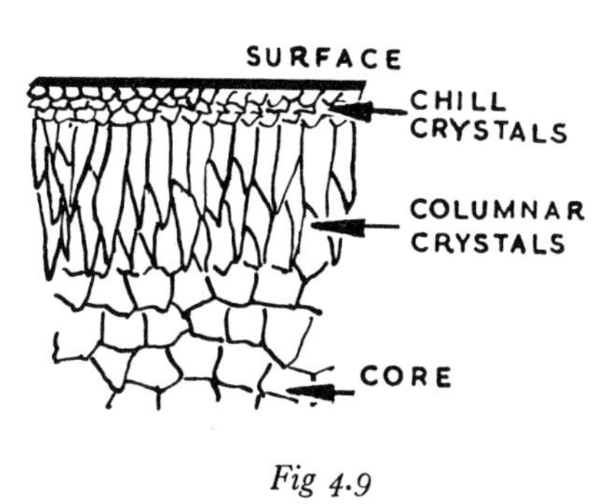

Fig 4.9

4.31 Hot Working Processes

4.311 FORGING

(*a*) *Hand Forging.* This is done by hammering the heated metal in conjunction with simple tools. The basic forging operations are upsetting, in which the section thickness is increased at the expense of length (see fig. 4.10), and drawing down, in which the length is increased at the expense of section thickness (see fig. 4.11(*a*)).

(*b*) *Machine Forging.* This is similar to hand forging, except that it is done to large pieces of metal, and a machine hammer or press is used; the tools used are large-scale versions of those used when hand forging, and the same basic operations are done. The ingot is suspended by a heavy chain called a 'burden chain' during the forging; during forging the ingot is positioned by the forging crane, and rotated by the burden chain; the ingot is counterbalanced by a 'porter bar' (see fig. 4.12).

During both hand and machine forging, only a small part of the material is worked at a time.

(*c*) *Drop Forging* (or Drop Stamping). This method is suitable for large

HOT WORKING PROCESSES—FORGING

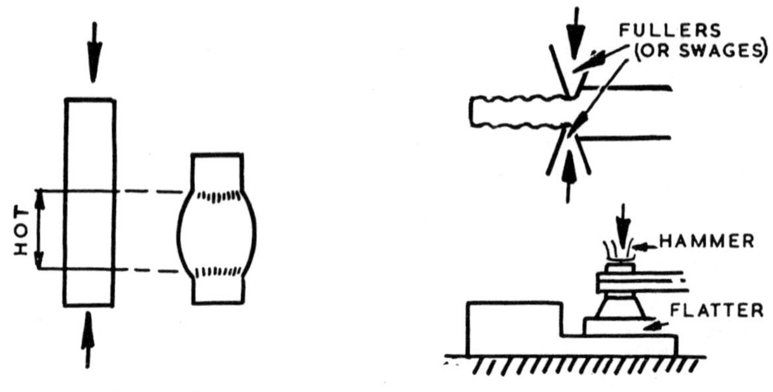

Fig. 4.10 Upsetting

Fig. 4.11(a) Drawing Down
Fig. 4.11(b) Setting Down

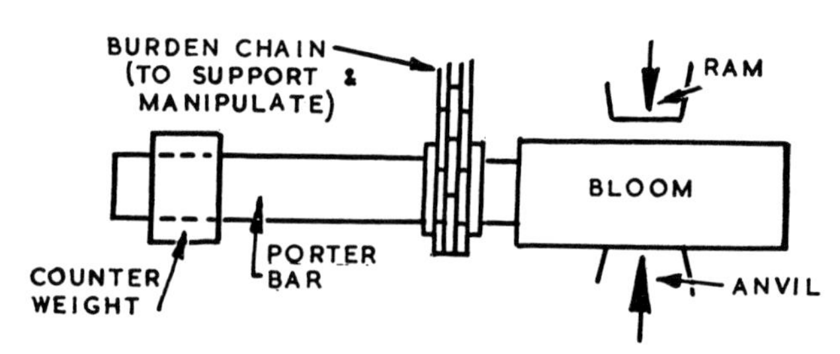

Fig. 4.12 Heavy Forging

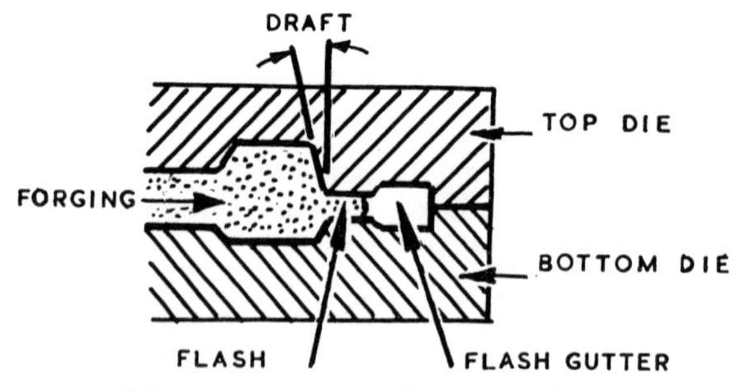

Fig. 4.13 Drop Forging Dies

quantities, and employs two **dies** of hard steel. Usually the upper die is dropped on to the heated metal, which rests in the lower die; forging is continued until the two dies make contact. The amount of metal to exactly fill the die cavity cannot be judged easily, and so the excess metal is allowed to flow into a gutter (see fig. 4.13). The **flash** so produced is severed from the finished forging. Simple shapes are produced by several blows using one pair of dies, but more complicated shapes required a number of dies. Drop forgings must be of simpler shape than castings, and when designing the forging, the position of the flash and the **draft** (see fig. 4.13) must be carefully considered; the fibre will follow the forging profile, and so the forging shape must be such that the required fibre direction is obtained.

4.312 HOT ROLLING

Heated metal can be rolled into long lengths by passing it between heavy rollers; before each pass the distance between the two rollers is reduced so that the metal becomes progressively thinner. Channel and other 'sections' can be rolled by shaping the rollers so that the series of gaps between them gradually produce the required section (see fig. 4.14).

4.313 EXTRUSION

In this process a heated billet of metal is placed in the heated container of a large hydraulic press and pushed through an orifice (called the **die**), to produce a continuous length with a constant cross section of the same size and shape as the die opening. Solid and hollow sections can be produced, and this process can be applied to any material that can be made plastic under suitable conditions. Steel is difficult to extrude because it demands high pressures and high temperatures. Figures 4.15, 4.16, and 4.17 illustrate the principle of extrusion.

4.32 Cold Working Processes

4.321 COLD ROLLING

Material that has been hot rolled can be cold rolled to improve its surface quality, give better dimensional accuracy, and to increase its hardness and strength. Before cold rolling, the hot rolled metal is **pickled** (immersed in hot dilute sulphuric acid) to remove the surface scale caused by the hot rolling.

4.322 IMPACT EXTRUSION. In this process (illustrated in fig. 4.18), a slug of metal is placed in the die and struck by the punch; the metal can be extruded forwards, backwards, or in both directions as required.

4.323 PRESSING. Sheet metal can be pressed into shape between formers as illustrated in fig. 4.19. Motor car bodies are produced in this way.

4.324 DEEP DRAWING. Very ductile metals, in sheet form, can be drawn and stretched into a cup-like shape using punch and die; this is illustrated in fig. 4.20.

4.325 STRETCH FORMING. Sheet metal can be formed by clamping the edges of the sheet and stretching it over a former as illustrated in fig. 4.21. This technique is used in the aircraft industry.

4.326 DRAWING

Metal can be made into wire by pulling it through a tapered hole (in the **die**), the combined pulling and squeezing action (the squeezing action is

HOT WORKING PROCESSES—
HOT ROLLING AND EXTRUSION

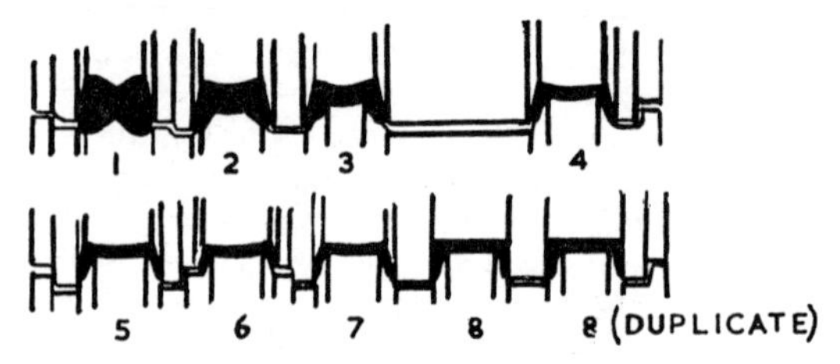

Fig. 4.14 Sequence when Hot Rolling a Channel using Two Pairs of Rolls

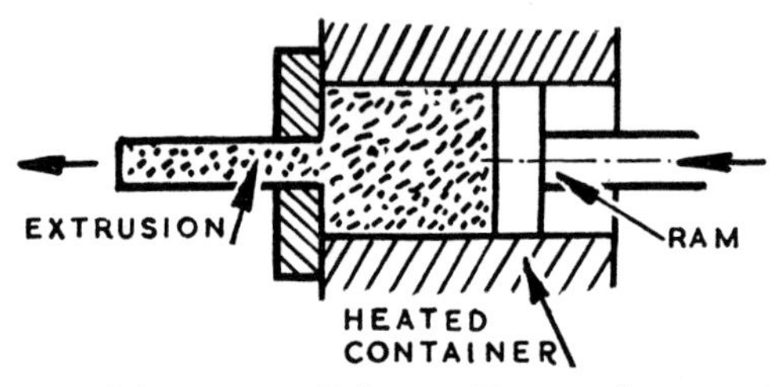

Fig. 4.15 Direct Extrusion

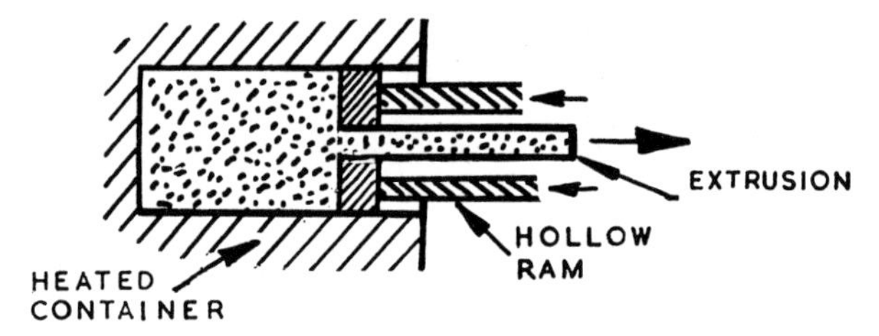

Fig. 4.16 Indirect Extrusion

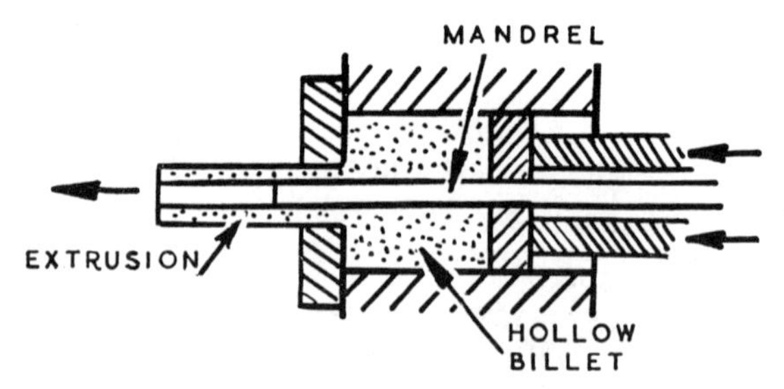

Fig. 4.17 Extruding a Hollow Section

The Principles of Extrusion

COLD WORKING PROCESSES

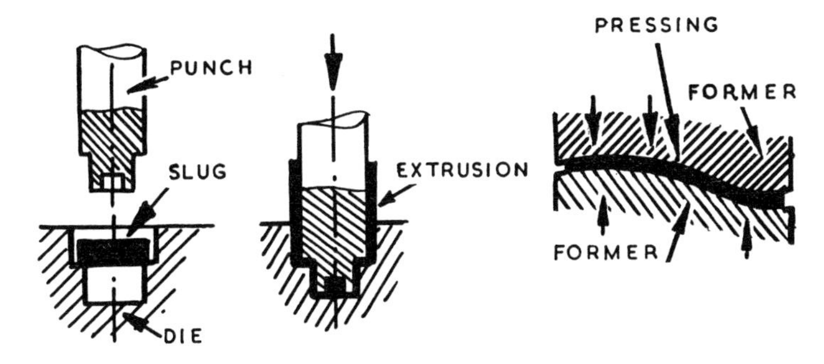

Fig. 4.18 Impact Extrusion *Fig. 4.19* Pressing

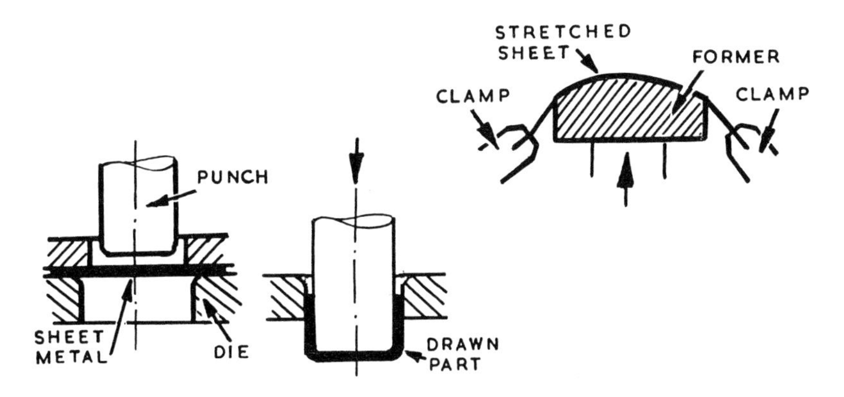

Fig. 4.20 Deep Drawing *Fig. 4.21* Stretch Forming

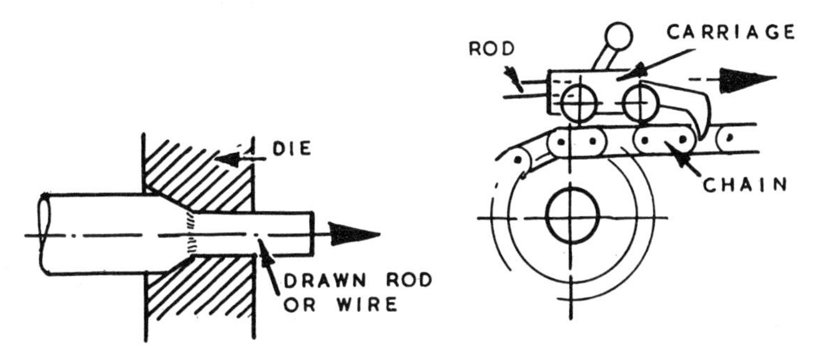

Fig. 4.22 Drawing *Fig. 4.23* Part of Drawbench

produced by the tapered hole) makes the metal longer and thinner, with a corresponding alteration of mechanical properties. The principle of drawing is illustrated in fig. 4.22.

When bright steel bars and similar sections are produced by drawing, a **drawbench** is used. The principle is the same as when wire drawing, but the drawbench incorporates an endless chain that is used to pull the metal through the die (see fig. 4.23).

4.327 EMBOSSING AND COINING

These are similar operations which use a punch and die set. Embossing (see fig. 4.25) is used to form thin sheet, and it has little effect upon the thickness of the sheet; this process can be regarded as local bending and forming.

Coining causes thin material to flow and fill the die cavity by local indentation and extrusion; this process is illustrated by fig. 4.24.

4.328 SPINNING

Spinning is a working process that is usually done in a machine shop. In this process, sheet metal that is sufficiently soft and ductile is forced against a rotating former to produce a hollow solid of revolution. The original process is a hand process that employs a simple lathe; a modern development of this process is **power spinning**, which is basically the same as hand spinning but the metal is worked by a roller. Spinning is illustrated in fig. 4.26.

4.329 FLOW FORMING

Flow Forming is a similar process to spinning, but the displacement of the metal is parallel to the axis of rotation; the diameter of the blank is almost the same as that of the finished component, but its thickness is greater. Flow forming is done using a machine that is heavier than that used for power spinning, and has been used to advantage for parts such as turbine shafts and diaphragms that were previously turned from necessarily heavy forgings. Flow forming is illustrated in fig. 4.27.

Powder Metallurgy

4.40 If metals are to be mixed using the more conventional methods, they must be heated to make them molten, and must form a homogeneous liquid solution. Powder metallurgy can be used to mix metals (or metallic compounds) that have a very high melting point, mix metals that have very different melting points, and to mix metals that do not form a homogeneous liquid solution; this process is also used when a special quality, or special properties, are required.

4.41 METHOD

The metal is first refined and if necessary made into a metallic compound (as in cemented carbide for cutting tools); the metal or compound is ground, or otherwise treated to put it in fine powder form, and then mixed with other fine metallic powders, and if necessary with a suitable lubricant to assist in the pressing operation.

The mixture is pressed in steel dies at a suitable temperature to form a briquette of the required shape, and then **sintered** at a suitable high tempera-

COLD WORKING PROCESSES

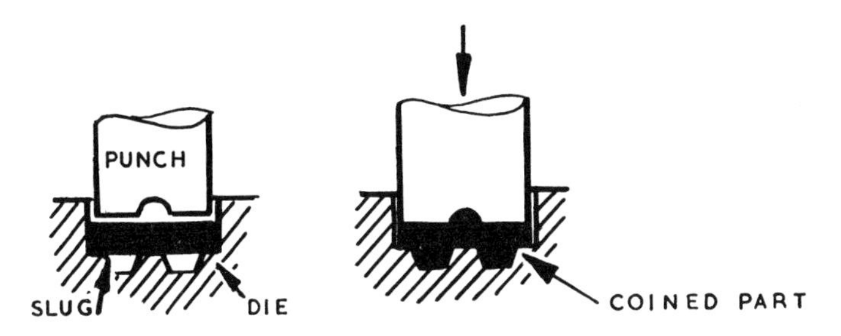

Fig. 4.24 Coining

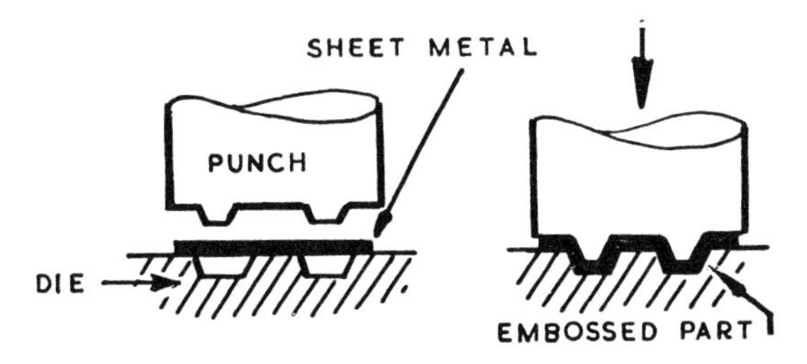

Fig. 4.25 Embossing

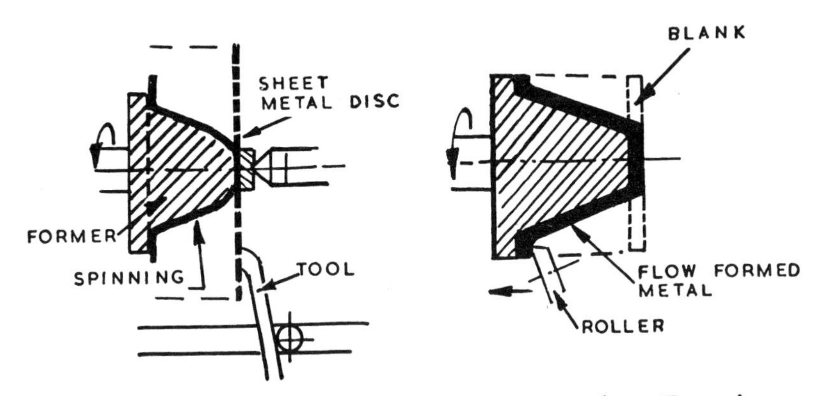

Fig. 4.26 Spinning

Fig. 4.27 Flow Forming

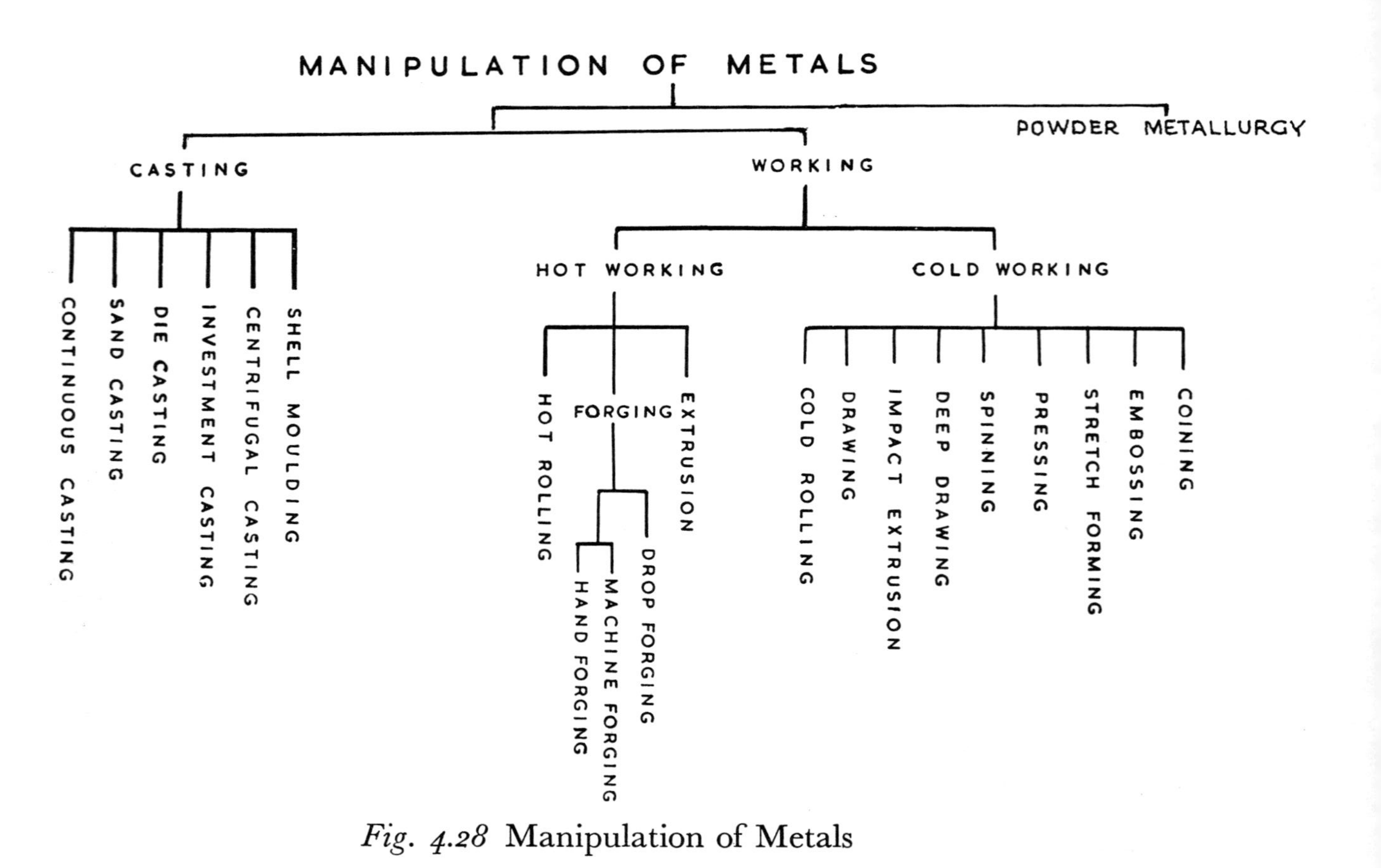

Fig. 4.28 Manipulation of Metals

ture. If special accuracy of shape is required, the sintered material is **sized** by a coining operation.

4.42 The main limitations of this method are the necessity for parts so shaped to be of simple form so that they can be pressed, the poor strength and toughness of material so produced, and the high cost of the equipment, equipment maintenance, and labour. Cemented carbides for cutting tools, electrical contact materials, refractory metals, and porous bearings are produced economically using powder metallurgy techniques.

CHAPTER 5

THE CONTROL OF THE MECHANICAL PROPERTIES OF METALS AND ALLOYS BY MANIPULATION AND BY HEAT TREATMENT

5·10 The mechanical properties (see page 48) of a metal or alloy may be controlled by its manipulation, its heat treatment or by a combination of its heat treatment and manipulation; heat treatment is a cycle of heating and cooling done upon the solid material. The principles of the main treatment are explained in this chapter, but the treatment that is applied varies from material to material, and so more precise details are given in the chapters that follow.

The control of properties can be classified as:

1. Control of the grains (*a*) by manipulation and (*b*) by heat treatment.
2. Strengthening by a heat treatment that produces a condition of non-equilibrium.

5·20 The control of the grains

The mechanical properties of a metal or alloy are influenced by the size and the shape of the grains, and the degree of work-hardening produced by cold working; this is best understood by studying the effects of heating and slowly cooling a metal or alloy.

If a piece of metal or alloy is heated to a suitably low temperature, there will be no change in its microstructure, but any small stresses produced by previous light manipulation or rapid cooling will be liberated. If the heating is continued, a temperature will be reached at which new grains are formed from the old ones; the temperature at which this **recrystallisation** occurs depends upon the melting point of the material as shown in table 5.1, but is slightly altered by the extent of previous treatment.

TABLE 5.1

	Recrystallisation temperature °C.	*Melting point °C.*
Tungsten	1200	3410
Molybdenum	900	2620
Nickel	600	1458
Iron	450	1535
Brasses	400	900–1050
Bronzes	400	900–1050
Copper	200	1083
Silver	200	960
Aluminium	150	660
Magnesium	150	651
Zinc	70	419
Lead	20	327
Tin	20	232

Continued heating will cause the whole structure to consist of new, equiaxed grains, and recrystallisation is said to be completed (a grain is equiaxed

EFFECT OF ANNEALING AND COLD WORKING UPON STRUCTURE OF COPPER

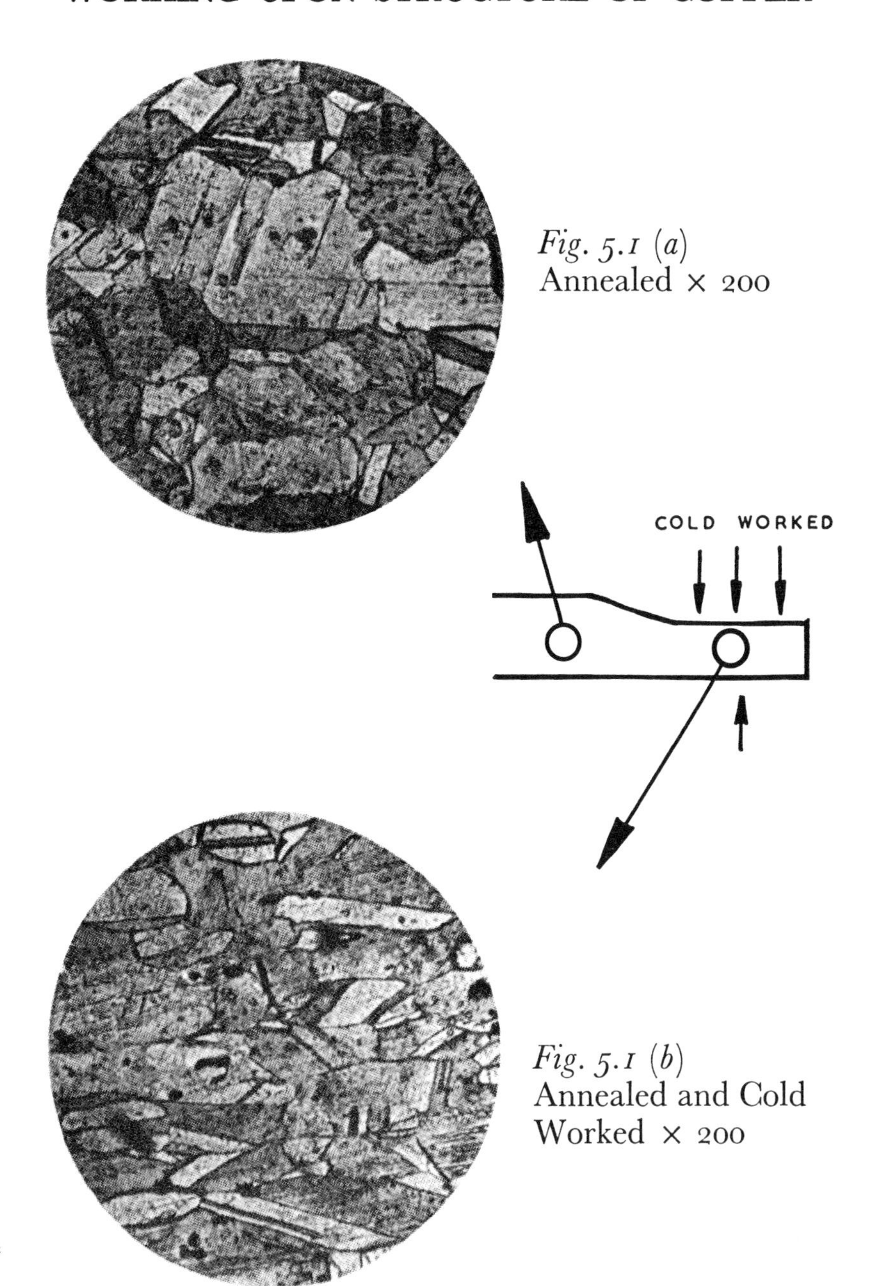

Fig. 5.1 (a)
Annealed × 200

Fig. 5.1 (b)
Annealed and Cold Worked × 200

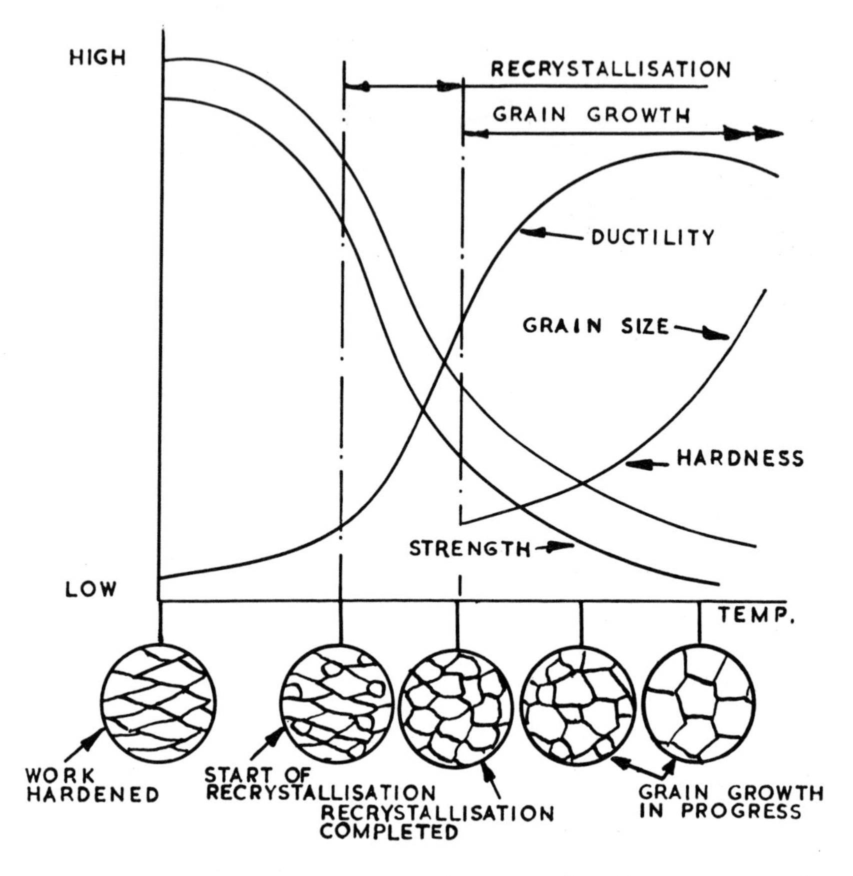

Fig. 5.2 The Effect of Heating on the Structure and Mechanical Properties of Cold Worked Metal

Note: Grain Growth Continues During Cooling above Recrystallisation Temperature

if its axes are approximately of equal length). These new grains will be equiaxed even if the old ones were not, and so the distortion and hardness produced by previous cold working is removed; these new grains will, at the completion of recrystallisation, be no smaller than the old ones, and so this process cannot be used on its own to change a coarse grained material into a fine grained one. If the heating is continued the larger grains will grow at the expense of the smaller ones, producing a coarse structure; this **grain growth** continues, even during cooling, as long as the material is above its recrystallisation temperature. Heating to produce a controlled, small amount of grain growth is known as **annealing**; this is a heat treatment process done to make a material soft and weak in preparation for cold working, and to remove the effects of cold working so that further cold work can be done without damage to the material. Fig. 5.2 shows the effect of heating a cold worked metal.

5.21 Cold working and hot working

When a pure metal or suitable alloy is cold worked it becomes stronger and harder because of distortion of the grains, and it is said to be **work hardened. Cold working** can be defined as 'working that produces residual stresses' and also as 'working at a temperature below that of recrystallisation'. Fig. 5.1 shows how the microstructure of annealed copper is altered by cold working.

Working at a temperature above that of recrystallisation will change the shape of the material, but the 'damage' to the grains will be 'repaired' by recrystallisation, work hardening will not occur, and the material is said to be **hot worked. Hot working** can be defined as 'working that does not produce residual stresses' and also as 'working at a temperature above that of recrystallisation'. Hot working causes the grains to be broken down, become equiaxed and to be arranged in an orderly way at right angles to the working force and so improve the strength of the material. This grain fibre can only be produced by hot working, and in most cases (steel is the exception) hot working is the only way that a metal can be made to have a finer grain without melting it and starting again.

5.30 Strengthening by heat treatment

If an alloy undergoes a phase change during slow cooling in the solid state it may be strengthened by a heat treatment process that prevents that change from taking place, or produces a different structure. This heat treatment usually involves heating the alloy to produce a solid solution and then quenching it so that there is insufficient time for the equilibrium condition to be achieved (quenching implies rapid cooling); the heating and quenching is usually followed by further heating at a lower temperature. This treatment can only be applied to alloys of the 'limited solid solubility' type (see page 22) of suitable composition and whose strength is sufficiently increased to make the treatment worth doing.

Alloy systems that are likely to respond to strengthening heat treatment can be classified as:

(*a*) Systems in which limited solid solubility at room temperature increases gradually when the alloy is heated.

(*b*) Systems in which a very limited solid solubility at room temperature becomes much less limited when the alloy is heated, because of an allotropic transformation that occurs at the higher temperature (an element is said to be allotropic if it can exist in more than one form in one state).

5·31 Heat treatment of alloys of the type where limited solid solubility is gradually increased by heating

Fig. 5·3 includes part of the equilibrium diagram for a system of this type. The alloy of composition 'X', will, if slowly cooled, consist of a solid solution of metal 'B' in metal 'A', in which are embedded particles of metal 'B' (or particles of an intermetallic compound of metals 'A' and 'B'). When this alloy is heated to a high enough temperature, the excess metal 'B' will be taken into the solid solution. If this alloy is slowly cooled from this tempera-

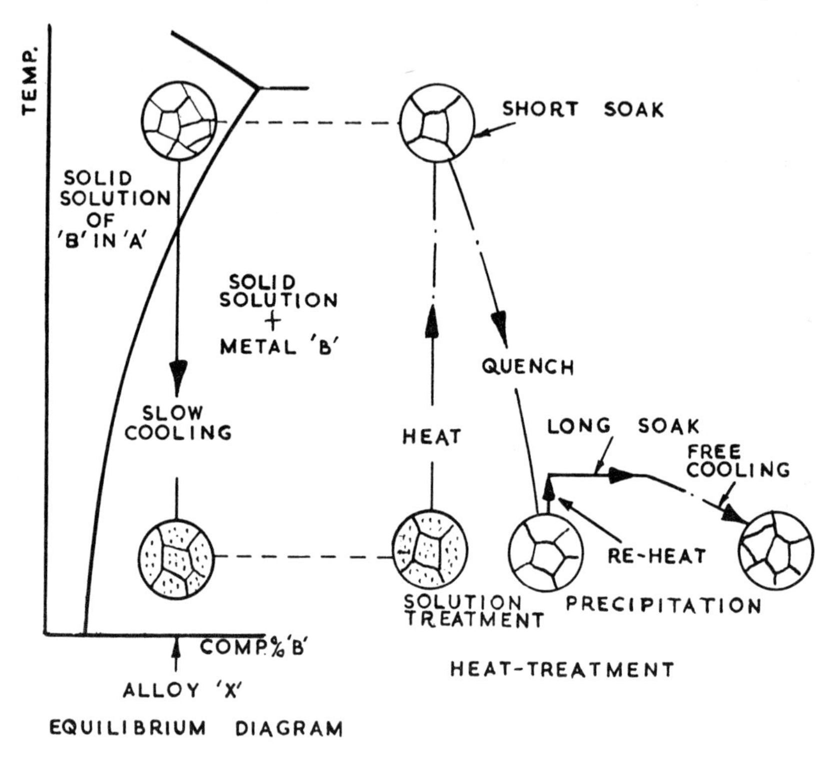

Fig. 5·3

ture, the excess metal 'B' atoms will be precipitated from the solid solution as indicated by the equilibrium diagram; but if it is quenched, there will be insufficient time for this to occur, and the excess 'B' atoms will be trapped in the solid solution, and the alloy will be in a condition of non-equilibrium. At this stage the excess 'B' atoms will be scattered throughout the structure and the **overall effect** will be to produce softness, weakness and ductility. Heating and quenching to produce this effect is called **solution treatment**, and is the first step towards increasing the strength of the alloy; but because it produces weakness, it is often followed by any cold working that needs to be done.

If the alloy is reheated, but to a lower temperature (see fig. 5·3), the atoms of metal 'B' will have enough energy to start their precipitation from the solid solution so that equilibrium is restored; but provided the temperature is not too high, they will not leave the solid solution, but form regions within it where the 'B' population is higher, and so locally strengthen the solid solution; the **overall effect** will be to produce increased strength and hardness at the expense of ductility. This second heat treatment is called **precipitation treatment**; it usually takes a long time, and is followed by free cooling to room temperature.

In the case of some alloys, this precipitation occurs at room temperature, starting very soon after quenching and takes about four days. Alloys of this type usually known as **naturally ageing** alloys (an aluminium alloy containing 4% copper is a typical example); these alloys are useful because they can be worked after solution treatment, when they are soft and weak, and develop their full strength without the distortion associated with heating.

Most heat-treatable alloys are heat treated by solution treatment followed by precipitation treatment, and a small number of heat-treatable alloys are of the naturally ageing type.

5.32 Heat treatment of alloys where a very limited solid solubility becomes less limited with temperature increase because of an allotropic transformation.

If the base (solvent) of the alloy undergoes an allotropic transformation so that it accepts more of the alloying addition (the solute) at a suitable temperature, a condition of non-equilibrium can be produced by quenching the alloy from that temperature. Quenching will not necessarily prevent the reverse allotropic change from taking place, but it will prevent the excess quantity of the solute from being precipitated; the structure so produced will be a **supersaturated solid solution**, and the hardness and strength of the alloy will be increased by distortion of the lattice of the solvent metal caused by the excessive quantity of the solute.

This is the most uncommon method of strengthening by heat treatment; the only important example being steel. Steel is an alloy of iron (which is allotropic) and carbon (which enters into solid solution in a much larger quantity at higher temperatures); it is heat treated by quenching from a suitable temperature to produce a structure that is modified by a second, lower temperature heating; by careful combination of the quenching rate and the reheating temperature, a range of properties between those of the slowly cooled alloy and those of the fully hardened alloy can be produced.

CHAPTER 6

THE MECHANICAL TESTING OF ENGINEERING MATERIALS

6.10 Mechanical tests are done to determine the **mechanical properties** of a material; a mechanical property is determined by deformation or by destruction. Properties that are determined by other methods are called **physical properties**; density, electrical resistivity, and thermal conductivity are typical physical properties.

Mechanical Properties

6.11 *Strength.* Strength is the ability to resist the application of force without rupture; the force may be tensile, compressive, or shear.
Hardness. This is a complex property, and may be taken to be the resistance to abrasion, deformation, or to indentation.
Elasticity. The property by which a material returns to its original dimensions after the removal of a stress is called elasticity.
Plasticity. Plasticity is the capacity to undergo deformation by hot or by cold working.
Ductility. This is the ability to undergo cold plastic deformation, usually by tension.
Malleability. This is the capacity for undergoing deformation in all directions, usually cold deformation by hammering or squeezing.
Toughness. Toughness is the capacity to withstand shock loads.
Brittleness. A tendency to fracture without visible plastic deformation is called brittleness.

Mechanical Tests

6.12 Mechanical tests can be divided into two groups. These groups are **design tests**, that are done to determine the properties of a material, and **routine tests**, that are done to determine if raw material is to the required standard, or as a check upon heat treatment.

The main routine tests are the tensile test, and the hardness test. Other routine tests, such as impact and ductility tests, may be done, depending upon the requirements.

6.20 The Tensile Test

The tensile test is used as a routine test because it is simple to do; the properties so measured are called **tensile properties**. Tensile strength and ductility are the properties usually determined during a routine test; the elasticity of a material can also be determined by this test, but it is not usual to do so during a routine test.

6.21 *The Test Piece.* In order to eliminate the effect of variation of shape, material is machined to a standardised shape before tensile testing it. Two typical British Standard Test Pieces are illustrated in figs. 6.1 and 6.2. It will be seen that the test is conducted over a part of the test piece that is accurately machined; this length is called the **gauge length** and is usually $5{\cdot}65\sqrt{S_0}$, where S_0 = cross-sectional area of test piece.

6.22 THE BEHAVIOUR OF MATERIAL DURING A TENSILE TEST

If a test piece is subjected to a tensile test during which an axial force is applied, and the extension of the gauge length produced by each force is measured using an **extensometer**, a graph can be plotted to show the connection between force and extension. Figure 6.3 illustrates a typical curve obtained in this manner, and it will be seen that when small forces are applied, the extension is proportional to the force; if the force is removed, the material will return to its original size and shape, and is said to be **elastic**. When the **limit of proportionality** is reached (point 'P' on the curve) the extension will cease to be proportional to the force, although the material is still elastic. Eventually a point will be reached at which the material will no longer return completely to its original dimensions; this point 'E' is called the **elastic limit**. After this point has been passed, the material will be partly elastic and partly plastic; points 'P' and 'E' are often very close together.

If the test is continued, the extension will become localised, and a **waist** will be developed. As a result of this waisting, the stress will increase without further force, as indicated by the broken line on fig. 6.3. The extension and waisting continues until fracture occurs.

If necessary, the true stress can be recorded and plotted against strain; but to do this, the diameter of the specimen must be measured continually during the test. To avoid this measuring, it is conventional to plot either the force against the extension, or the **nominal stress** against strain; the nominal stress is the force divided by the original area.

This convention is justified because when in service, materials are stressed well below their elastic limit, and at these stresses little change in diameter occurs, and so the nominal stress differs little from the true stress at the lower forces. The value for **tensile strength** (see below for the calculation method) obtained using this method is less than the stress necessary to produce fracture; it will be appreciated that the tensile strength is the stress that causes waisting to occur, and is the limiting stress. When calculating sizes, this stress value is used, and a **safety factor** is applied to it to bring the stress that the part is designed to withstand well below the elastic limit for the material. It will be seen that the shape of the stress/strain curve obtained using this convention is the same shape as the force/extension curve, and so only the scales need be altered to convert one curve into the other.

6.23 THE BEHAVIOUR OF A SOFT STEEL DURING A TENSILE TEST

It will be seen from fig. 6.4 that when soft steel is subjected to a tensile test, a point is reached when elongation occurs without increase in load; this is called the **yield point**. Although the material will withstand stress much higher than the yield stress, the latter must not be exceeded because the sudden extension could cause failure of other parts of the assembly, if not to the part itself.

TENSILE TEST

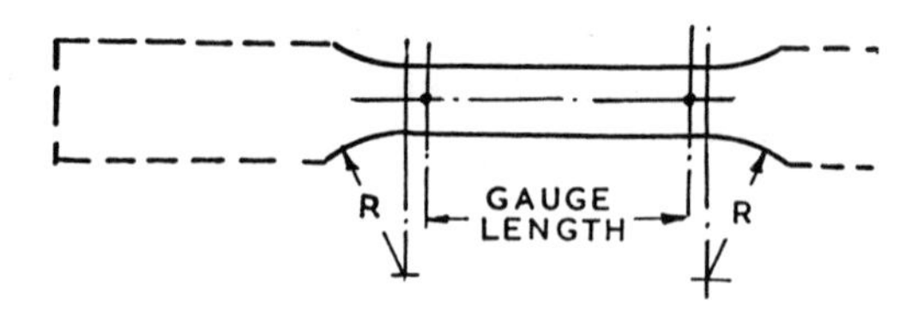

Fig. 6.1 British Standard Flat Test Piece

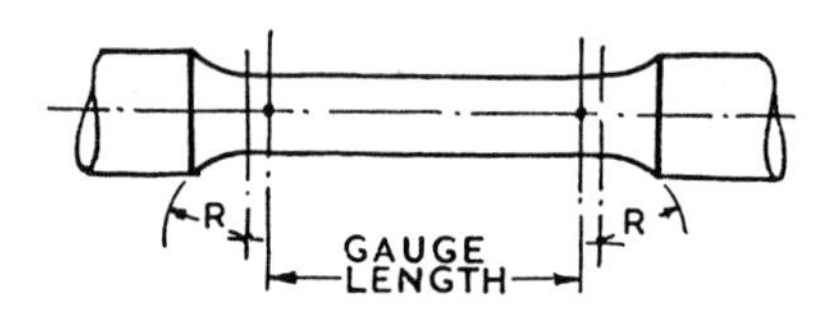

Fig. 6.2 British Standard Round Test Piece

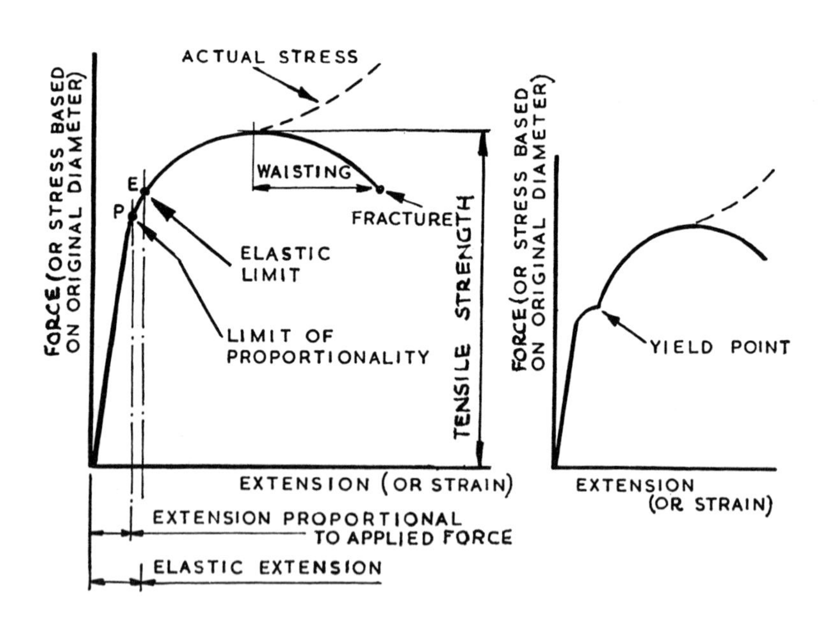

Fig. 6.3
Typical Tensile Test Curve

Fig. 6.4
Tensile Test Curve for Soft Steel

6.24 TENSILE PROPERTIES

If a nominal-stress/strain curve is drawn from the information recorded during the test, Young's Modulus of Elasticity, 'E', can be determined.

$$E = \frac{\text{increase in stress}}{\text{increase in strain}}$$

where $\text{stress} = \dfrac{\text{force}}{\text{original area}}$ $\qquad$ $\text{strain} = \dfrac{\text{extension}}{\text{original length}}$.

It will be apparent that 'E' is the slope of the straight portion of the nominal-stress/strain curve.

6.25 When conducting a routine test, it is not usual to record forces and extensions or to plot a curve; usually the maximum force and the yield point is noted during the test, and the test piece measured after fracture to obtain the extension and the diameter at the waist. This information is used to determine the tensile strength of the material and to give an indication of its ductility.

$$\text{tensile strength } (R_m) = \frac{\text{maximum force}}{\text{original cross-sectional area of the test piece}}$$

The percentage elongation, and the percentage reduction of area both give an indication of the ductility of the material; the percentage elongation is the more reliable because it is easier to measure the extension of the gauge length than the reduction of area, and because the material may not still be rectangular or circular in section at the waist after fracture.

$$\text{percentage elongation after fracture. } (A) = \frac{L_u - L_o}{L_o} \times 100$$

where L_o is the original gauge length,
L_u is the final gauge length.

When quoting the percentage elongation, the gauge length or the specification number of the test piece form must be quoted also, because the local extension is independent of the gauge length.

$$\text{percentage reduction of area } (Z) = \frac{S_o - S_u}{S_o} \times 100$$

where S_o is the original cross-sectional area,
S_u is the minimum cross-sectional area after fracture.

6.26 PROOF STRESS (R_p)

It has been explained that the yield stress is very important, and must not be exceeded; if a material does not display a clearly defined yield point, a substitute for it must be employed. The proof stress value is the usual one to use, and is defined as *the tensile stress (force divided by the original area of cross section of a test piece) which is just sufficient to produce, under force, a non-proportional elongation equal to a specified percentage of the original gauge length.* Usually a value of 0·2% is used, and the proof stress is then referred to as the '0·2% proof stress'. When proof stress is to be determined, it is usual to start with an initial force of 10kN, to ensure that the test piece has settled down in the grips before fitting the extensometer; the forces and equivalent extensions are recorded and a curve drawn. The proof stress is obtained from this curve by drawing a line parallel to the straight portion of the curve, at a distance from it by an amount representing the required non-proportional extension; the force at which this line cuts the curve divided by the original cross-sectional area of the gauge length is the proof stress. This is illustrated in fig. 6.5.

DETERMINATION OF PROOF STRESS

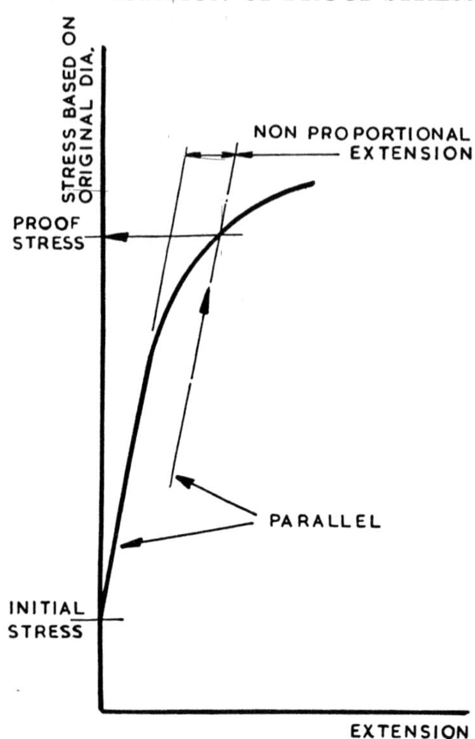

Fig. 6.5 Usually the stress to just produce under force, a non-proportional extension of 0·2% of the gauge length is quoted and called '*The 0·2% Proof Stress*'

Sometimes proof stress in compression is required; this is difficult to obtain, especially when the material is in sheet form, because of the tendency for buckling to occur. Various systems are used to prevent this buckling; the equipment must support the material, but present only the minimum resistance to axial movement of the material during the compression test.

6.30 Hardness and Hardness Testing

Hardness is a complex property that cannot be defined simply. It can be taken to be one of the following:

(*a*) The ability to scratch other material.
(*b*) The ability to resist scratching.
(*c*) The ability to resist plastic spreading under indentation.
(*d*) The ability to resist elastic deformation under indentation.
(*e*) The ability to resist deformation by rolling.

There is a definite relationship between hardness and tensile strength, and so a hardness test is a simple, virtually non-destructive test that can be used to give an indication of the strength of a material as well as its resistance to wear. It can also be used as a test of heat treatment, because it can be applied locally; it also gives an indication of the machinability of a material.

All hardness tests are comparative tests involving the comparison between the material under test and some other material.

6.31 HARDNESS TESTS

There are a number of hardness tests in use because of the large number of definitions of hardness, and the method used depends upon the conditions anticipated when the material is in service, or when it is being fabricated, and upon the ease with which the test must be performed.

6.32 1. *Scratch Tests.* Tests of this type measure the resistance of the material to scratching. In **Moh's Scale**, a number of substances are arranged so that each substance will scratch the one preceeding it in the scale but not that which succeeds it. Ten styli are used, one with each of the substances in the scale, and the hardness number of the material under test is one number less than that of the substance that just scratches it. This test is useful for mineralogists, but it is not convenient as an engineering test.

Moh's Scale

1. Talc	6. Felspar
2. Gypsum	7. Quartz
3. Calcspar	8. Topaz
4. Fluorspar	9. Corundum
5. Apatite	10. Diamond

Attempts have been made to produce a machine that tests scratch resistance, as this is often required, but so far these have not been particularly successful.

6.33 2. *Indentation Tests.* These tests are the most common hardness tests used in engineering because they are simple to perform; it is usual to consider hardness as the resistance to plastic deformation. These hardness tests involve forcing an indenter into the surface of the material under test, and then basing the hardness value either upon the surface area of the impression, or upon the depth to which the indenter enters the material.

The Brinell Hardness Testing Machine (fig. 6.6), the Firth Brown Hardometer (fig. 6.7), and the Vickers Hardness Testing Machine (fig. 6.8) all produce hardness values based upon surface area of impression:

$$\text{Hardness number} = \frac{\text{force}}{\text{surface area of impression}}$$

6.331 *The Brinell Hardness Testing Machine.* This machine consists of a cylinder into which oil is forced by hand pump (in some machines by motor); at the lower end of the cylinder is a piston to which is attached the ball indenter. At the top of the cylinder another piston supports the dead weights, and the oil is pumped into the space between these two pistons so that when the dead weights are floating the desired force is attained. The force is allowed to act upon the material under test for 15 seconds to ensure that plastic flow occurs. The surface diameter of the indentation is measured using a microscope and the Brinell Hardness Number (HB) calculated or obtained from charts.

6.332 *The Firth Brown Hardometer.* In this machine the force is applied by compressing a calibrated spring; the indenter can be a steel ball or a diamond. The surface diameter is measured using a microscope that can be swung into position, and the hardness number obtained from charts. The hardness value obtained using this machine with a steel ball is the same as the Brinell Hardness Number.

6.333 *The Vickers Hardness Testing Machine.* This machine uses a diamond with 136° apex angle between facets, and the force automatically applied by a lever. The force can be altered to suit the material under test, and the surface size of the indentation is measured using a microscope with shutters, and the distance recorded by a counter; the hardness number (HV) is obtained from charts that take into account the force, the shape of the indenter, and the microscope magnification.

6.334 *The Rockwell Hardness Testing Machine* (see fig. 6.9) produces hardness numbers based upon depth of impression. To eliminate surface roughness effects or zero errors, a small force is applied, and then a suitable 'major' force is applied; the increase in depth of impression due to the major force is noted and used as a measure of hardness. The indenter can be a steel ball or a diamond cone; Rockwell Hardness 'B' scale is associated with the ball, and Rockwell Hardness 'C' scale with the diamond cone.

6.34 3. *Rolling Tests.* The Herbert Pendulum Test (fig. 6.10) is a test for the resistance to rolling load; it uses an arched pendulum that rests on a steel ball or a spherical-ended diamond, and is balanced using weights. A spirit level is incorporated into the arch of the pendulum. Two main tests can be done using this apparatus, the **time hardness test**, and the **scale test**. The time hardness test is done by making the pendulum oscillate through a small arc, and using the time taken for it to complete 10 single swings as the hardness value; the time hardness for lead is 3 and for glass 100. The scale hardness is obtained by tipping the pendulum so that the bubble is at zero at one end of the spirit level scale, and then allowing the pendulum to swing; the scale number to which the bubble travels at the end of the first swing is the scale hardness number.

6.35 4. *Rebound Tests.* The **Shore Scleroscope** (fig. 6.11) is an example of a dynamic test; it uses a small diamond-tipped hammer that is allowed to fall freely from a height of 250 mm in a graduated glass tube, on to the material under test. The height of the rebound is used as the hardness number; the softer the material, the more energy will be absorbed when the hammer strikes it, and the smaller will be the height of the rebound.

6.40 IMPACT TESTING

The toughness of a material is tested by impact; toughness is not revealed by tensile testing, and two materials may have identical tensile strengths, but behave quite differently when under impact. Impact testing is used to compare the shock resistance of different materials, to reveal brittleness produced by heat treatment, and to indicate the effect of shape upon the shock resistance of a material.

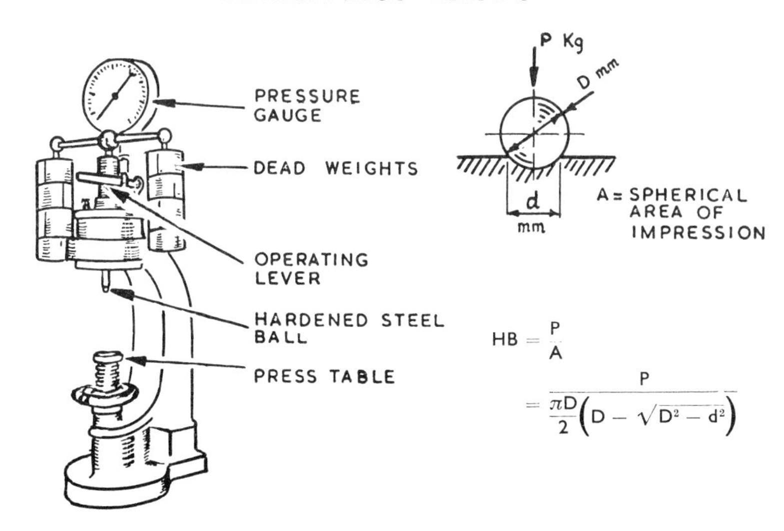

Fig. 6.6 The Brinell Hardness Test

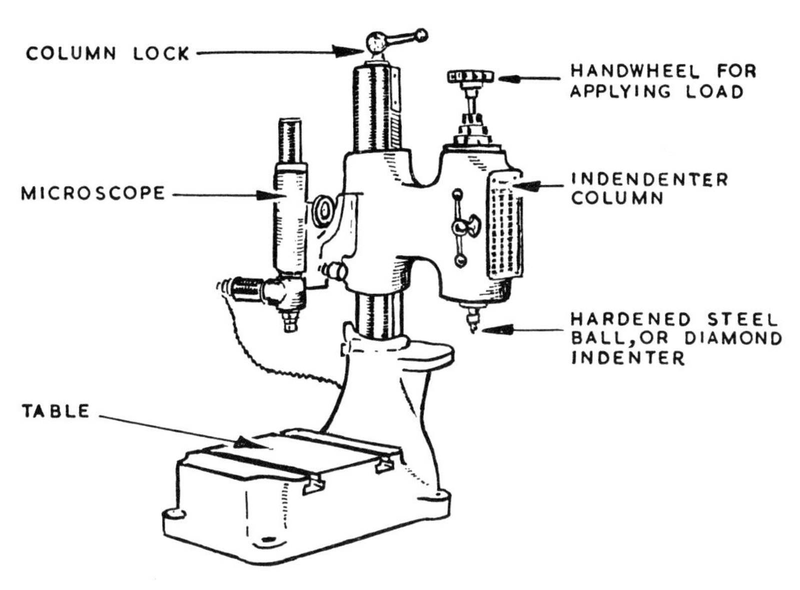

Fig. 6.7 The Firth Brown Fixed Load Hardometer (Microscope Shown Swung into Position)

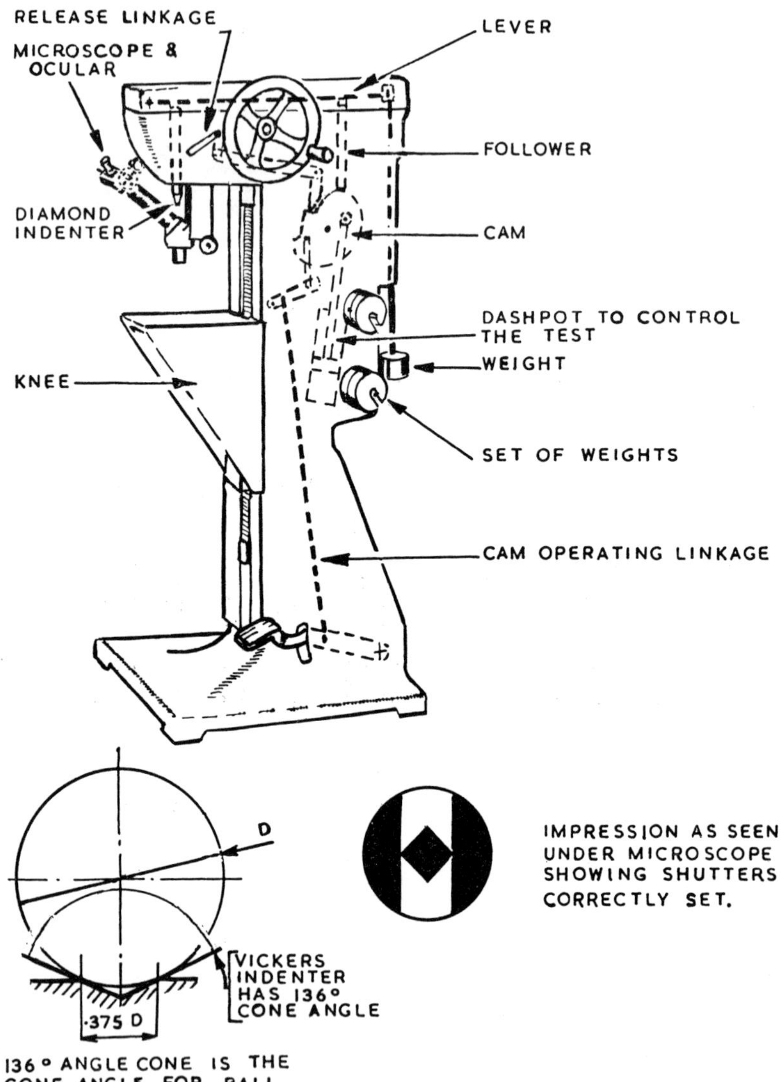

Fig. 6.8 Vickers Pyramid Hardness Testing Machine

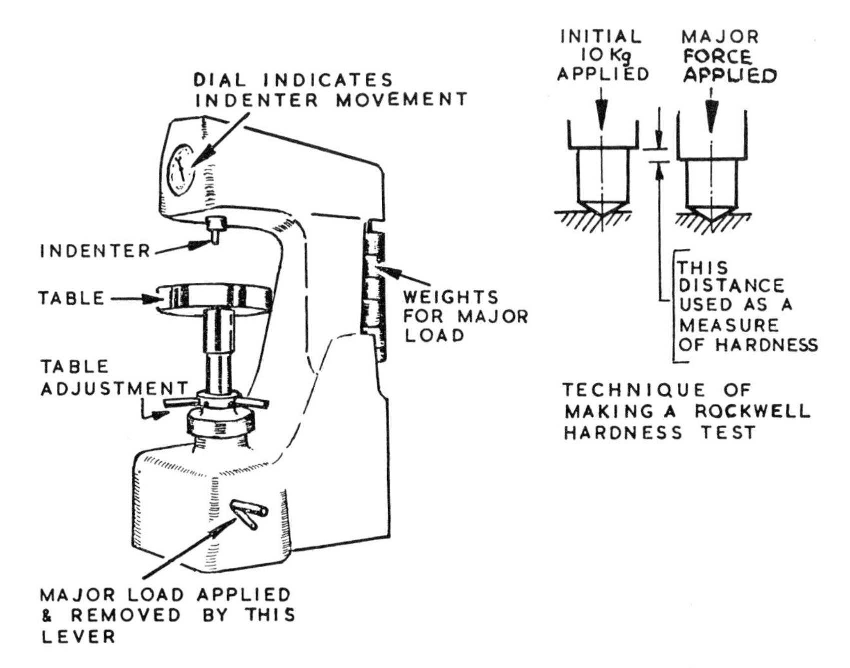

Fig. 6.9 Rockwell Hardness Testing Machine

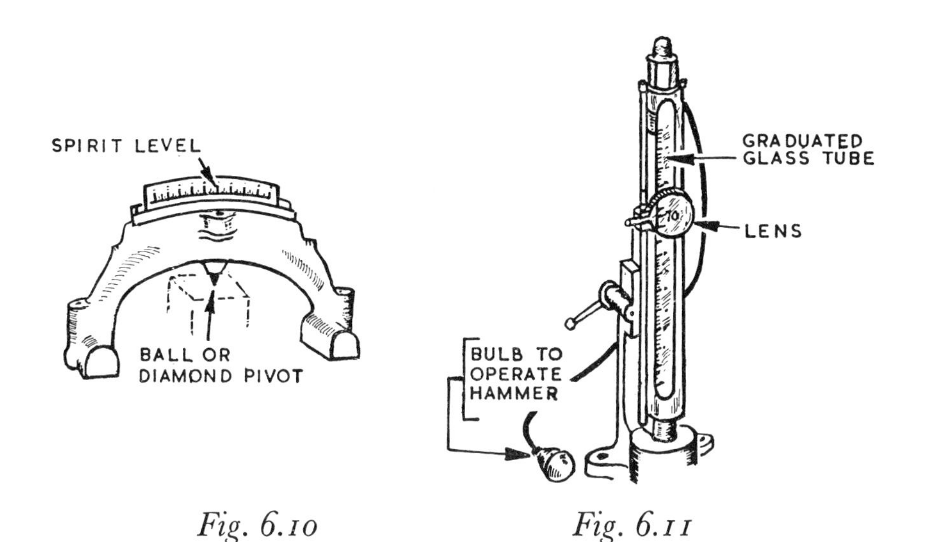

Fig. 6.10
Pendulum Hardness Tester

Fig. 6.11
Shore Scleroscope

6.41 The pendulum impact testing machine is illustrated in fig. 6.12 and is a common method of impact testing. The Izod machine uses a cantilever-type test piece, and the Charpy machine uses a beam-type test piece. In both machines the extreme swing position of the pendulum after striking the test piece is used as an indication of the impact strength. The tougher the material the greater amount of energy absorbed in fracturing it, and the smaller will be the extent of the swing after it has been fractured.

6.50 DUCTILITY TESTS

A **bend test** is a simple test of ductility that does not require special equipment or a specially shaped test piece. Figure 6.17 illustrates the simple bend test, in which a straight, solid test piece of round or rectangular section is subjected to plastic deformation in one direction. In order to be acceptable the test piece must, after bending through a specified angle, be unbroken and free from cracks that are visible to the unaided eye, on the outside surface. This test may also be done using roller supports, vee block, a soft steel block, or similar methods; as an alternative, the material may be wrapped around a mandrel by hammering it (see fig. 6.18), or by using a bend testing machine.
6.51 Bend tests for sheet metal can be classed as single bend tests, and reverse bend tests. The single bend tests can be subdivided into close bend, angle bend, and 180° bend (see fig. 6.19); the reverse bend tests can be subdivided into 180° reverse bend and 90° reverse bend (see figs. 6.20 and 6.21).
6.52 Other bend tests include the drift test, flatting and bending tests for tubes, and the wrapping test for wire.
6.53 The **cupping test** is a ductility test that is used in conjunction with press-tool work. In the **Erichson Test** (see fig. 6.22), the sheet metal to be tested is pushed into the die by the punch, which is screw operated. The operation is continued until fracture occurs, and the depth of the cup at the point of fracture is the 'Erichson Value'. In Continental practice, the test piece is gripped between the die and the clamp, but in America and Britain clearance is allowed so that the metal can draw down. This test is very valuable as a comparison test, but it is not regarded as being as discriminating as tensile and bend tests, and is not recommended by the British Standards Institution as a test for specification purposes.

Materials Specifications

6.60 Specifications are used to standardise the quality and properties of material, and, where applicable, its dimensions. A specification states the composition and mechanical properties, and gives particulars of the test piece dimensions and the test procedure to be adopted. If the specification relates to drawn, rolled, or extruded section, the standard sizes and tolerances are also stated.

A specification is intended to be a document to form the basis of purchase agreement, and the inspection of material; it is not, in itself, a design instruction because not all the characteristics of a material are listed in its specification. When further details are required about a material, the manufacturer should be consulted.

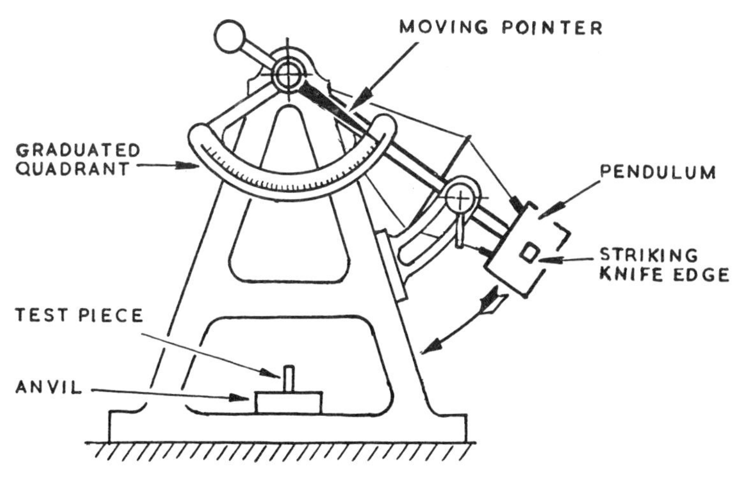

Fig. 6.12 Izod Machine

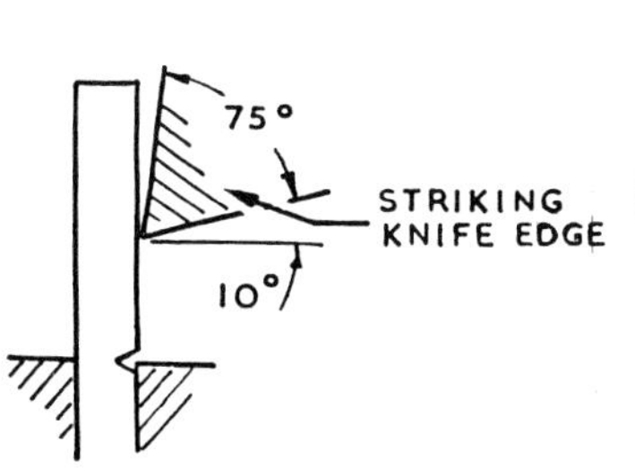

Fig. 6.13 Cantilever Impact Test (Elev.)

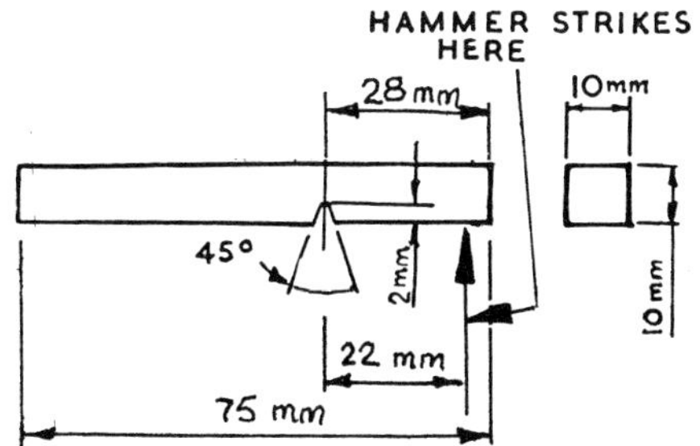

Fig. 6.14 One-Notch British Standard Cantilever Type Test Piece

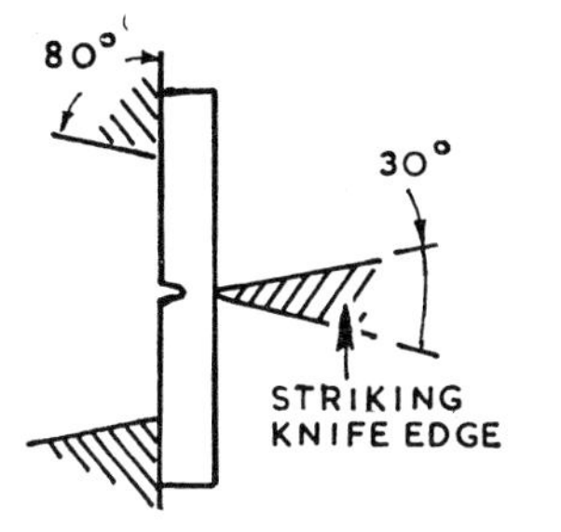

Fig. 6.15 Beam Impact Test (Plan)

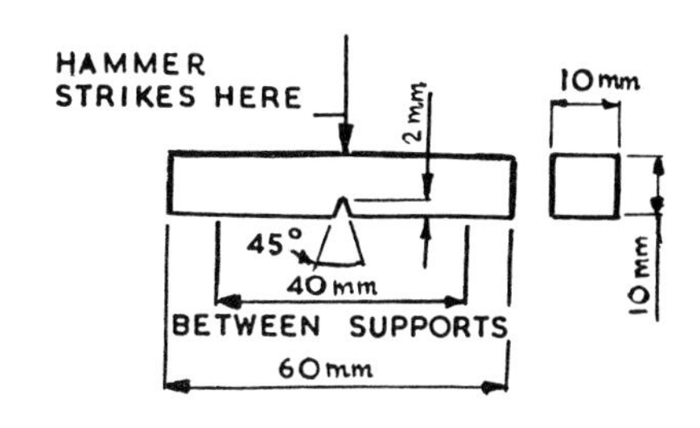

Fig. 6.16 British Standard Beam Type Test Piece

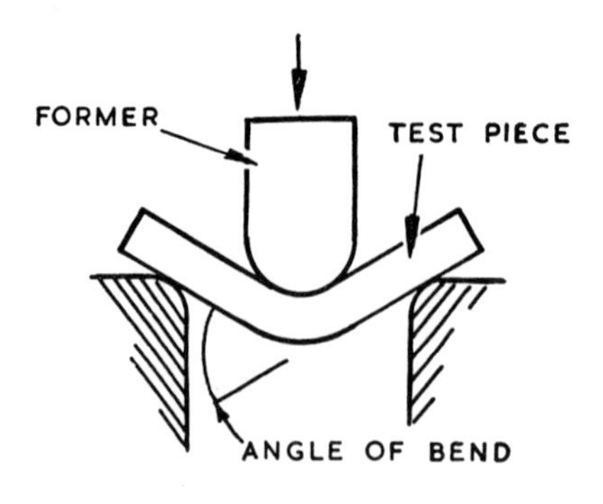

Fig. 6.17
Simple Method of Test

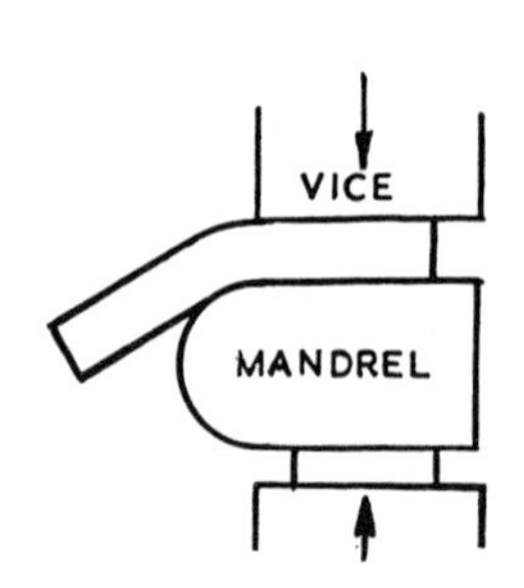

Fig. 6.18
Bending Round a Mandrel

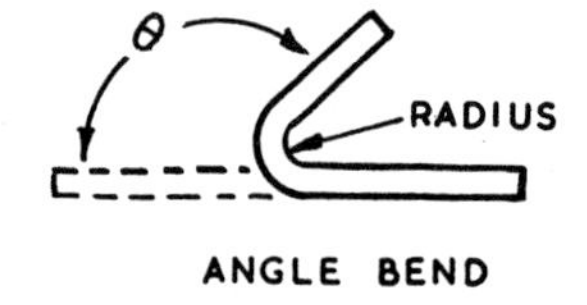

Fig. 6.19 Single Bend Tests on Sheet Metal

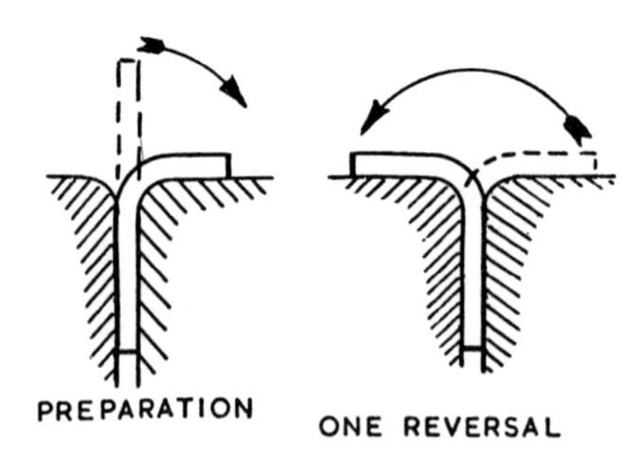

Fig. 6.20
180° Reverse Bend on sheet metal

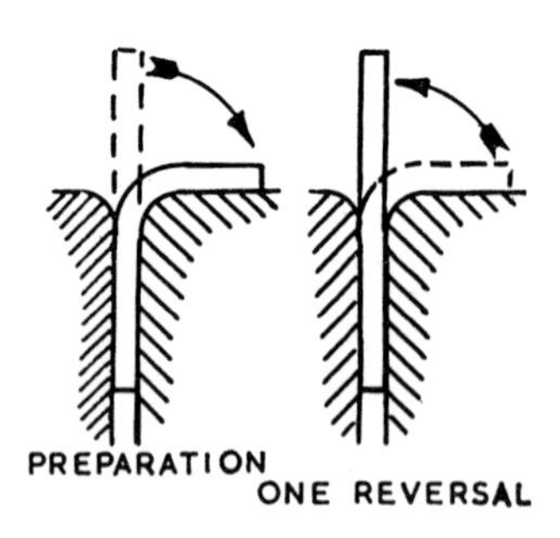

Fig. 6.21
90° Reverse Bend on sheet metal

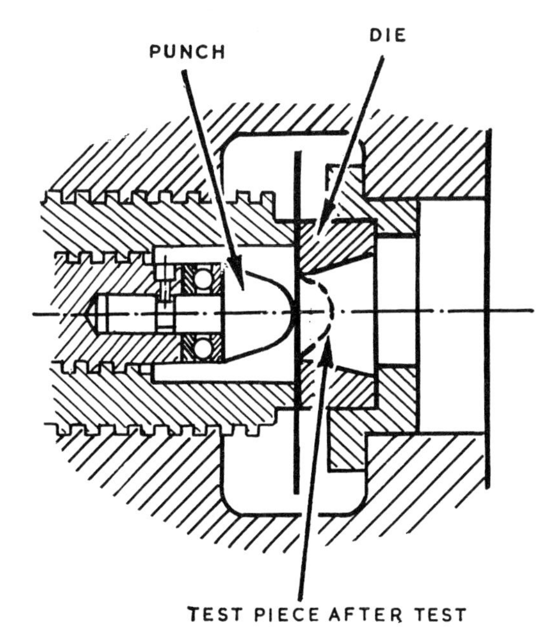

Fig. 6.22 The Principle of the Erichson Test

6.61 British Standard Specifications

The British Standards Institution is the approved body for the preparation and issue of the British National Standards, and it issues standards for a wide range of commodities and procedures; these standards are identified by the prefix 'BS' and the reference number of the specification is followed by the date of issue. A selection of British Standards for material and test procedures is listed on page 240.

Steels are specified by a system which indicates the type of steel, condition of supply and the specific steel.

6.62 Material for use in aircraft must be of an especially high quality. Aircraft steels are identified by the symbol 'S', and reissues of each specification are indicated by the issue number, which is put in front of the 'S'. For example, '3 S 14' is a case hardening steel that conforms to issue 3 of the specification 'S 14'.

Light alloys for aircraft use are identified by the symbol 'L', brass, copper, etc., by the symbol 'B', cast irons by the symbol 'K', and plastics by 'PL'. Reissues of the specification are indicated by the prefix number.

6.63 D.T.D. Specifications

Specifications which are approved by the Directorate of Technical Development for use in aircraft purchased by the government but which are not covered by British Standards for Aircraft are given a D.T.D. reference number. These specifications and procedure may later be given the status of a British Standard, but will remain D.T.D. specifications if of limited national use.

CHAPTER 7

CREEP AND CREEP TESTING

7.10 When a material is loaded for long periods, it may gradually deform, and fracture at a stress that is well below the ultimate tensile stress as determined by short-time tensile testing; this continuous gradual extension under a **steady force** or **steady stress** is known as **creep.**

Creep must be considered when a material is to be used at temperatures approaching its recrystallisation temperature (see page 42, section 5.22); for example, creep must be considered when steel is used at temperatures above 500°C., and when low-melting-point metals, such as lead and tin, are used at room temperature.

Creep is very important in gas turbines. For example, the blades must be made from a creep-resisting material because the high temperatures and rotational speeds produce creep, and the clearance between the tip of each blade and the turbine casing cannot be large, otherwise the engine efficiency will suffer.

7.20 Creep Testing

Figure 7.1 illustrates the essential features of a creep test; this is usually done using a parallel, circular-sectioned specimen, under simple tensile stresses. The results obtained by the test are corrected if other types of stress and loading is expected in service.

Creep tests are usually done at high temperatures, and over long periods of time; it is therefore necessary to include a furnace that can be controlled to fine limits, and also a thermocouple so that the temperature of the material under test can be recorded. At certain stages in the test the rate of extension of the test piece will be very small, and so means of accurately measuring small extensions must be included.

7.30 BEHAVIOUR OF SPECIMEN DURING CREEP TEST (see fig. 7.2)

After the strain produced by the initial force, creep proceeds in three stages. During the **primary creep period** the rate of creep decreases, to become steady throughout the **secondary creep period**; during the **tertiary creep period** the rate of creep increases and eventually causes failure of the material. The secondary creep period is usually of long duration, and this, followed by the sudden increase in creep rate, makes extrapolation of results obtained by testing into the secondary creep period very dangerous. When a material is used at high temperatures it will be in the secondary creep period during most of its working life.

Creep tests of up to 10 000 hours duration are used to obtain design data, but short-time creep tests of at least 48 hours duration are used as acceptance tests; these short-time tests must only be used to compare the behaviour of the material under test with the results of long-time tests.

CREEP AND CREEP TESTING

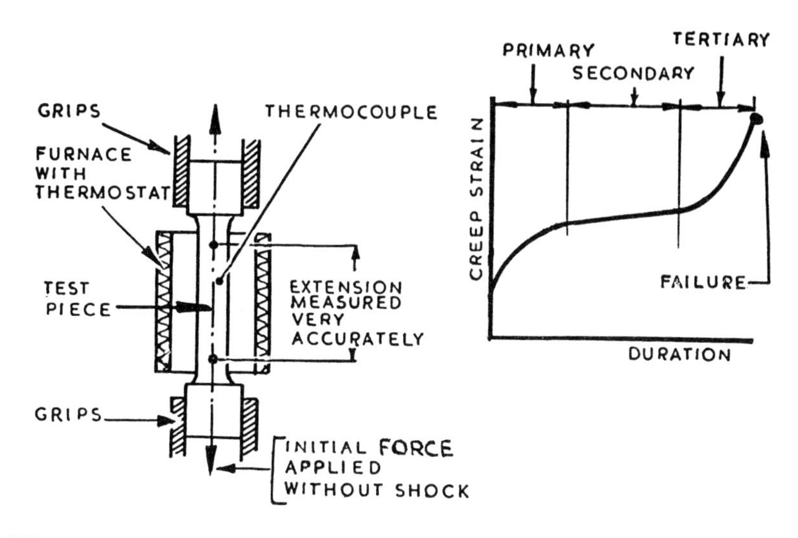

Fig. 7.1 Essential Features of Creep Test

Fig. 7.2 Behaviour of Specimen during Creep Test

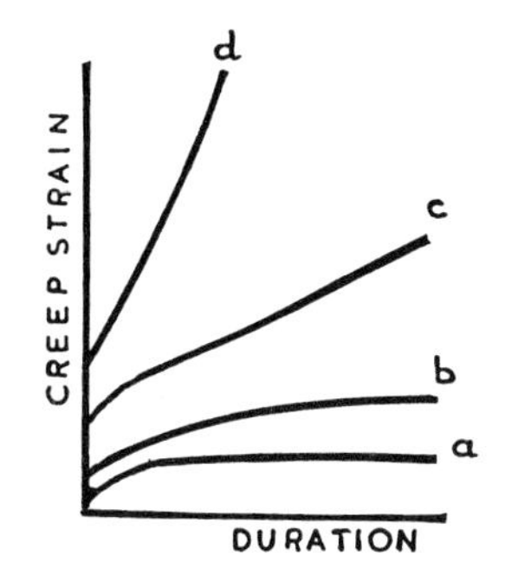

Fig. 7.3 Effect of Increasing Initial Force

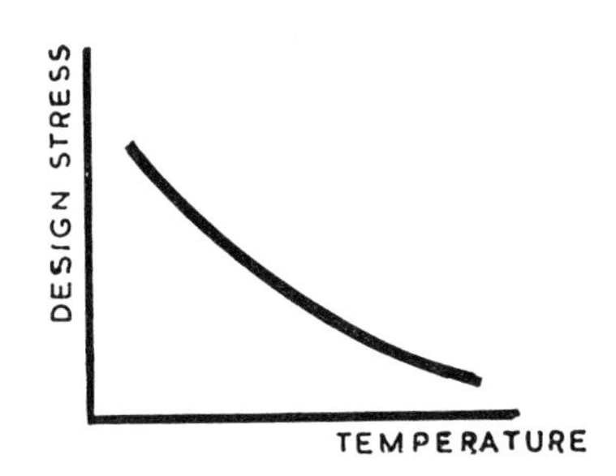

Fig. 7.4 Presentation of data (Design Stress against Temp on Basis of a Permissible Creep Strain in a given Lifetime)

7·40 FACTORS INFLUENCING CREEP

Initial Loading. Figure 7.3 illustrates the effect of increasing the initial force, but keeping the temperature constant. Curve (*a*) illustrates the behaviour of a material with a small initial force, and curve (*d*) the behaviour of the same material with a very much larger initial force. It will be seen that the specimen with the small force is still in the secondary creep period at the termination of the test, but the specimen with the large force is in the tertiary creep period at the end of the test.

Temperature. If a number of specimens of a material are tested with the same initial force but at different temperatures, it will be seen that the rate of creep increases with temperature; the effect will be similar to that produced by increasing the initial force.

Grain Size. When a material has a coarse grain it has a better creep resistance than when it has a fine grain.

7·50 PRESENTATION OF CREEP DATA

Figure 7.4 shows one method of presentation of creep data; this gives the variation of design stress with temperature to produce a certain permissible creep strain in a given lifetime.

CHAPTER 8

FATIGUE AND FATIGUE TESTS

8.10 Fatigue failure is caused by repeated stress cycles such as reversed or alternating stresses (reversal of direction of bending or torsion, or alternating compressive and tensile stresses), repeated stresses (application and removal of stresses), and fluctuating stress (variation of the intensity of stress). Fatigue failure is encountered very frequently in engineering, and although much publicity has been given to fatigue of aircraft structures, this form of failure is very common in more ordinary circumstances; motor-car half-shafts, crown wheel and pinion assemblies, and pedal-cycle crank spindles are susceptible to fatigue failure.

8.11 The appearance of the material after a fatigue failure is illustrated in fig. 8.5; ductile materials display a smooth zone and a crystalline zone as shown, but these zones are less marked in the case of brittle materials. The smooth zone is produced by the gradual progression of the fatigue crack and the rubbing of the surfaces of the crack; the crystalline zone is produced by the sudden fracture when the remaining sound material can no longer withstand the increased stress caused by the reduction in the area carrying the load.

8.12 A fatigue crack often starts at some point of stress concentration; if the material is subjected to intermittent stressing, the surface of the smooth zone will display a number of curved lines as indicated in fig. 8.5.

8.13 The stress that produces fatigue failure is considerably smaller than the tensile strength as determined by a static tensile test, and there is no perceptible distortion before failure. The fatigue crack is very fine, but it can often be detected when about 90% of the fatigue life of the component has been reached.

8.20 Fatigue-testing Machines

Fatigue-testing machines can be grouped according to the type of fatigue test made by them.

BENDING-STRESS MACHINES

(*a*) *Rotating type* (machines of the Wöhler reverse bend type; see fig. 8.1). These machines use a test piece that is rotated in a chuck, and a force is applied in one direction at the free end of the test piece; the rotation produces a reversal of bending.

(*b*) *Reciprocating type.* These machines produce bending of the material under test by magnetic impulses; finished components, welded joints, etc., can be tested.

TORSIONAL-FATIGUE MACHINES

In these machines, the test piece is held in a chuck at one end and subjected to a small oscillating movement at the other end.

DIRECT-STRESS MACHINES

These machines produce alternating or fluctuating stresses.

In addition to these machines, more complicated machines that simulate the conditions expected in service are sometimes used; a typical example is one that simulates the movement of an aircraft wing when in flight.

8.30 PROCEDURE FOR FATIGUE TESTING, AND THE RESULTS OBTAINED

A number of test pieces are manufactured from the material under test; each test piece is tested to destruction, and the number of stress reversals to cause fracture is recorded. Each test is done at a lower stress than that of the previous test, and in the case of some materials, a stress is reached, below which the material will not fracture, even if subjected to an 'infinite' number of stress cycles. This stress is known as the **fatigue limit** or **endurance limit** of the material; very few non-ferrous materials display a fatigue limit.

8.31 The results of the series of tests are used to produce a curve of stress plotted against the number of stress cycles to cause fracture; this curve is usually known as an 'S–N curve'. Figure 8.6 illustrates two typical S–N curves; curve A is the type obtained when testing a material that displays a well-defined fatigue limit, and curve B is the type obtained when testing a material that does not display a well-defined fatigue limit. The S–N curve also indicates the fatigue life that a material is likely to have when subjected to a specific stress.

FATIGUE TESTING METHODS

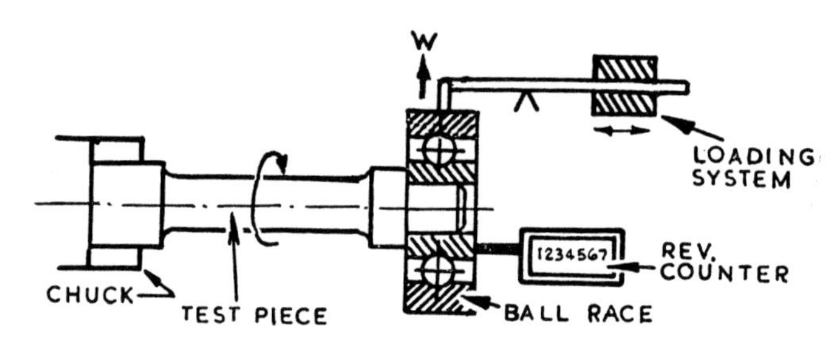

Fig. 8.1 Wöhler Reverse Bend Test

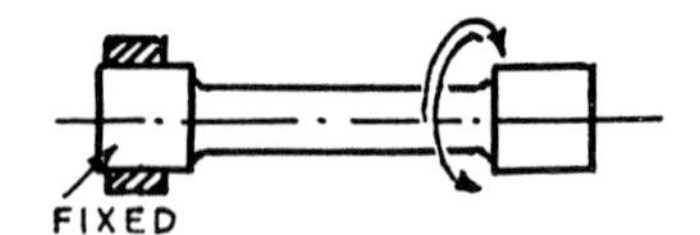

Fig. 8.2 Torsion Test

Fig. 8.3 Tension-Compression Test

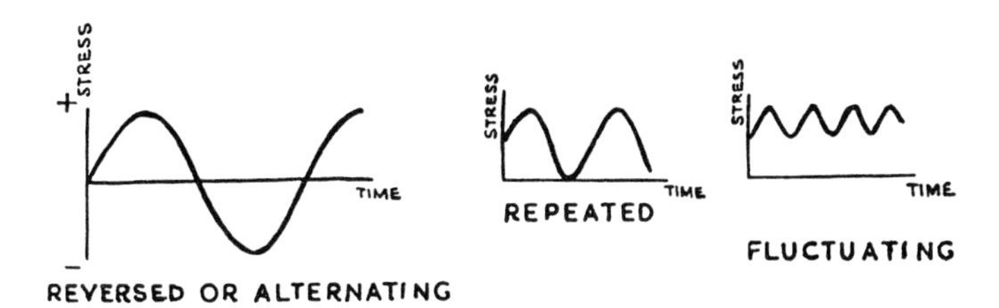

Fig. 8.4 Force Systems

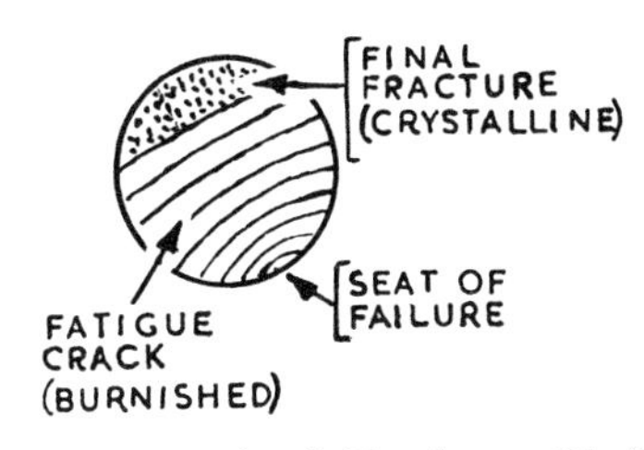

Fig. 8.5 Typical Fatigue Failure

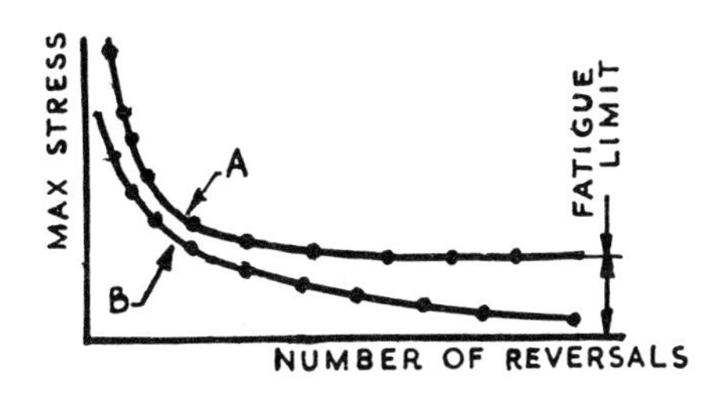

Fig. 8.6 Typical 'S–N' Curves

8.32 THE CONNECTION BETWEEN FATIGUE LIMIT AND THE TENSILE PROPERTIES OF A MATERIAL

(*a*) *Fatigue Limit and Tensile Strength*

$$\frac{\text{fatigue limit}}{\text{tensile strength}} = 0{\cdot}35 - 0{\cdot}65$$

It is found that materials with a good strength have a lower fatigue strength/tensile strength value than those with a poor strength.

(*b*) *Fatigue Limit and Yield Point.* There is no reliable connection between fatigue limit and yield point.

8.33 OTHER FACTORS THAT INFLUENCE FATIGUE STRENGTH OF A COMPONENT

Grain Size. When a material has a coarse grain it has a poorer fatigue resistance than when it has a fine grain.

Component Shape. It has already been stated that a fatigue crack often starts at some point of stress concentration and so stress-raising features such as an abrupt change of section, sharp corner, keyway, etc., should be avoided if possible.

Surface Finish. Tooling marks act as stress raisers and so the fatigue resistance of a component can be improved by polishing, etc.

Residual Stresses. Stresses produced by the machining operations will affect the fatigue resistance of a component; tensile stresses reduce the resistance, and compressive stresses improve it. Compressive stresses can be produced by shot peening the surface with chilled cast iron or steel shot.

Corrosion. Corrosion produces a pitted surface and so introduces stress raisers; the fatigue strength of a component is reduced very considerably by corrosion.

Temperature. At high temperatures materials tend to lose their strength, and also suffer grain growth (see page 42, section 5.23), and so the fatigue strength falls when the temperature is high.

CHAPTER 9

THE INSPECTION OF MATERIAL

9.10 The previous chapters have dealt with the mechanical testing of materials; in addition to the tests already described, the raw material must be inspected to ensure dimensional accuracy and soundness; the component must also be inspected during its machining to ensure that the desired properties have been developed as a result of heat treatment, and that heat treatment or machining has not caused craking.

9.11 The mechanical properties of cast material can be verified by casting a test piece at the same time and subjecting it to a suitable test; the surface hardness of a casting can be checked using a hardness-testing machine. The properties of a material after heat treatment can be determined by hardness testing or by subjecting a test piece to the heat treatment at the same time.

The inspection techniques described in this chapter are those other than mechanical tests, and can be classified as (*a*) destructive inspection and (*b*) non-destructive testing.

9.20 Destructive Inspection

9.21 *Check for Grain Flow of Forgings.* The direction of grain flow produced by forging is important because it produces directional strength; it can be verified by cutting up a sample forging, grinding the surface of the section, and then etching it to reveal the grain flow. The etched section can be used like a printing block to produce a record of the grain flow. Figure 9.1 shows a drawing of a component, the outline of the stamping from which it is to be machined, and a macroprint taken from the stamping; the grain will be seen to follow the profile of the stamping. The structure shown in fig. 9.1 is called a **macrostructure** because it can be seen by the unaided eye; the structure revealed by the microscope is called a **microstructure.**

9.22 *Examination Using a Microscope.* The examination of material under a microscope is used to obtain information about the manufacture, structure, heat-treatment, and cause of failure of material. The material to be micro-examined must have a flat reflective surface; the surface is ground, using a suitable paper, and then polished to remove the scratches so produced; this polishing will produce a thin 'flowed' layer which hides the micro-structure. The flowed layer is dissolved by applying a suitable etching reagent which also attacks the underlying layers to reveal the grain boundaries and the micro-constituents. The magnification employed depends upon the information required, but is usually between $\times$ 50 and $\times$ 480.

9.30 Non-destructive Testing

'Non-destructive testing' implies the inspection, examination and testing of materials and components without detriment to their mechanical and physical properties or their performance in service.

9.31 *Visual Examination.* Surface cracks and blemishes can often be seen using a low-power magnifying lens or a low-power binocular microscope. Light etching often reveals defects that are not detected by other methods;

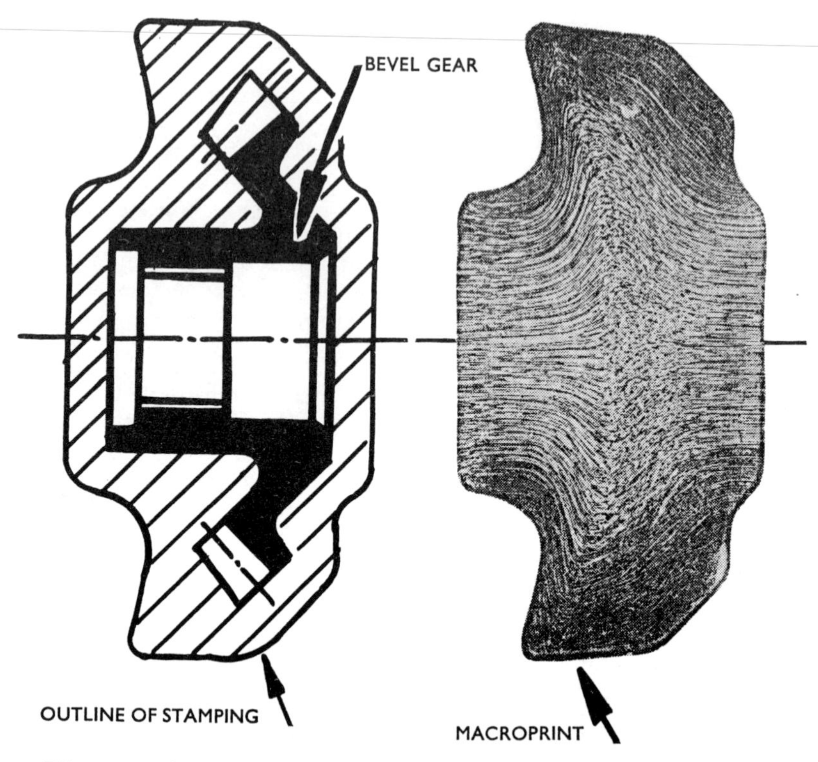

Fig. 9.1 Stamping Drawing and Macroprint

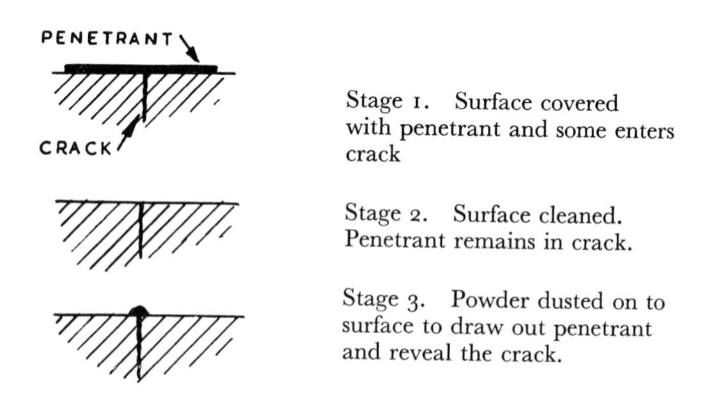

Fig. 9.2 Crack Detection using Penetrant

it is to some extent destructive. Coins are, for example, inspected under a powerful lighting system to ensure that the impression is correct.

The external dimensions of castings and forgings can be checked by marking out the material as for small-quantity production to ensure that it will clean up as a result of machining; certain wall thicknesses can be checked by measuring using suitable calipers, or by using a comparator. Internal walls and pockets in castings can be examined by radiography (see below) otherwise a trial casting is cut up.

9.32 *Pressure Testing.* Castings can be checked for porosity by blanking off all ports, and introducing paraffin at the required pressure; porosity is indicated by fall in pressure, and located by seepage of paraffin.

9.33 *Acoustic Test.* A simple test for soundness is the acoustic test, in which the material is tapped with a light hammer, and its soundness judged by listening to the quality of the sound so produced. The test for the soundness of a grinding wheel, the railway wheel tapper's checks and the china expert's test for cracks are applications of acoustic testing.

9.34 *Penetrants.* Figures 9.2 illustrates the use of penetrants. The simplest method is the hot oil and chalk test; if a better contrast is required, a dyed or a fluorescent penetrant is used. This test reveals flaws at the surface.

9.35 *Magnetic Detection Methods.* Figure 9.3 illustrates the principle of the magnetic flaw-detection methods. In these methods, a magnetic flux is set up in the part under test; a defect in the part will distort the flux lines, which can be detected by a magnetic powder. The powder can be dusted on to the surface of the part, or suspended in paraffin which is poured on to the part. These methods reveal defects at, or near the surface of magnetic material, but it is to some extent directional, and flaws that lie along the flux lines may not be revealed.

9.36 *Ultrasonic Testing Methods.* Defects within the material can be detected by passing pulses of energy into the material being tested using a piezo-electric crystal (one in which the application of an alternating voltage results in the generation of an alternating strain, and vice versa). These pulses travel through the material as stress waves that are reflected back from the far side or from defects within the material. The usual frequency range is 0·25–10 MH_z, and a *coupling* oil film is applied to the surface at the entry side to ensure that the pulses are not reflected before they enter the material. Figure 9.4 illustrates the principle of the **pulse reflection** method in which the transmitted and reflected pulses are caused to produce a *blip* on a cathode ray tube display; a defect free material will cause two blips to be produced on a time base, and the distance between them therefore represents the thickness of the material. A defect will cause some energy to be received *early*, so producing a blip that can be used to indicate not only the presence, but the depth at which the defect lies. The transmitting and receiving functions can be performed in quick succession by one crystal, which is then described as a *transceiver*. The equipment can be arranged to use the **transmission** method, in which the transmitter is placed on one side and the receiver on the other; two blips are displayed, but the blip produced by the received energy will be shorter than that transmitted if a defect is present because some energy will be reflected back; this method does not require such good contact conditions as does the pulse reflection method. Storage tanks can be checked for internal corrosion by producing a condition of **resonance** by adjustment of the input frequency

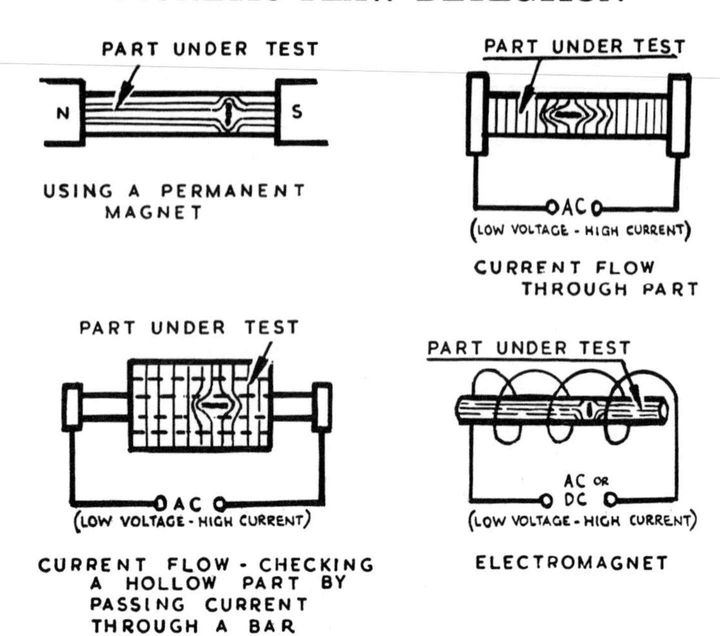

Fig. 9.3 Magnetic Flaw Defection (effect of defect on Magnetic Flux)

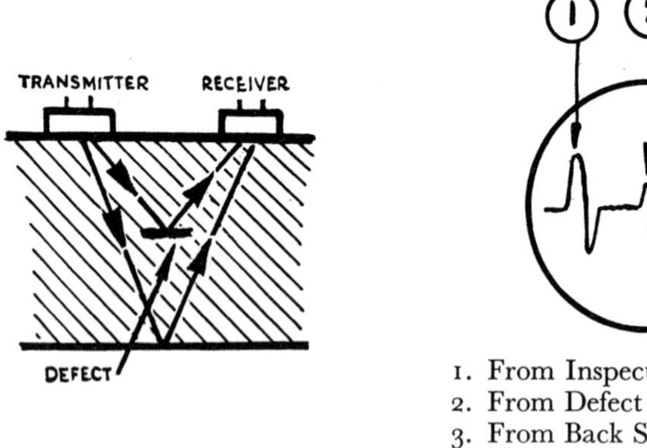

THE PRINCIPLE OF THE PULSE REFLECTION METHOD

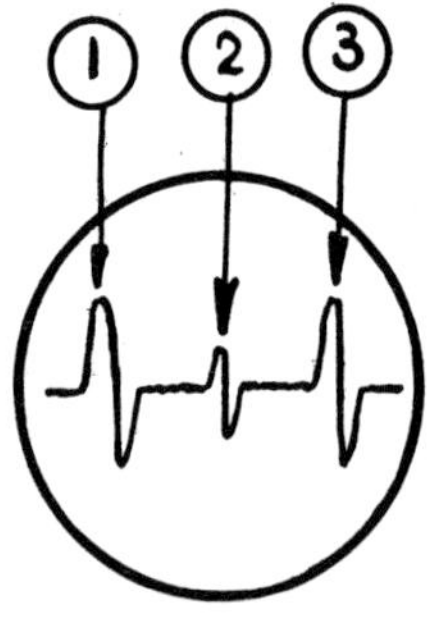

1. From Inspection surface
2. From Defect
3. From Back Surface

CATHODE-RAY TUBE DISPLAY

Fig. 9.4 Ultrasonic Testing

and relating the wall thickness to the wavelength. Ultrasonic testing does not indicate the shape of the defect except by *exploring* in the region of the defect and 'mapping' the position of the defect.

9.37 Radiography. X-rays and gamma-rays behave like light rays, except that they pass through solid material, and attack a photographic plate. The extent of this attack depends upon the density of the material, and so the image of defects will appear on the plate.

X-rays are produced by applying a high electrical voltage to the end of the X-ray tube, whereas gamma-rays are produced spontaneously in certain substances. The X-ray equipment is rather expensive and more bulky than gamma-ray equipment, and gamma-rays can penetrate thicker material than can X-rays (250 mm in steel compared with 100 mm by X-rays). The radiation output from an X-ray tube is greater than from a gamma-ray source, and so the exposure time is measured in minutes, compared with hours when using gamma-rays; the quality of the X-ray picture is better than that of a gamma-ray picture. Both X-rays and gamma-rays are dangerous to health and a strict operating procedure must be adopted.

Radiography is often done in conjunction with ultrasonic testing, because radiography can indicate the shape of a flaw at right angles to the direction of testing but a single exposure cannot indicate the depth at which it lies. Also, radiography is less able than ultrasonic testing to detect a thin flaw that lies in the direction of testing, but is more able to detect flaws at right angles to the direction of testing.

CHAPTER 10

STEEL AND ITS PRODUCTION

10.10 Steel can be defined as an alloy of carbon and iron, which can be hot worked, and in which the carbon is in the combined state; it also contains other elements in controlled amounts. The carbon content is between about 0·1% and about 1·7%, and the other elements may be controlled impurities, or alloying elements that are introduced to alter the response to heat treatment or to produce special properties.

10.20 Carbon

Carbon is a very important constituent; the quantity present and the form it takes affects the properties of steel very considerably. It must be realised that the main object of adding alloying elements to steel is to alter the behaviour of the carbon, and that compared with the carbon content, very large amounts of alloying elements are required to produce the desired properties.

10.21 Carbon can be present with iron in slowly cooled steels at room temperatures in the following forms:

1. Dissolved in iron to form the solid solution **ferrite**, which can contain up to 0·006% carbon when at room temperature, and which increases to 0·03% carbon at about 725°C. Ferrite is soft, weak, and ductile.
2. As a chemical compound with iron. This compound is called **cementite** and is of the formula Fe_3C; it contains 6·67% carbon. Cementite is hard and brittle.

   Cementite can be present as **free cementite**, or laminated with ferrite to produce the structure **pearlite**; pearlite is so named because when etched, and viewed with the naked eye, it has the appearance of 'mother of pearl'. Pearlite combines the good properties of ferrite and cementite.

10.22 The form taken by the carbon in slowly cooled plain carbon steels (steels not containing alloying elements) depends upon the amount of carbon present; this is illustrated in fig. 10.1, which also shows how the microstructure influences the mechanical properties.

10.23 If steel is heated and then cooled rapidly, equilibrium will be upset, and the carbon will be present in other forms, so that a range of properties can be produced by subjecting steel to various heating and cooling cycles. The properties and microstructures shown in fig. 10.1 are those existing before such heat treatment has been done.

10.30 Impurities Present in Steels

Phosphorus. This element forms iron-phosphide, which lowers the melting point of steels, and also tends to produce hardness and brittleness. Phosphorus is regarded as a deadly impurity and the quantity of phosphorus present in steel is rigidly controlled by specifications; maximum, about 0·05%. Iron ores are graded according to their phosphorus content.

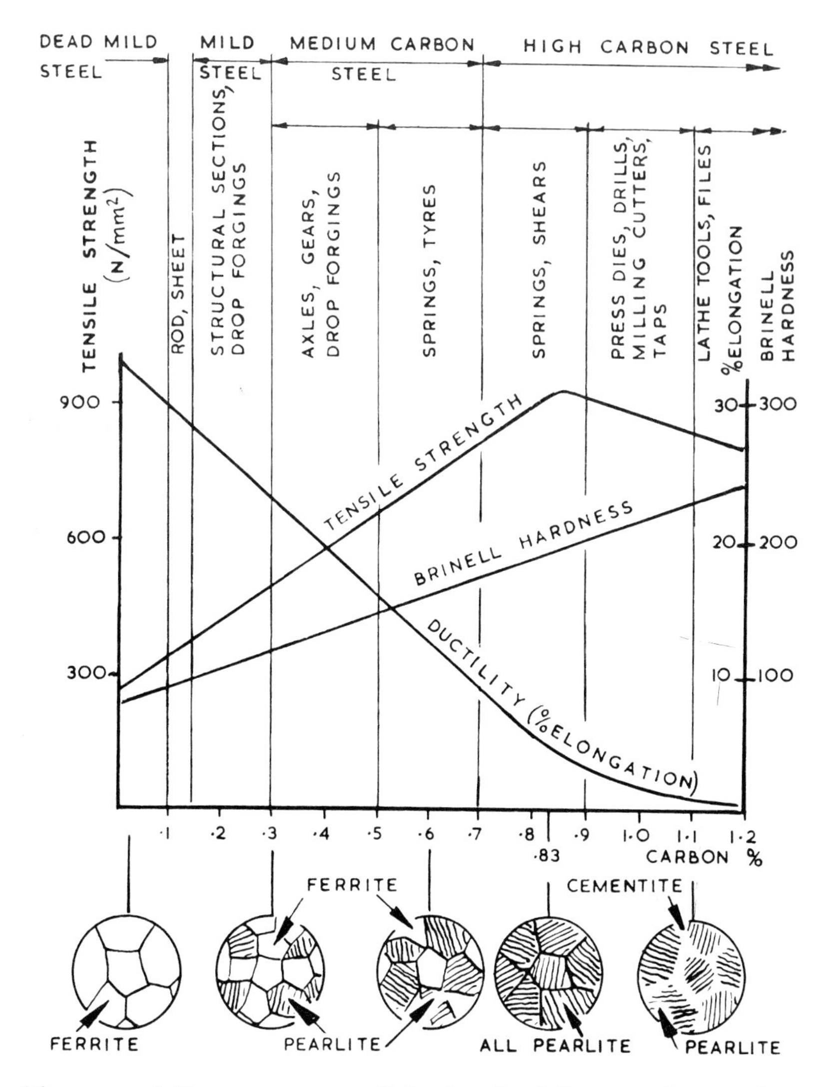

Fig. 10.1 Microstructure, Mechanical Properties, and Uses of Plain Carbon Steels (the Structures and Properties are those before Hardening Treatment)

Sulphur. This produces the harmful constituent iron-sulphide, which is brittle and has a low melting point. The iron-sulphide collects at the grain boundaries making steel cold-short (unsuitable for cold-working) because of its brittleness; it also makes steel hot-short (unsuitable for hot-working) because it melts at hot-working temperatures and so causes the steel to crumble. The sulphur content must be kept to below about 0·05%.

Silicon. Silicon makes steel fluid, but it tends to produce graphitisation (the breakdown of cementite to produce **graphite**), causing the steel to become weak. Steel contains between 0·1 and 0·3% Silicon.

Manganese. This combines with sulphur to form manganese-sulphide instead of allowing it to form iron-sulphide. Manganese-sulphide is not harmful, and so the ill effects of sulphur are offset. The manganese content must, however, be controlled to ensure uniformity of properties from one batch of steel to the next. Carbon steels contain up to 1% manganese.

10.40 The Acid and Basic Steelmaking Processes

The terms **acid** and **basic** refer to the chemical nature of the slags produced and to the furnace linings.

The acid process is used to refine pig irons that are low in phosphorus and sulphur, because these pig irons are produced from ores that are rich in silicon, which produces an acid slag. The furnace lining is constructed of silica bricks so that it will be of the same nature as the slag and so prevent reaction.

The basic process is used to refine pig irons that are rich in phosphorus. This element can only be removed if a large amount of lime is used during the refining process; as this produces a basic slag, the furnace lining must be of a basic refractory to prevent reaction between it and the slag. About 85% of steels produced in Britain are of the basic type, and with modern techniques they are almost equal in quality to the acid steels produced from the superior ores.

10.50 The Development of Steelmaking Processes

A form of steelmaking was practised in Asia Minor in about 1400 BC, based upon the absorption of carbon when iron is heated for a long time in a carbonaceous atmosphere. In this process wrought iron (see page 85, section 11.24) was packed together with charcoal into boxes, which were sealed and then heated for several days; the carbon absorbed by the iron formed cementite at the surface of the wrought iron, and the process is accordingly called the **cementation process**. After this treatment, the bars were heated, bundled together and forged in order to produce a more even carbon distribution across the section, but a good distribution could never be obtained. This process was successful, however, for small articles and for edged tools; it is used today as the **carburising** operation when casehardening (see page 104, section 13.30).

10.51 In 1740 the clockmaker Benjamin Huntsman realised that in order to produce a steel that would be suitable for clock springs, the carbon should be introduced when the iron was molten; the **crucible process** which he developed is still used for cutlery and tool steels, and the **induction process** used in the production of alloy steels is the modern version of this process. The crucible process is essentially one of alloying, and in the original process, wrought iron treated by cementation, Swedish iron, and alloying elements were melted together in 20 kg fireclay pots, and poured into moulds after the slag was skimmed off. This process produced good-quality steels, but the rate of production was low.

10.52 In 1856, Sir Henry Bessemer announced that steel could be produced by blowing air through molten pig iron in a vessel called a converter, so that the impurities would be removed by oxidation. At that time a rapid steel production method was urgently needed because of the rapid expansion of the railways and similar undertakings. This process was potentially a good method of steel production because since only air was introduced, further contamination of the metal was minimised; when Bessemer worked on his process he used good-quality low-phosphorus pig iron, but when the steelmakers used this method in conjunction with the British ores, they found that the phosphorus could not be removed, and a poor-quality steel was produced. The problem of phosphorus removal was eventually solved in 1878 by Sydney Gilchrist Thomas and his cousin Percy Gilchrist, who introduced lime and the basic lining system now used in the basic steelmaking process; by this time the **open-hearth process** was in favour, and very little Bessemer steel was produced in Britain until after the Second World War, when interest in the converter method of steelmaking was renewed. A similar process using a converter had been developed in the United States of America by William Kelly, who did not apply for a patent until 1856, when he learned that Bessemer had been granted an American patent. His claim was proved in 1857, and Bessemer's application for renewal of patent was rejected, but by that time Kelly had become bankrupt; the Bessemer process has remained popular in America until the present time.

10.53 The open-hearth process, based upon the reverberatory furnace (see page 85, section 11.24) and upon the dilution of pig iron with wrought-iron scrap before refining, as patented by Pierre Martin, was developed by Sir William Siemens in 1867, and is the method now used for the production of the bulk of steel in Britain.

10.54 Since the Second World War, there has been a renewed interest in the Bessemer process, and various versions of that process, using converters operating with oxygen, air, and oxygen-steam are in use in many countries.

Modern Steelmaking Processes

10.60 These processes can be grouped as follows:

1. Processes using a converter.
2. The open-hearth process.
3. Electric processes.

10.61 Processes Using a Converter

The converter is a steel shell that is open mouthed, refractory lined, and mounted upon a trunnion so that it can be swung into a horizontal position for charging and pouring, and into a vertical position for blowing. In the original Bessemer process air at about 140 kN/m^2 is blown through the molten pig iron from a large number of small holes in the bottom of the refractory to oxidise the impurities and the carbon; the carbon content is finally adjusted by adding manganese-rich pig iron, and the steel is poured into a ladle, and then teemed into ingot moulds. The converter capacity is between 25 and 60

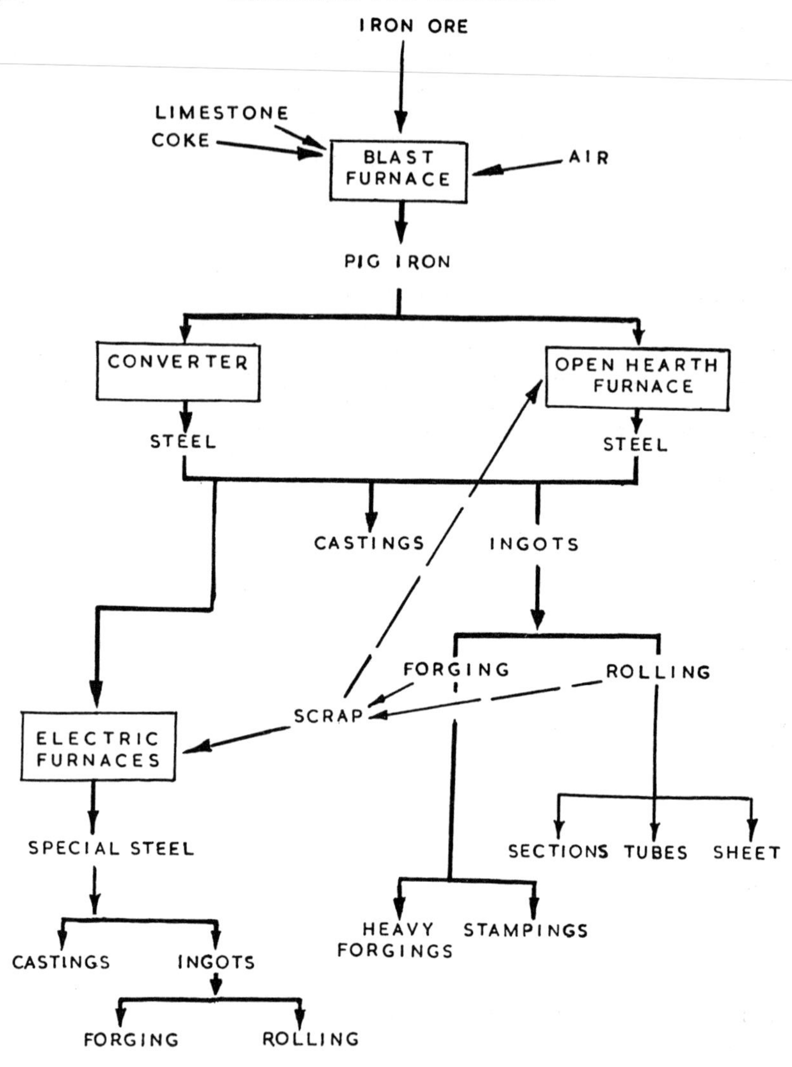

Fig. 10.2 Steelmaking

tonnes, and the process takes about 25 minutes. The Bessemer converter is shown in fig. 10.3.

10.611 During recent years a variation of the Bessemer process using oxygen has become popular; this process produces higher temperatures, and permits up to 15% scrap to be employed instead of only about 5% as in the original process.

On the continent, variations of the Bessemer process using oxygen blown on to the surface of the molten pig iron are being used. In the **Linz-Donawitz**

(L.D.) **process** (shown in fig. 10.4), developed in Austria, oxygen is blown on to the top of the molten pig iron, in a vertical converter; this allows low-phosphorus irons to be treated (the Bessemer process requires phosphorus as a fuel); the original L.D. process is of little interest to British steelmakers because British home ores are rich in phosphorus; but this process is being developed to use pig irons made from ores with more than 2% phosphorus. The **rotor process** (see fig. 10.5), developed in Germany, employs a horizontal converter with two nozzles; one blowing oxygen into the metal, and the other blowing oxygen into the surface to produce heat by burning the CO to CO_2; during refining, this converter is rotated at between ½ and 2 rev/min. The **Kaldo process** (see fig. 10.6), developed in Sweden, uses a converter that is inclined at 17° to the horizontal, and oxygen is blown on to the surface of the pig iron whilst the converter is rotated at up to 30 rev/min for even and rapid transmission of the heat to the metal. The Kaldo process is suitable for irons with up to 2% phosphorus, and takes about 90 minutes; this allows a closer control of the steel than do the other processes that use a converter.

10.62 The Open-hearth Process

The open-hearth furnace is used to produce low and medium carbon content steels by basic or acid methods, according to the nature of the furnace lining. This furnace, illustrated in fig. 10.7, has a capacity of between 150 and 300 tonnes, and is fired by producer gas and coke-oven gas, or by fuel oil. It uses the regenerative principle, and the stoves attain a temperature of between 900°C. and 1200°C.; these stoves enable the necessarily high temperatures to be attained, and at the same time save fuel. In this process, the furnace is charged with pig iron and steel scrap, which is melted to cause some of the impurities to form a slag on the surface of the melt; iron ore or millscale is then added, mainly to remove carbon by oxidation. Upon completion of the refining, the tapping notch is broken open and the steel is tapped into a ladle. The steel leaves the furnace before the slag, and so some of the slag can be prevented from leaving the furnace until the steel has all been tapped off; the slag that does enter the ladle will float on the top of the steel, and is allowed to overflow into a smaller ladle. The steel is teemed from the ladle into ingot moulds from the bottom so that any slag still in the steel ladle will be the last to leave, and can be isolated by teeming into a small ingot mould. The open-hearth furnace is tapped about once every twelve hours; during the later stages of refining, a number of samples are taken and analysed to ensure that the composition will be correct. The basic slag is used as a fertiliser.

10.63 Electric Processes

If the quality of the steel is to be high, it is necessary that the temperature be controlled, and that the impurities entering the furnace during the refining be minimised. These requirements can only be met if electric furnaces are used; in Britain the initial steel refining is done using the open-hearth furnace, and further refining is done using the **electric arc furnace**. The **high-frequency induction furnace**, the modern version of the crucible furnace, is used for the melting and alloying of special steels, but it is not a refining furnace.

STEELMAKING USING A CONVERTER

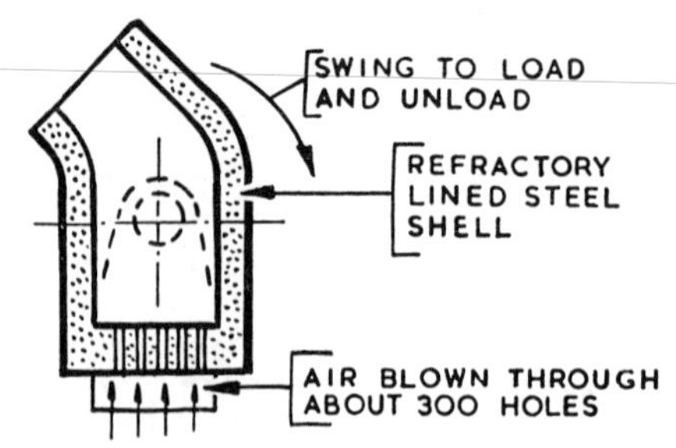

Fig. 10.3 The Bessemer Converter

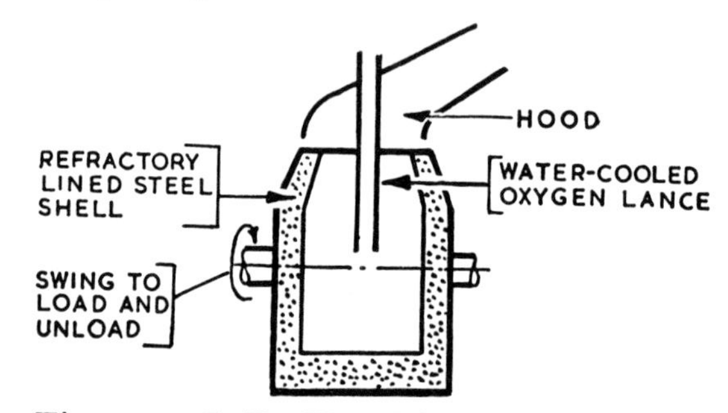

Fig. 10.4 L.D. Top Blown Converter

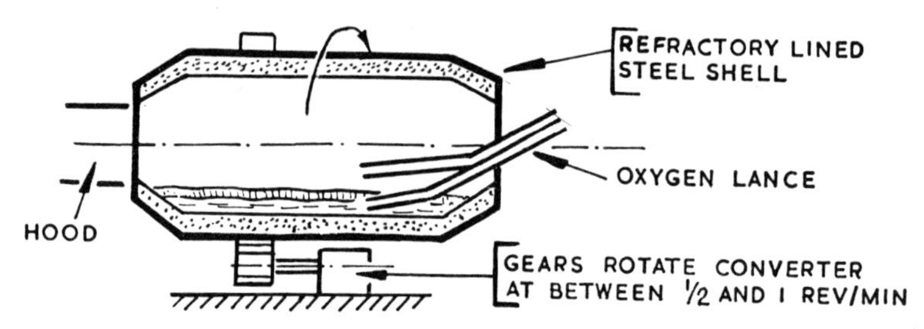

Fig. 10.5 The Rotor Mixed Blown Converter

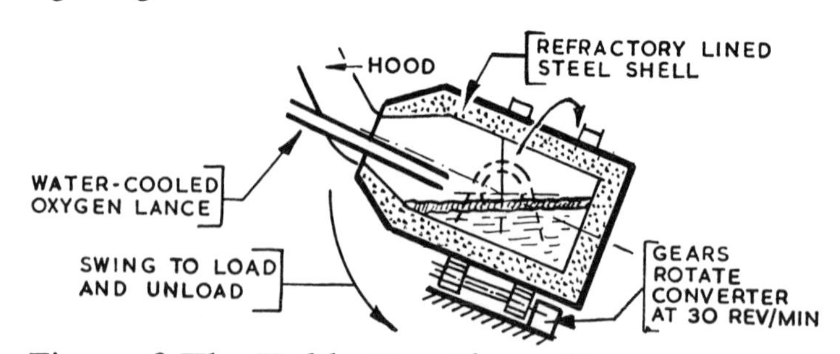

Fig. 10.6 The Kaldo Top Blown Converter

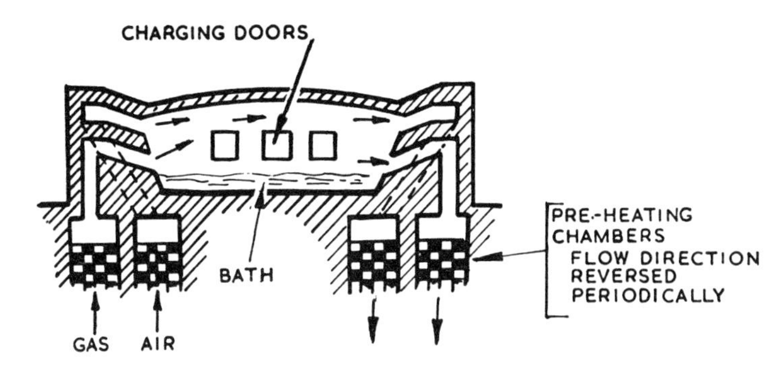

Fig. 10.7 Open-hearth Furnace. Capacity: 150–300 tonnes

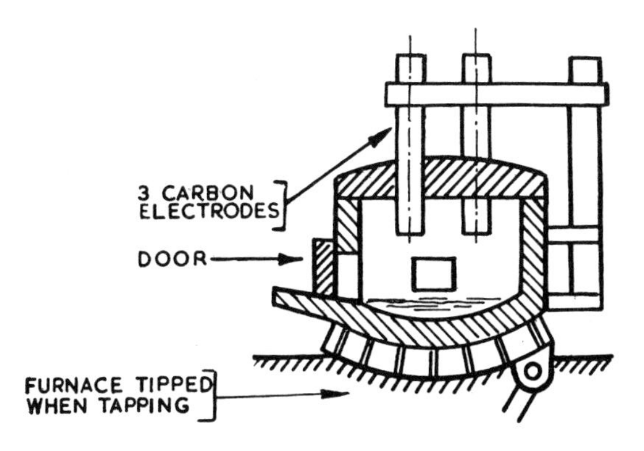

Fig. 10.8 Electric Arc Furnace (Rocking Type)
Capacity: 25–100 tonnes

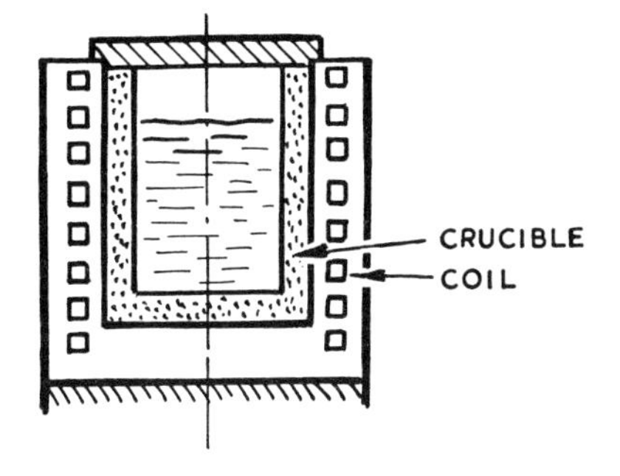

Fig. 10.9 High-frequency Induction Furnace
Capacity: 350 kg–6 tonnes

10.631 The electric arc furnace is illustrated in fig. 10.8 and is of between 25 and 100 tons capacity. It is fitted with three carbon electrodes in the roof, which are adjusted automatically to strike an arc directly with the metal. This furnace can be lined to suit either the acid or basic system, and the material charged into it can include scrap of known composition. When the basic process is worked, an oxidising slag composed of lime and millscale is employed to remove the impurities, and then raked off so that a reducing slag, which consists mainly of lime, can be added to prevent oxidation when the alloying elements are added before tapping.

10.632 The high-frequency induction furnace (shown in fig. 10.9) consists of a coil of wire wound around a refractory crucible so that when energised with an electric current, it will produce circulating currents within the metal, and so cause melting; when the material is molten, these currents produce a stirring action. The capacity of this type of furnace is between 350 kg and 6 tonnes, and it is used for the production of special alloy steels.

10.7 British Standard Specifications for Steels

A fixed six digit system has been adopted to allow flexibility and because of the extensive use of computers. The first three digits are numbers, and are used to indicate the type of steel and the group to which it belongs; these are followed by a letter, to give information such as condition of supply; the final two digits are numbers that are used to indicate the actual alloy.

The series up to 199 are all carbon steels, including casehardening steels. The first three digits indicate the mean manganese content × 100, the fourth digit indicates condition of supply (i.e. by mechanical properties—'M', or by analysis—'A'), and the final two digits indicate the mean carbon content × 100. For example, 015A03 is a carbon steel with up to 0·30% manganese, supplied by analysis, and containing up to 0·06% carbon.

The series 200 to 299 are all free-cutting carbon steels (indicated by the first digit); the second and third digits indicate the manganese content × 100; and, as before, the remaining digits indicate the condition of supply and the carbon content.

The series 300 to 499 are all stainless steels; the first three digits is an arbitrary indication of the grouping (e.g. 303 group is 18%/9% chromium-nickel free-cutting, and the 347 group is 18%/9% chromium-nickel + niobium). The final two digits are an arbitrary indication of the specific alloy. The numbers are separated by the letter 'S' to indicate that the alloy specified is a stainless steel.

The series 500 to 999 are all alloy steels. The first three digits are an arbitrary indication of the group, the final two digits indicate the carbon content × 100, and the separating letter indicates the condition of supply (by analysis—'A', by mechanical properties—'M', or by hardenability—'H').

Wrought steels are covered by British Standard BS 970, and Cast steels by British Standard BS 3100.

CHAPTER 11

IRON-CARBON ALLOYS

11.10 Various quantities of carbon are alloyed with iron to produce a series of alloys that have properties that are different from those of both iron and carbon. Iron-carbon alloys undergo structural changes during cooling from the liquid state, and these changes must be understood before the theory of the heat treatment and alloying of steel and of cast iron can be fully appreciated.

The behaviour of iron-carbon alloys during cooling from the liquid state will be considered in two stages:

1. Liquid to solid changes.
2. Changes when in the solid state.

Liquid to Solid Changes

(Refer to the portion of the iron-carbon-equilibrium diagram illustrated in fig. 11.1)

11.20 When iron is cooled from the liquid state it will solidify instantaneously

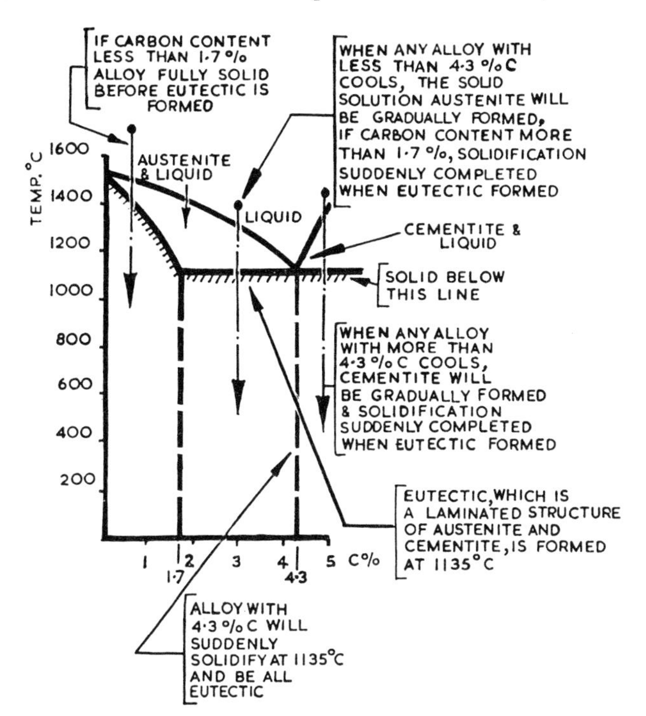

Fig. 11.1 Liquid to Solid Changes

when a temperature of 1535°C. has been reached; when 4·3% carbon is alloyed with iron the **eutectic** (see page 21, section 3.60) for the system is produced, which will solidify instantaneously when a temperature of 1135°C. is reached. Any iron-carbon alloy with a different carbon content will solidify gradually, and pass through a **pasty condition** during its cooling from the liquid state.

If the carbon content is less than 4·3% a **solid solution** (see page 16, section 3.31) of carbon in iron will be produced during its solidification; this solid solution can contain no more than 1·7% carbon and consequently the *percentage* of carbon in the remaining liquid will rise during the solidification.

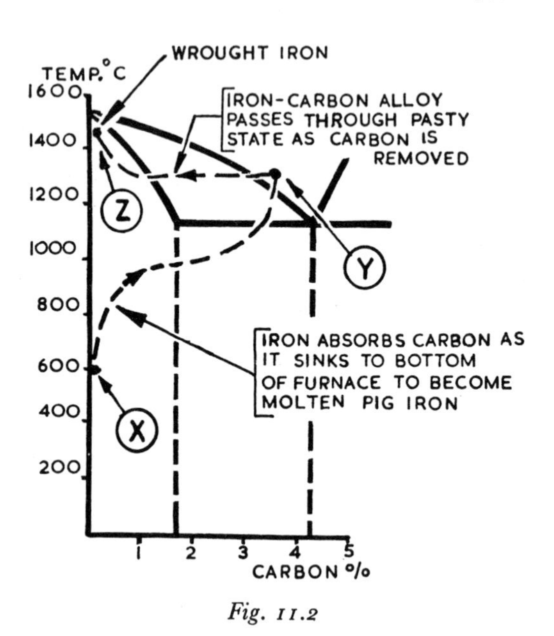

Fig. 11.2

If the alloy contains more than 4·3% carbon the compound **cementite** (which contains 6·67% carbon) will be produced during the solidification; due to the large amount of carbon in cementite, the *percentage* of carbon in the remaining liquid will fall during the solidification.

11.21 Any alloy containing more than 1·7% carbon will not be completely solid even when its temperature has fallen to almost 1135°C., but when the temperature has reached 1135°C. the remaining liquid will contain 4·3% carbon and it will therefore solidify instantaneously because it will be of eutectic composition.

11.22 It will be seen from fig. 11.1 that the iron-carbon alloy with about 3·5% carbon, known as **cast iron** is an ideal iron-carbon casting alloy because it has a relatively low melting point, which not only produces fluidity, but also reduces the cooling range in the solid state, so that the problems associated with cooling after casting are minimised. It will also be seen that this alloy passes through a pasty state during solidification; this ensures that the streams of molten metal unite before solidification, and so prevents 'cold shuts' and similar defects.

11.23 The blast furnace provides a good example of the lowering of the solidification temperature by increasing the carbon content. Iron is produced in the stack where the temperature is 600°C., and so it is solid; as it sinks to the bottom of the furnace, this iron becomes hotter and also absorbs carbon from the carbon monoxide that is rising to the top of the furnace. Line 'XY' on fig. 11.2 indicates the composition-temperature track taken by the iron;

WROUGHT IRON

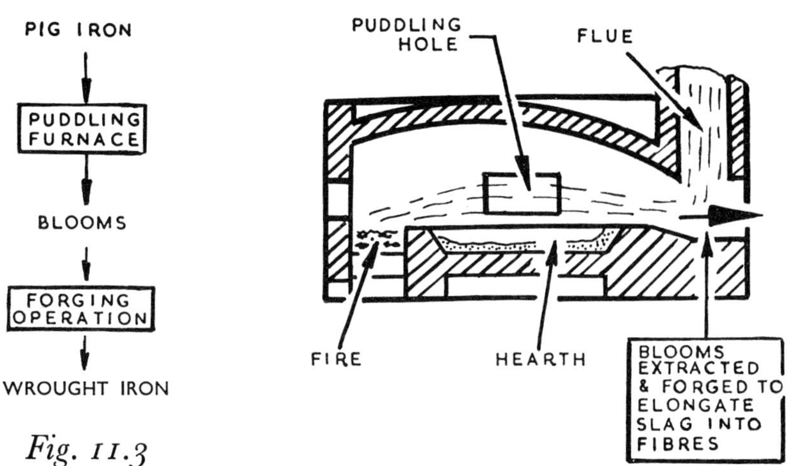

Fig. 11.3
Flow Diagram Showing Production of Wrought Iron from Pig Iron

Fig. 11.4
Puddling Furnace

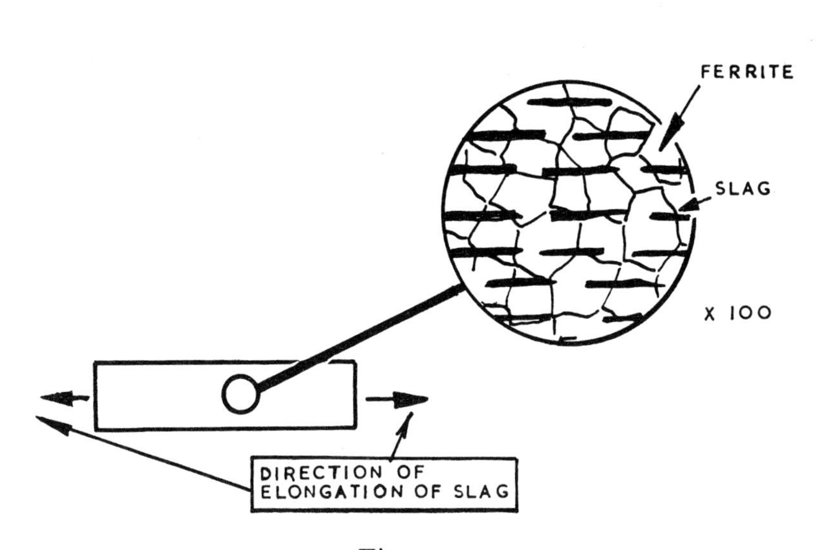

Fig. 11.5
Typical Microstructure of Wrought Iron

it can be seen that when the iron has reached the bottom of the furnace, where the temperature is about 1250°C., it will have absorbed about 3·5% carbon, and will be molten and can be tapped from the furnace (see also page 10, section 2.26).

11.24 The production of **wrought iron** is a good example of the effect of removal of carbon and of the pasty state so produced. Wrought iron, now produced in only small quantities owing to its high cost, contains about 0·02% carbon, and is made from pig iron in a **puddling furnace**. The puddling furnace (shown in fig. 11.4), is an example of the reverberatory furnace, in which the fuel is burned in a grate at the end of the furnace where it is out of contact with the charge; the fumes pass over the charge and the heat is reflected from the roof of the furnace on to the charge to melt it; the open-hearth furnace is a modern version of this type of furnace. To produce wrought iron, the pig iron is heated with millscale until molten, when the carbon will be removed by oxidation to form a slag on the surface of the melt; the slag is then raked off. The oxidation is continued but this time the small amount of slag is stirred back into the melt; as the carbon is removed, the material will enter the pasty condition as indicated by the line 'YZ' on fig. 11.2. Towards the end of the process the temperature is raised so that the material can be worked into 'blooms' and removed from the furnace to be rolled and forged to elongate the slag into fibres, and so produce the characteristic structure and properties of wrought iron.

Figure 11.5 represents a typical wrought-iron microstructure. Wrought iron is extremely ductile and tough, resistant to atmospheric corrosion, and very easy to weld and to forge; it is used for certain chains and lifting hooks where distortion as a warning of impending failure is essential.

Changes in the Solid State

(Refer to the portion of the iron-carbon-equilibrium diagram illustrated in fig. 11.6)

11.30 In order to appreciate the changes that take place when an iron-carbon alloy is cooling in the solid state, it is necessary to study the **allotropy of iron** (if an element is allotropic, it can exist in more than one physical form).

When a metal is in the liquid state the atoms are in a random arrangement, but when the metal is solid, these atoms are arranged in an orderly manner within the grains.

11.31 When pure iron has a temperature of more than 900°C., the atom centres are arranged as shown in fig. 11.7 (see page 88); it can be seen that the 'unit arrangement' is an imaginary cube with an atom at each corner, and an atom at the centre of each 'face'. This arrangement is called a 'face-centred cubic lattice'; iron with this atomic arrangement is called **γ iron**.

When a temperature of 900°C. is reached upon cooling, the atoms take up a different arrangement as shown in fig. 11.8. It will be seen that the centres of the atoms are again arranged in a cubic system, but with an atom at the centre of each cube. This arrangement is called a 'body-centred cubic lattice', and iron with this atomic arrangement is called **α iron**.

These two allotropic forms of iron have the following important characteristics:

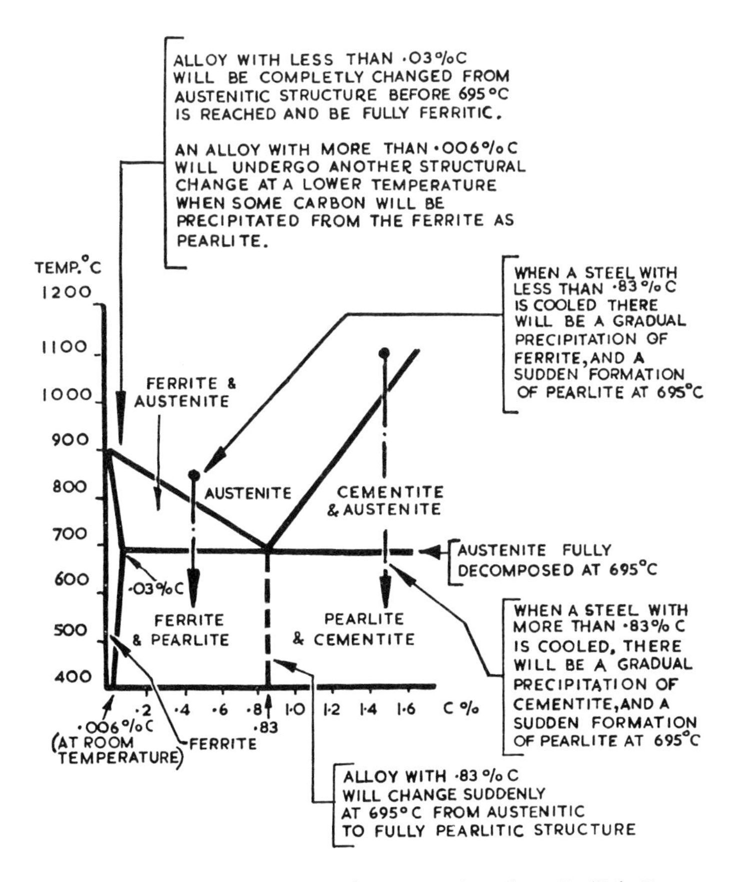

Fig. 11.6 Structural Changes in the Solid State

(*a*) γ iron is of denser atomic packing than α iron and so iron with this arrangement has a smaller volume; when iron changes from one form to the other, the sudden change in volume enables the temperature, when the change takes place, to be recorded, but this volume change can cause cracking during heat treatment.

(*b*) γ iron will accept up to 1·7% carbon in solid solution, producing the micro-constituent **austenite**. Austenite is non-magnetic, and relatively weak; it cannot exist at temperatures below 695°C. and will be fully decomposed when the temperature of a plain carbon steel or ordinary cast iron has fallen below that temperature. α iron will accept only up to 0·03% carbon in solid solution, producing the micro-constituent **ferrite**.

11.32 When the temperature of pure iron falls to 900°C., the γ iron changes

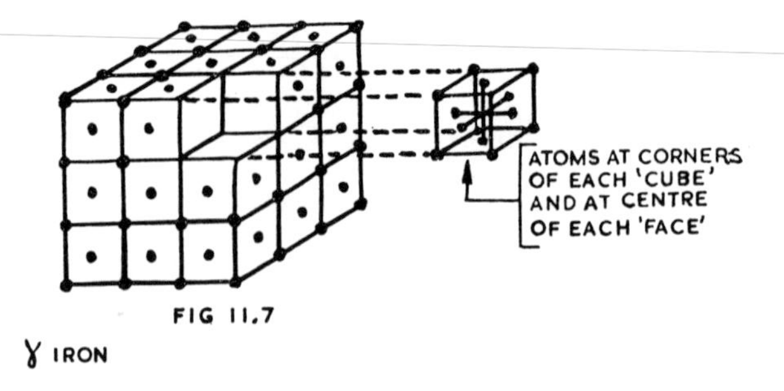

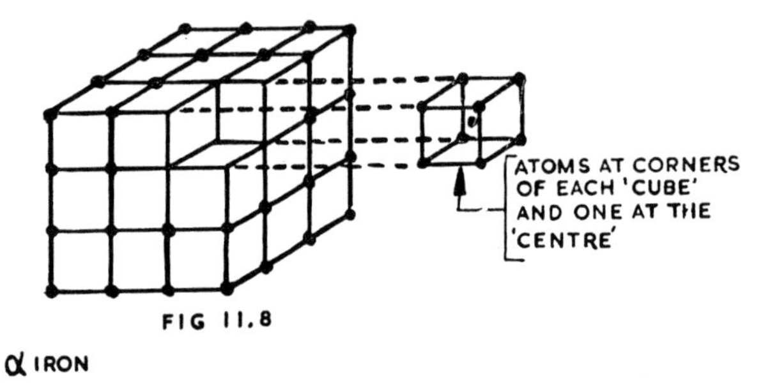

Figs. 11.7 and 11.8 Allotropic Forms of Iron

to α iron; when 0·83% carbon is alloyed with iron, the temperature of this change is lowered to 695°C. and the austenite changes instantaneously to **pearlite.** Pearlite is a laminated structure, and consists of laminations of ferrite and cementite. The iron-carbon alloy with 0·83% carbon is called the **eutectoid.**

If an iron-carbon alloy contains other than 0·83% carbon the breakdown of austenite will be gradual. If the carbon content is less than 0·83%, ferrite will be precipitated during the breakdown of austenite; ferrite contains only a small amount of carbon and so the *percentage* carbon in the remaining austenite will rise, and reach 0·83% when the temperature of the steel has fallen to 695°C., when the remaining austenite will suddenly break down to form pearlite.

11.33 If the carbon content is greater than 0·83%, cementite will be precipitated during the breakdown of austenite; cementite contains 6·67% carbon, and so the *percentage* carbon of the remaining austenite will fall, and reach 0·83% when the temperature of the steel has fallen to 695°C., when the remaining austenite will suddenly break down to form pearlite.

11.34 The solid solubility of carbon in α iron falls from 0·03% to 0·006% with fall in temperature, and so if an iron-carbon alloy has a carbon content

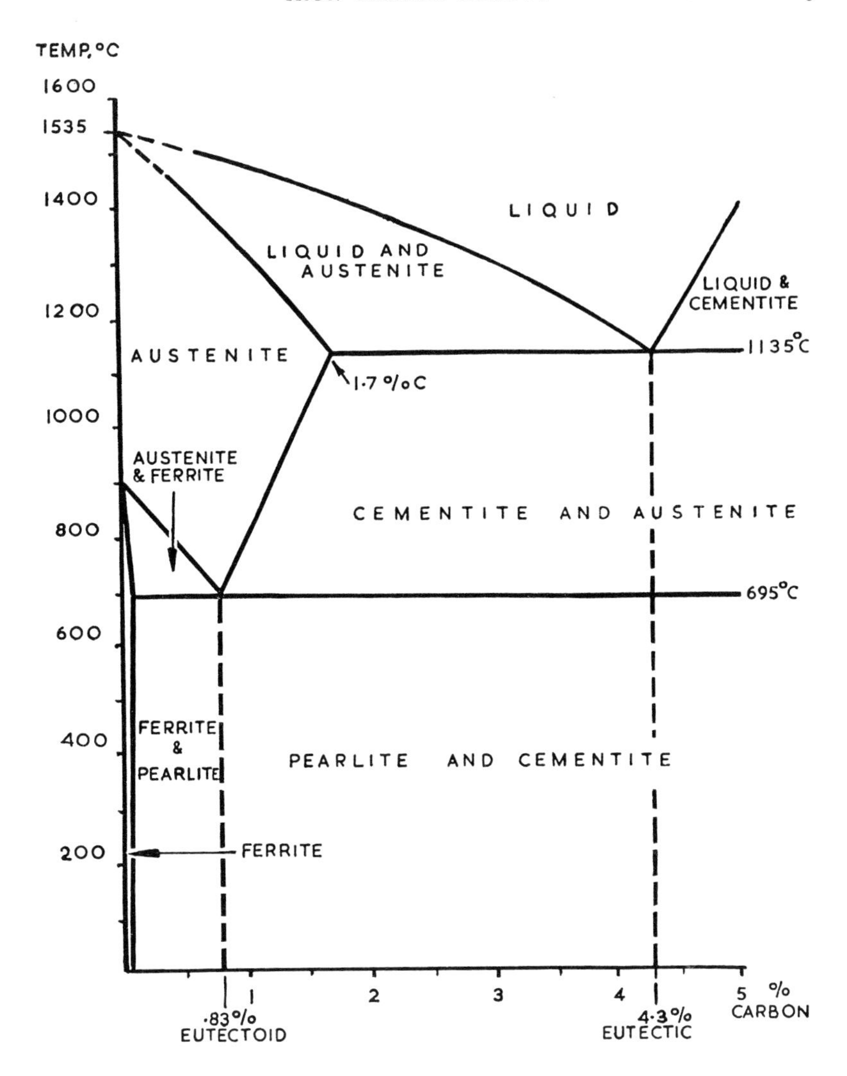

Fig. 11.9 Simplified Iron-carbon Equilibrium Diagram

of more than 0·006%, some carbon will be precipitated from the ferrite during further cooling and so produce more pearlite.

Figures 11.1 and 11.6 are combined to produce the simplified iron-carbon equilibrium diagram shown in fig. 11.9. This diagram has been simplified by omitting phases associated with an allotropic change that takes place when iron-carbon alloys with up to 0·55% carbon are passing from the liquid state into the solid state.

The Heating and Cooling of Plain Carbon Steels

11.40 When plain carbon steels are heated in a furnace they pass through a temperature range during which their temperature will not rise at a uniform rate even though the furnace temperature continues to rise at a uniform rate. The temperatures at which there is a change in the rate of temperature

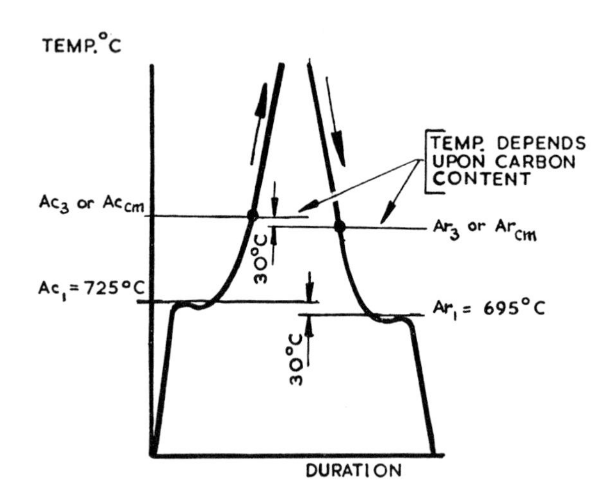

Fig. 11.10 Heating and Cooling Curves for Steel

rise are called the **arrest points**, or **critical points**. Figure 11.10 shows these changes in the rate of temperature rise; it will be seen that at the first arrest point (the Ac_1 point) there is a sudden check in the temperature rise, because the heat is used to bring about the change from α iron to γ iron. After this check there is a gradual recovery of the original rate of temperature rise as the steel passes into the fully austenitic condition, and the original rate of temperature rise is reached at the Ac_3 point (steels with up to 0·83% carbon) or the Ac_{cm} point (steels with more than 0·83% carbon). The Ac_1 point is 725°C., but the Ac_3 and Ac_{cm} points depend upon the carbon content of the steel. ('A' is an abbreviation for 'arrest' and 'c' is an abbreviation for 'chauffage', which is French for 'heating'). The temperature range between the Ac_1 and the Ac_3 or Ac_{cm} points is called the **critical** or **transformation range.**

11.41 When these steels are allowed to cool freely, they will pass through a similar critical range. The upper arrest point is called the Ar_3 or Ar_{cm} point (the 'r' is an abbreviation for 'refroidissement', which is French for 'cooling'), and the lower arrest point is called the Ar_1 point. Figure 11.10 shows these points.

11.42 The temperature at which steel ceases to be ferromagnetic upon heating is called the Ac_2 point, or the Curie point. At one time it was believed that this magnetic change was associated with another allotropic form of iron, called

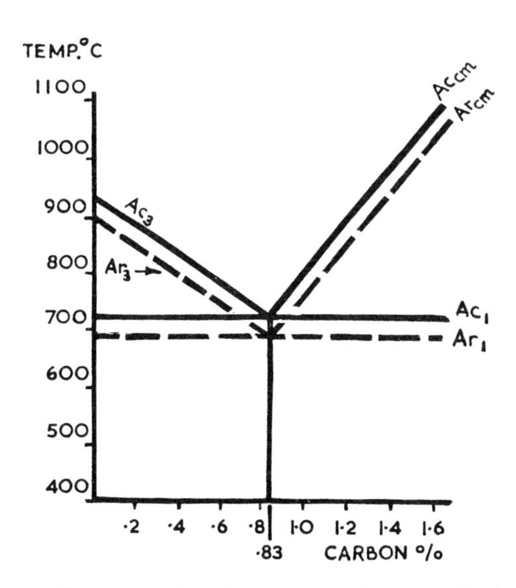

Fig. 11.11 Connection between Arrest Points and Carbon Content

β iron; it is now believed that the steel becomes non-magnetic when a sufficiently large amount of austenite is present. The steel regains its magnetism when the austenite breaks down upon cooling.

The connection between the arrest points and the carbon content is shown in fig. 11.11; it will be seen that there is a difference of 30°C. between corresponding points, due to a sluggishness of the allotropic transformations.

CHAPTER 12

THE HEAT TREATMENT OF STEEL

12.10 Heat treatment can be defined as 'a process in which the metal in the solid state is subjected to one or more temperature cycles, to confer certain desired properties'. Steel is an important engineering material because although cheap, it can be given a wide range of mechanical properties by heat treatment.

Heat treatment can alter the properties of steel by changing the size and the shape of the grains, and by altering the micro-constituents. The shape of the grains can be altered by heating the steel to a temperature above that of recrystallisation; the size of the grains can be controlled by the temperature and the duration of the heating, and the speed at which the steel is cooled after the heating. The micro-constituents can be altered by heating the steel to a temperature that is sufficiently high to produce the solid solution **austenite** so that the carbon is dispersed, and then cooling it at a rate that will produce the desired structure.

Heat treatment processes can be broadly classified as:

1. Treatments that produce equilibrium conditions.
2. Treatments that produce non-equilibrium conditions.

When a steel is in a state of equilibrium it is less strong and hard, but more ductile than when it is in a state of non-equilibrium. Annealing is an example of an equilibrium-producing treatment, and hardening is an example of a non-equilibrium-producing treatment. Tempering tends to restore equilibrium, but it is used in conjunction with hardening to produce a controlled degree of non-equilibrium.

Treatments that Produce Equilibrium Conditions

12.20 When steel is heated to temperatures up to 500°C., any small residual stresses will be liberated, to cause only a slight reduction in hardness and strength. When a temperature of about 500°C. is reached, recrystallisation (see page 42, section 5.22) will take place, producing new, small grains that will be equiaxed even if the grains were deformed by cold working before this heating. If heating is continued the grains will become enlarged, and the ductility will be increased at the expense of hardness and strength. If the temperature of the treatment is high enough to produce an austenitic structure, and if the cooling rate is low enough, the microstructure indicated by the equilibrium diagram will be produced, even if the material was not in equilibrium before this heating. The mechanical properties of the steel at the end of the heat treatment will depend upon its carbon content, the temperature to which it was heated, the duration of the heating, and the cooling rate.

The principal heat treatments in this group are:

Stress relief
Annealing
Normalising

12.21 Stress Relief

Lightly stressed components are often given stress relief (or stabilising) treatment, in which they are heated to a temperature below that of recrystallisation and then cooled freely in air. Stabilising is often done after hardening to relieve quenching stresses; it will not seriously affect the hardness if the temperature of the treatment is about 150°C.

12.22 Annealing

Annealing can be defined as 'heating to, and holding at a suitable temperature, followed by cooling at a suitable rate, for such purposes as inducing softness, improving cold working properties, obtaining a desired structure, and removing stresses'. The properties listed in this definition imply that the steel must be heated through the recrystallisation temperature to remove stresses, held at a high temperature to produce slight grain growth and an austenitic structure, and then cooled very slowly to produce a pearlitic structure to induce softness, and to improve the cold working properties.

There are a number of variations of the annealing process:

Full annealing, isothermal annealing, and sub-critical annealing will be considered in this chapter.

12.221 FULL ANNEALING

This process can be defined as 'heating to, and holding at some temperature above the transformation range, followed by slow cooling through the transformation range'.

Full annealing aims at producing all the effects listed in the definition of annealing. The steel is therefore heated through the recrystallisation range to a temperature that is sufficiently high to produce an austenitic structure (see fig. 12.1), soaked (that is, held at that temperature to produce the necessary uniformity and slight grain growth), and then cooled very slowly. The duration of the soaking will depend upon the thickness of the material and the properties required but it is about two hours. The slow cooling is done either in the furnace, or by removing the steel from the furnace and burying it in ashes to make it cool slowly.

12.222 ISOTHERMAL ANNEALING

It will be appreciated that the slow cooling can take a considerable time, and that if done in the furnace will take up valuable capacity. Isothermal annealing is an alternative to full annealing, which aims at overcoming these difficulties; it can be defined as 'heating to, and holding at some temperature above the transformation range, then cooling to, and holding at some temperature below the transformation range until the austenite has changed completely to pearlite, and finally cooling freely'.

In order to obtain softness it is necessary that the steel is cooled very slowly through the lower critical temperature and so ensure that the main equilibrium change, that of austenite into pearlite, takes place; slow cooling through this temperature is produced by transferring the steel, after heating and soaking, to a salt bath (see page 232) that is maintained at an appropriate sub-critical temperature, until the steel attains that temperature. When the steel has cooled to the temperature of the salt bath, it is removed and cooled freely in air. The salt-bath temperature is usually about 650°C.

12.223 SUB-CRITICAL ANNEALING

This process can be defined as 'heating to, and holding at some temperature below the transformation range, followed by cooling at a suitable rate'. Sub-critical annealing is introduced during an extensive cold working operation in order to remove deformation of crystals caused by it, so that the cold working can be continued (this process was formerly called 'process annealing').

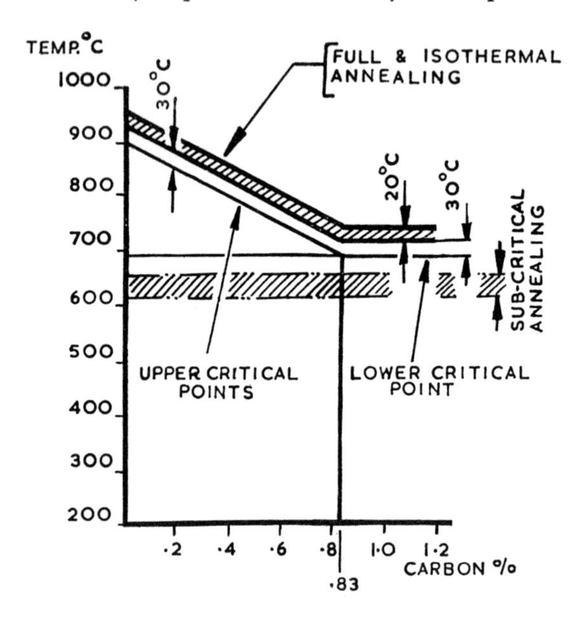

Fig. 12.1 Annealing Temperatures

It will be appreciated that full annealing is done before the commencement of the cold working, which will have affected the grain shape but not the micro-constituents; no attempt is therefore made to alter the micro-constituents and it is therefore neither necessary to heat the steel to a temperature that is high enough to produce an austenitic structure, nor to cool it slowly.

In this process steel is heated to about 650°C.; this temperature is high enough to produce both recrystallisation and uniformity of structure. After the heating it is cooled freely in air.

When applied to higher carbon steels this process causes the cementite to assume a spherical shape, and so makes machining and working easier to do (see fig. 12.12).

12.224 PREVENTION OF SCALING DURING ANNEALING

When steel is heated for long periods at a high temperature, oxidation causes scaling to occur; this scaling can be prevented by the following methods:

1. Heating the steel within refractory-lined and sealed boxes. The steel is surrounded within the box by a suitable material which supports it, and also minimises the amount of air in the box. Iron will accept or reject carbon when at high temperature according to the atmosphere surrounding it, and the carbon content of the steel; a high carbon steel must therefore be surrounded by a carbonaceous material otherwise some decarburising will occur during the heating; similarly, a low carbon steel must be packed with a neutral material otherwise it will absorb carbon.

2. The steel can be heated in a controlled atmosphere furnace (see page 230); when this method is used, the steel need not be packed into boxes.

12.23 Normalising

Normalising can be defined as 'heating to, and holding at a suitable temperature above the transformation range, followed by cooling freely in

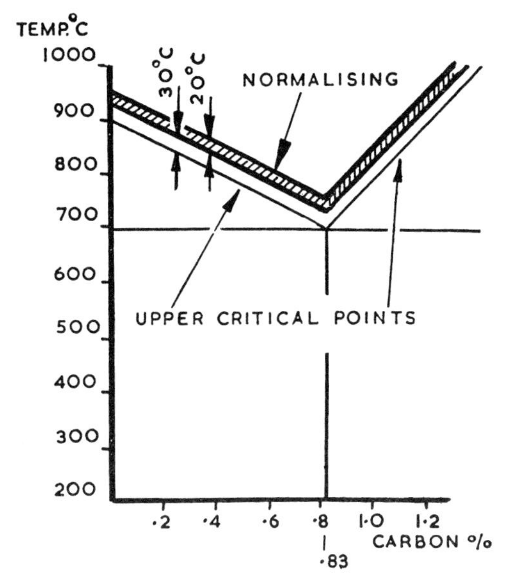

Fig. 12.2 Normalising Temperatures

air, in order to modify the grain size, render the structure more uniform, and usually to improve the mechanical properties'. In this process, the steel is heated to form an austenitic structure (see fig. 12.2), soaked, and then cooled freely in air. Free cooling will produce a finer structure than that produced by annealing, and so a better surface can be produced by machining. Normalising is often done before hardening to produce uniformity; if the steel was soaked during hardening in order to produce uniformity, the grain would become coarse, and the properties produced by hardening would be poor as a result; any coarseness caused by the normalising process would be removed during the heating of the steel through the recrystallisation temperature when its temperature is raised to the hardening temperature.

Treatments that Produce Non-equilibrium Conditions

12.30 When steel is heated to a high temperature, the iron will pass from the α arrangement into the γ arrrangement and all the carbon present in the steel will be dispersed throughout the structure to form the solid solution **austenite**. When the steel is cooled, the iron will revert to the α arrangement in which carbon can only be present in small amounts in solid solution to form **ferrite** if the steel is in a state of equilibrium (see page 86, section 11.31). The precipitation of the excess carbon from solid solution when the iron arrangement changes, requires very slow cooling through the transformation range. If the steel is quenched (cooled very rapidly) from the austenitic condition, the excess carbon will not be precipitated, but will be trapped within the lattice to form the supersaturated solid solution of carbon in α iron called **martensite**, after Martens, who was one of the founders of modern metallurgy. Martensite is a fine, needle-like structure which, due to the enormous supersaturation that causes a distortion of the cubic lattice, is very strong and hard, but very brittle. Martensite is illustrated in fig. 12.10.

12.31 Hardening

In the direct hardening process, steel is heated to produce an austenitic structure and then quenched. The properties produced will depend upon the carbon content of the steel, the temperature to which it is heated, the duration of the heating, the temperature of the steel at the start of the quenching, and the cooling rate.

12.311 CARBON CONTENT

In order to produce a change in properties, sufficient carbon must be retained in solid solution after quenching, to produce the necessary lattice distortion. If the carbon content is less than about 0·15% there will be no change in the properties after quenching, but as the carbon content is increased, there will be a corresponding increase in hardness and strength as a result of quenching (see fig. 12.3) but there will be a reduction in ductility.

12.312 TEMPERATURE

In order to ensure supersaturation as a result of quenching, it is necessary that sufficient carbon is put into solid solution as a result of heating. Steels with less than 0·83% carbon are heated to above the upper critical point (see fig. 12.4) to put all the carbon into solid solution, and then quenched from that temperature; steels with more than 0·83% carbon are usually heated only to above the lower critical point (see fig. 12.4) so that only the pearlite is converted into austenite, which, upon quenching from that temperature will form martensite. It will be seen that when the carbon content is above 0·83%, no attempt is made to convert the free cementite into austenite because this constituent is already hard, and because the high temperature necessary to convert it into austenite would produce a coarse structure which would cause the steel to be even more brittle after quenching, without any appreciable increase in hardness and strength. The duration of the heating depends upon the thickness of the material, but must not be prolonged, otherwise a coarse structure will be produced.

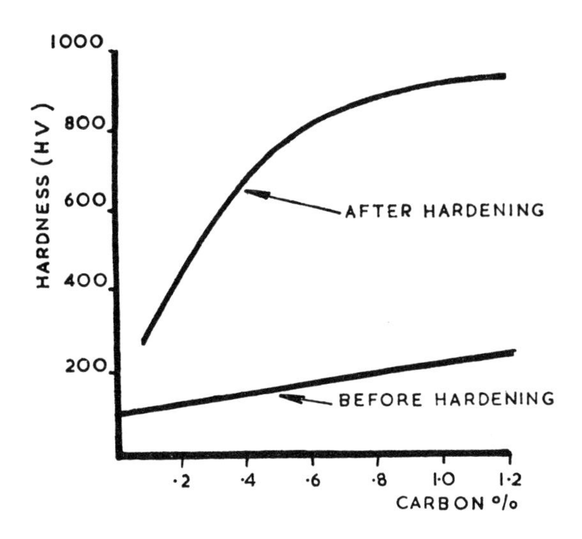

Fig. 12.3 The Connection between Carbon Content and Hardness of Steel

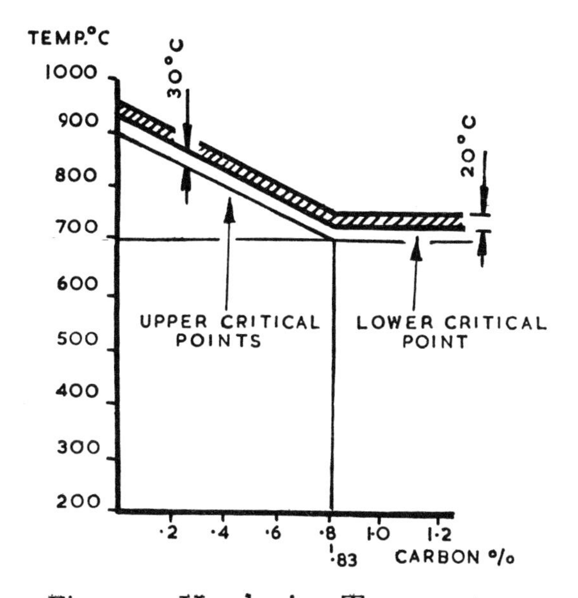

Fig. 12.4 Hardening Temperatures

12.313 COOLING RATE

If a steel is cooled at a certain minimum rate, called the **critical cooling rate**, all the austenite will be transformed into martensite, and so produce its maximum hardness. The critical cooling rate depends upon the chemical composition of the steel.

If the cooling rate is slightly lower than the critical cooling rate, **troostite** will be formed; if the cooling rate is lower still, yet higher than that which will allow pearlite to be formed, **sorbite** will be formed. Troostite and sorbite are stronger and harder than the equilibrium structures; when formed by quenching from the austenitic condition, these structures are a very fine form of pearlite and often called **troostitic pearlite** and **sorbitic pearlite** to distinguish them from the structures formed by reheating martensite (see 'tempering').

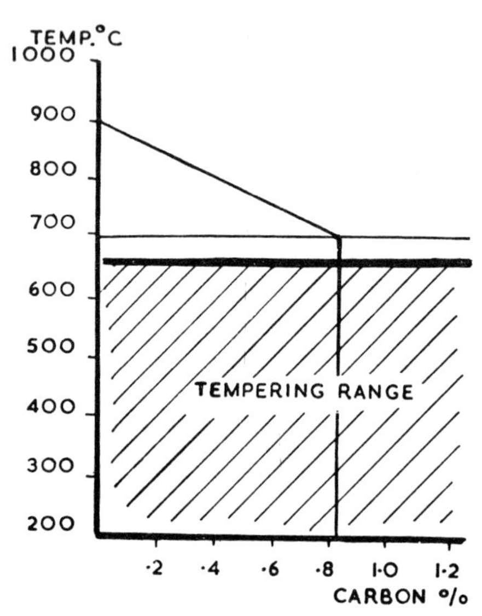

Fig. 12.5 Tempering Temperatures

The rate of cooling depends upon the quenching medium used; for a rapid quench a solution of salt or caustic soda in water must be used, and for a very slow quench, a blast of air is sufficient; water and oil are the most common media used.

12.314 HARDENING CRACKS

When a steel is cooled rapidly through the transformation range, it will expand due to the change in the packing arrangement (see page 86); after this change it will continue to cool, contracting as it does so. This change takes place progressively, as the effect of the quench travels towards the core; and so each 'layer' will expand against the outer 'layers' which, if the carbon content is high enough for the steel to respond to the quench, will crack because of their extreme brittleness.

12.315 CHOICE OF QUENCHING MEDIUM

In order to prevent cracking, and to minimise distortion, the quenching medium should be just drastic enough to produce the required properties. Most alloy steels can be quenched in oil, and certain special alloy steels can be quenched in a blast of air (see Chapter 14). Water is used if a plain carbon steel is to have a high hardness, but it must be realised that a high carbon steel can be oil quenched to produce a similar hardness to that produced when a lower carbon steel is water quenched.

12.316 EFFECT OF THICKNESS OF MATERIAL

When a very thick piece of steel is heated and quenched only the outside will be martensitic, and the core will be of a fine pearlite; this variation of structure will cause a variation of properties across the section, known as **mass effect**. Very often this variation of properties does not cause concern because the surface of the part is usually more highly stressed than its core; but when uniformity of properties, or a strong core is required, the thickness must not exceed a certain maximum, depending upon the composition of the steel. The effect of thickness is usually indicated in a specification by **ruling section**; this is the greatest thickness the material can be and still have uniform properties when quenched using the medium specified. The ruling section depends upon the chemical composition of the steel.

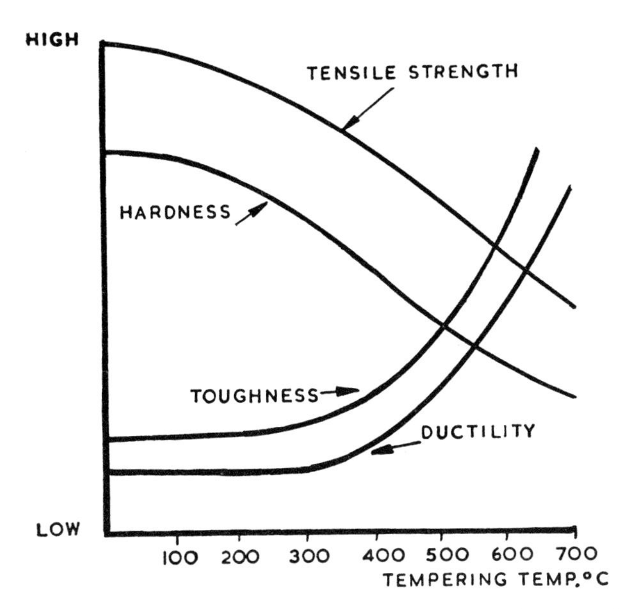

Fig. 12.6 Curves Illustrating how the Mechanical Properties of Hardened Steel can be Modified by Tempering

12.317 MATERIAL SHAPE

In order to minimise distortion during heating and quenching, it may be necessary to consider supporting the steel during its heating, and to pay special attention to the way in which the quenching is done. Hardening problems can be reduced by careful component design; uniform section thickness will allow uniformity of cooling, and fillets will reduce the tendency for cracks to form at corners.

12.32 Tempering

Steels are usually reheated to a sub-critical temperature after hardening to improve their toughness and ductility, at the expense of hardness and strength,

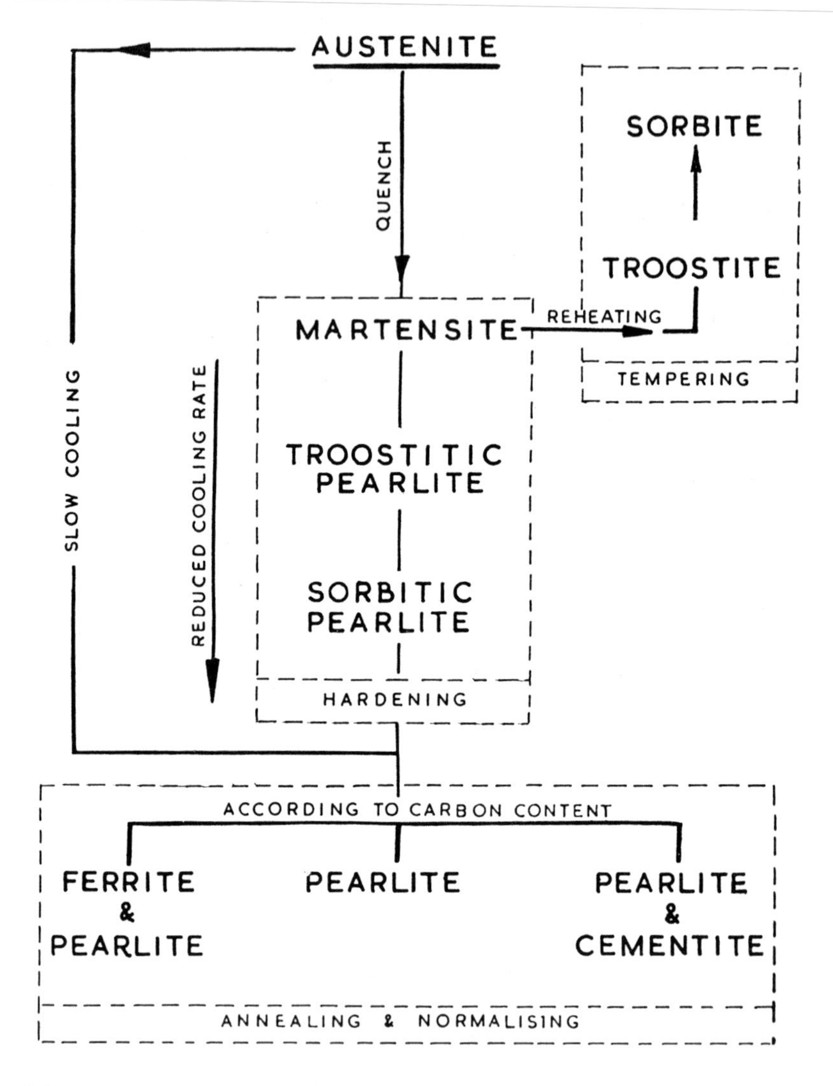

Fig. 12.7 Structures Produced when Carbon Steel is Cooled from an Austenitic Condition

and so make them more suitable for service requirements. This reheating process is called **tempering**, and it causes the martensite to be transformed into **troostite** or **sorbite** according to the tempering temperature (these forms of troostite and sorbite are fine dispersions of carbide in a ferrite matrix, and unlike the structures formed from austenite, which are laminated). The tempering temperature depends upon the properties required, but is between about 180 and 650°C., and the duration of the heating depends upon the thickness of the material. Heating is usually done in air-circulating furnaces, oil baths, salt baths, or lead baths, so that the temperature can be controlled accurately. Tools are usually tempered at low temperatures by judging the temperature by the colour of the oxide film produced upon heating (see table 12.1 below), but this method is unsuitable for accurate temperature assessment. Figure 12.6 illustrates the effect of hardening and tempering upon the mechanical properties of a steel, and it will be seen that a wide range of properties can be obtained from one steel according to the extent of hardening and the tempering temperature.

TABLE 12.1

Tempering temperatures

Temper colour	*Temperature °C.*
Pale straw	230
Dark straw	240
Brown	250
Brownish-purple	260
Purple	270
Dark purple	280
Blue	300

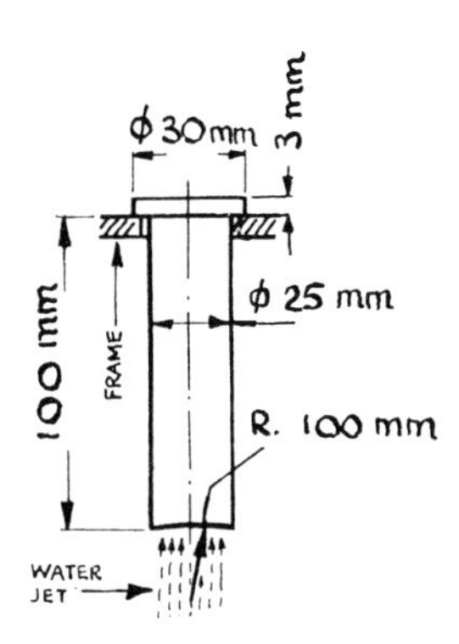

Fig. 12.14

The Jominy End-Quench Test

12.33 On page 98 it was explained that when a thick piece of steel is heated and quenched its hardness will vary across the section. The **hardenability** of a steel is that property which determines the depth and distribution of hardness after quenching under specific conditions; this property must not be confused with intensity of hardness. Hardenability can be determined using the Jominy end-quench test (fig. 12.14) in which a standard test piece is quenched from austenitic condition so that only the end is quenched, and thus the test piece is cooled at different rates along its length. The hardness along the length is measured at 2 mm intervals after 0·4 mm is ground off to produce a 'flat'. A graph of hardness/distance from quenched end is drawn to compare steels.

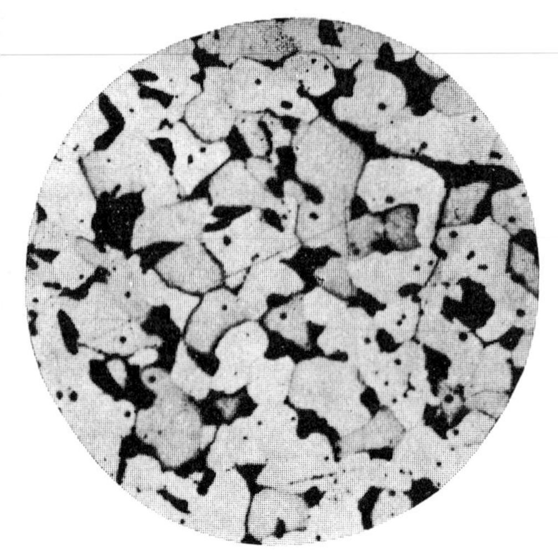

Fig. 12.8 0·13% C Steel in the Normalised Condition × 500* Pearlite (dark) and Ferrite (light)

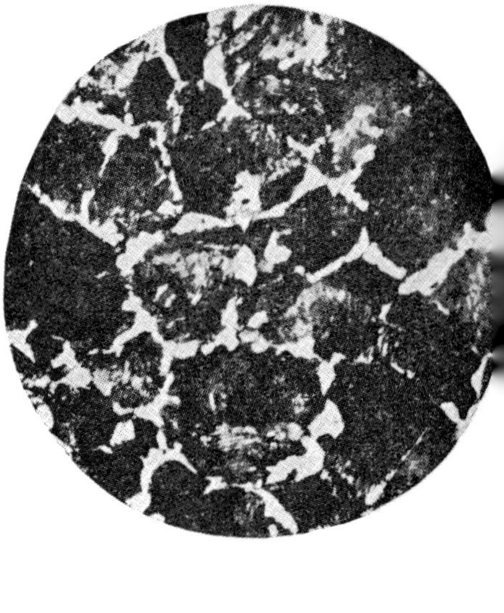

Fig. 12.9 0·52% C Steel in the Normalised Condition × 500* Pearlite (dark) and Ferrite (light)

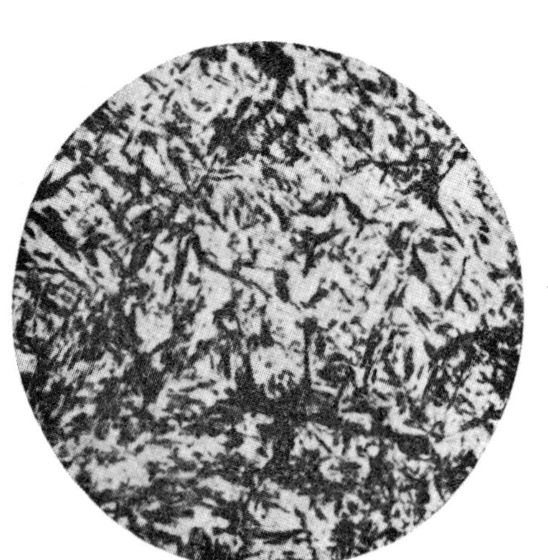

Fig. 12.10 0·52% C Steel after Normalising and then Hardened by Quenching in Water × 500*

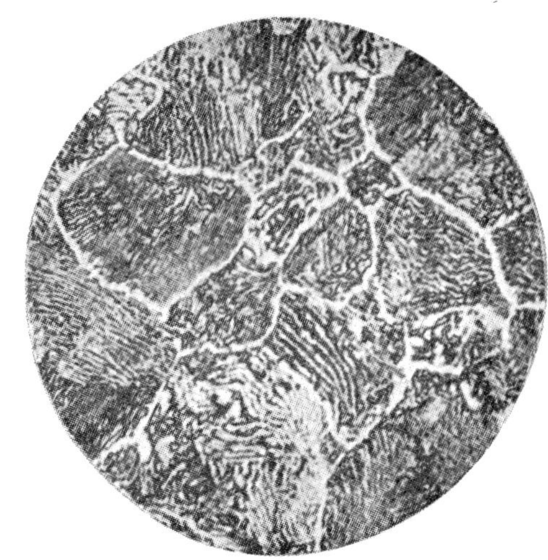

Fig. 12.11 1·1% C Steel in the Fully Annealed Condition × 200* Pearlite (laminated), Cementite (light) at Crystal Boundaries

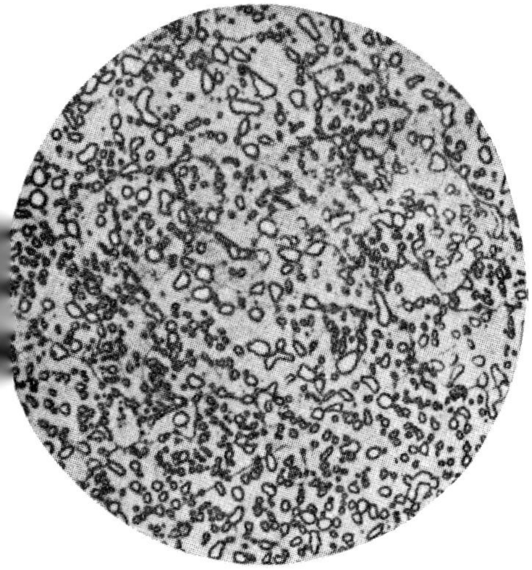

Fig. 12.12 1·1% C Steel in the Sub-critically Annealed Condition × 500.* Note that the Cementite has assumed a spherical shape

Fig. 12.13 1·1% C Steel after Quenching in Water then Tempering at 250°C.*

*Courtesy of British Iron and Steel Research Association

CHAPTER 13

THE SURFACE HARDENING OF STEEL BY HEAT TREATMENT

13.10 Very often a component must have a hard, wear-resisting surface that is supported by a tough, shock-resisting core. This combination of widely differing properties can be combined in a single piece of steel by surface hardening.

Surface-hardening methods can be broadly classified as:

1. Methods in which the whole component is heated.
2. Methods in which only the surface of the component is heated.

Methods in which the Whole Component is Heated

13.20 If the material or the heat-treatment process is such that only the surface of the component will respond to the treatment, the whole component can be heated during the treatment. Two methods of surface hardening that employ full heating are:

(*a*) *Casehardening.* In which the composition of the steel is such that it can be treated so that when it is later subjected to heating and quenching only the surface will become hardened.

(*b*) *Nitriding.* In which the composition of the steel is such that when subjected to heating in an atmosphere of nitrogen gas, the surface will become hardened.

13.30 Casehardening

In this process the component is usually made from a steel with a carbon content of about 0·15% so that it will not respond to direct hardening treatment, and is subjected to **carburising** (or cementation) to increase the carbon content of the surface layers, so that only the surface will respond to hardening. In the carburising process the steel is subjected to heating in a carbonaceous atmosphere; this is a similar process to that used in ancient times to make a kind of steel from wrought iron (see page 76, section 10.50) but which was considered to be unsatisfactory because the carbon was unevenly distributed across the section of the material. The uneven carbon distribution produces a high carbon 'case' surrounding a low carbon 'core'; when the component is heated up and quenched, only the case will respond and become hard, whilst the core will remain 'soft' and tough as required. If selected surface areas are to remain soft, they can be insulated during the carburising operation to prevent carbon from entering the steel at these points so that the surface remains low in carbon; an alternative method is to leave surplus metal on these parts of the surface, so that when machined after carburising, the high carbon surface will be removed to expose the core.

Casehardening is therefore a two-part process:

(i) *Carburising.* In which the carbon content of the surface is increased.

(ii) *Heat Treatment.* In which the core is refined, and the case is hardened.

13.31 CARBURISING

The steel is heated to above its upper critical point (see fig. 13.1) in a carbonaceous atmosphere, and kept at that temperature until the carbon has penetrated to the depth required. The carburising medium can be solid, liquid, or gaseous.

13.311 *Solid Carburising Media* (when a solid medium is used, the process is often called 'pack carburising'). In this method, the parts are packed into a suitable metal box and surrounded within the box by the carburising medium.

It is important that none of the carbon gas produced during the process is lost, and that air does not enter the box to cause decarburisation (loss of carbon) of the steel, and so a lid is placed on the box and sealed with a suitable fireclay. The carburising medium is basically wood, bone, or leather charcoal; an energiser is usually added to accelerate the process; barium carbonate and sodium carbonate are typical energisers. The carbon content produced at the surface can be controlled by blending new and used carburising media; the carburising rate is shown in fig. 13.2, but this can be accelerated by using higher temperatures. The surface can be insulated against carburising by coating with a suitable paste, or by plating to produce a copper deposit about 0·1 mm thick.

13.312 *Liquid Carburising Media.* A typical salt bath for carburising consists of sodium carbonate and sodium cyanide with either sodium or barium chloride. The liquid carburising process is suitable for cases with a depth of about 0·3 mm. The high speed of carburising when this method is used is a disadvantage if the part is to be highly stressed in service, because the rate at which the carbon is absorbed by the steel is greater than the rate at which it is diffused within the steel; this produces a thin case with a very high carbon content, which may flake or crack after hardening. The parts are held in baskets within the bath, and must be preheated to prevent an explosion.

13.313 *Gaseous Carburising Media.* Gas is a suitable medium for batch or continuous carburising to produce a case depth of about 1 mm, and takes about four hours, during which the parts are held in a basket within a heated furnace through which is passed a suitable carbon gas. The carbon content of the case can be controlled by adjusting the composition of the carburising gas.

13.32 HEAT TREATMENT

The lengthy carburising treatment will cause grain growth (see page 42, section 5.23) unless a nickel casehardening steel (see Chapter 14) is used; the object of the post-carburising heat treatment is to produce a fine grain as well as to harden the case. It must be understood that as a result of the carburising process, the steel will have a case with about 0·83% carbon, and a core with about 0·15% carbon; there will be a gradual transition from case to core composition (see fig. 13.3) that extends over about 0·5 mm. The heat treatment temperature for the core will be considerably higher than that for the case (see fig. 13.1), and it is convenient to consider the case and the core separately.

13.321 *Refining the Core.* The carburised steel is first reheated to about 870°C. to refine the core and to produce uniformity of structure, and then quenched to prevent grain growth during cooling. The temperature of this heating is much higher than that suitable for the case, and consequently the austenite so produced will be coarse, and therefore a coarse and extremely brittle martensite is produced when the steel is quenched. The case and the outer layers of the core must be refined after core refining.

13·322 *Refining the Case.* The steel is heated to about 760°C. according to the case composition (see fig. 13.1) to refine the case, and temper the outer layers of the core, and then quenched from that temperature. Very often the steel is finally tempered at about 200°C. to relieve quenching stresses.

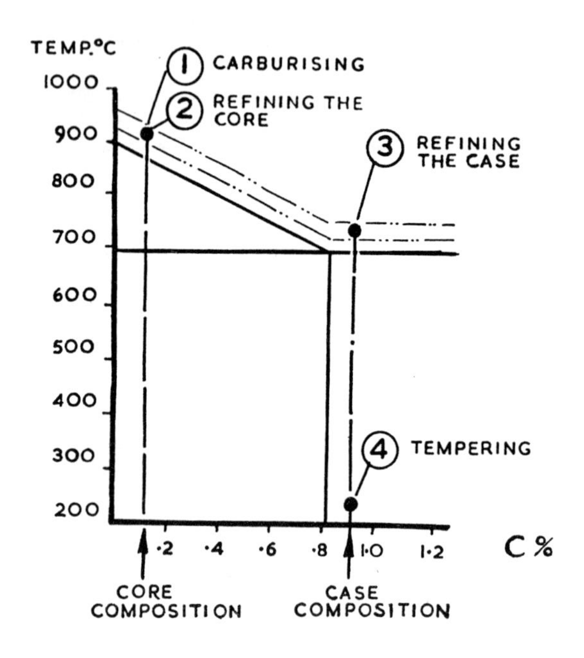

Fig. 13.1 Casehardening Temperatures

13·33 VARIATIONS OF THE CASEHARDENING PROCESS

1. When an alloy casehardening steel with about 3 or 5% nickel is used, the carburising process will not produce grain growth, and so core refining is unnecessary (see Chapter 14).

2. If the component is not to be subjected to high stresses when in service, the core-refining process need not be done, even if the steel does not contain nickel.

3. If the steel contains nickel, or if the component is not likely to be highly stressed in service, and provided that surplus metal is not left on parts of the surface for removal after hardening, the component can be quenched directly from carburising, and then tempered to remove stresses set up by this quenching. This technique is called 'pot quenching'.

MICROSTRUCTURES PRODUCED BY CARBURISING AND HARDENING

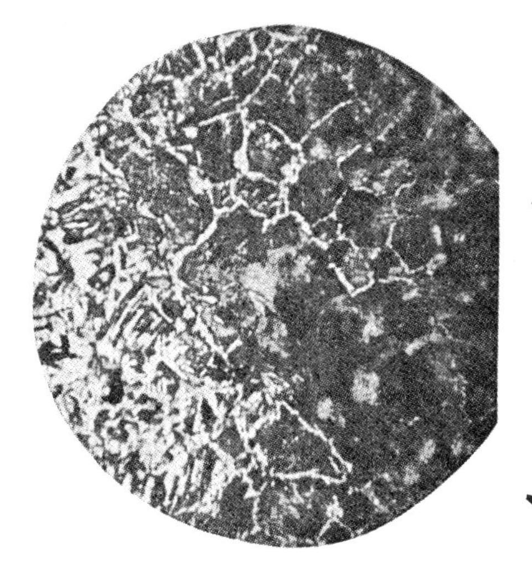

Fig. 13.3 (a)
Casehardening Steel, Pack Carburised for One Hour × 50
Pearlite and Ferrite (more Pearlite at Surface)

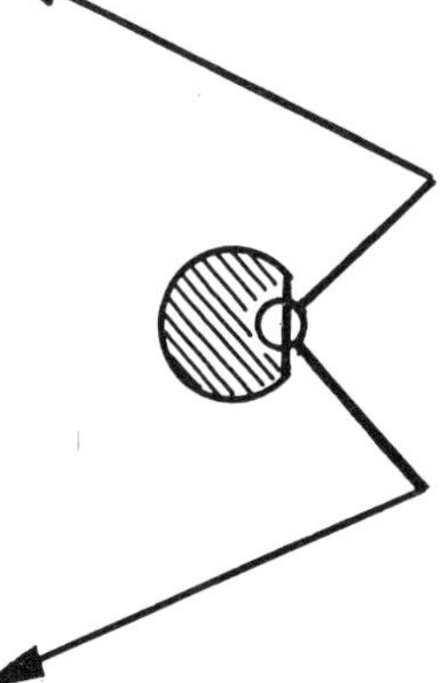

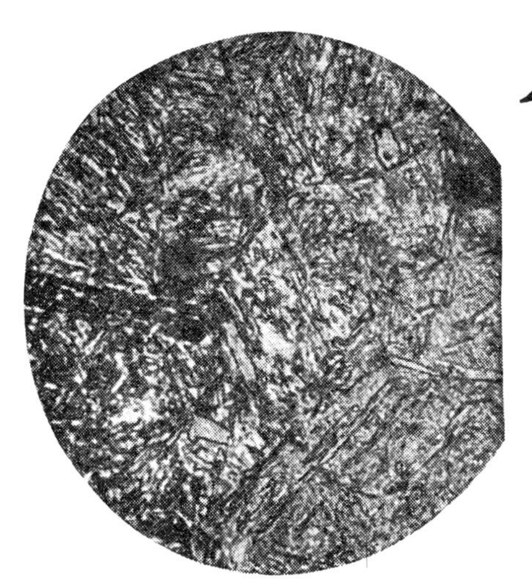

Fig. 13.3 (b)
Casehardening Steel, Pack Carburised for One Hour and then Hardened by Water Quenching × 50
Martensite Formed at Surface

13.40 Nitriding

Nitriding can be defined as 'a surface-hardening process in which a special alloy steel is heated for a considerable time in an atmosphere of gaseous nitrogen'.

As a result of this treatment, hard nitrides are produced at the surface. These nitrides are bulky and form a 'pegging' in the lattice structure of the steel. In order to produce surface hardness by this method it is necessary to use an alloy steel that contains a small amount of chromium, or small amounts of both chromium and aluminium, according to the hardness to be produced;

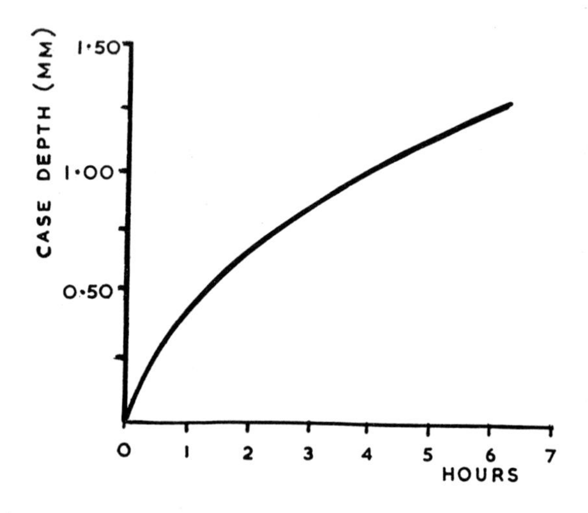

Fig. 13.2 Relation between Case Depth and Carburising Period

if a plain carbon steel was subjected to this process, nitrides would be formed throughout the structure with little effect upon the properties. The carbon content of a nitriding steel is between 0·2 and 0·5%, according to the core properties required; it will be realised that these steels will respond to direct hardening.

Parts that are to be nitrided are given heat treatment during the early stages of their machining to develop core strength; this treatment consists of hardening by oil quenching, followed by tempering at between 550 and 750°C. depending upon the composition of the steel and the properties required. Before final machining they are heated at about 550°C. for up to seven hours and slowly cooled to remove stresses and to minimise distortion during the nitriding. These parts can be finish-machined before nitriding because no quenching is done, and therefore they will not suffer from quenching distortion.

13.41 The nitriding process consists of heating the parts at 500°C. in a constant circulation of ammonia gas, for up to 100 hours; during the early stages of nitriding a case depth of about 0·1 mm is produced in 10 hours, but the rate of penetration decreases as the process is continued, and it takes about 100 hours to obtain a case depth of about 0·7 mm (see fig. 13.4). During the nitriding process the parts are in an externally-heated gas-tight box fitted with inlet and outlet ports for the ammonia. At the completion of the soaking the ammonia is still circulated until the temperature of the steel has fallen to about 150°C., and then the box is opened and the cooling completed in air. After this treatment the parts can be buffed if necessary to remove the film produced on the surface.

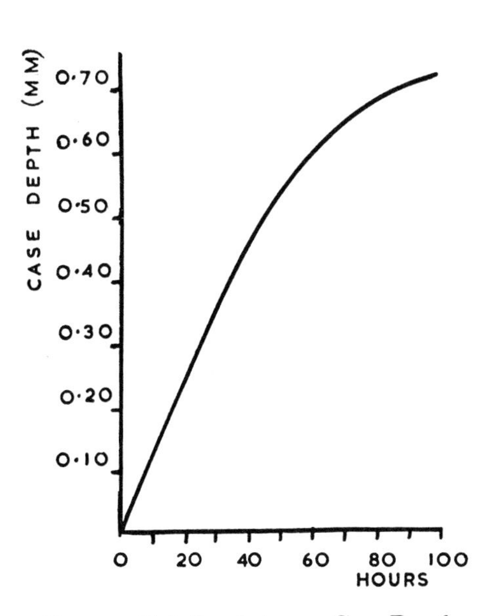

Fig. 13.4 Relation between Case Depth and Nitriding Period

13.42 Surface areas that are to be kept 'soft' can be insulated by tinning, by plating with copper or nickel to produce a 0·07 mm deposit, or by applying a suitable paste. Nitriding causes a growth of between about 0·02 and 0·05 mm on diameter, or about 0·015 mm on the sides of rectangular sections; for precision work a finishing allowance of between 0·02 and 0·07 mm of surface material is usually allowed.

13.43 The surface hardness produced depends upon the composition of the steel used; steels with 3% chromium develop about 850 HV, and steels with 1·5% chromium and 1·5% aluminium develop about 1100 HV.

13.44 Nitriding is an ideal surface-hardening process for large-scale production but it is uneconomical for small-scale production. It is particularly good where moderately high temperatures are to be encountered in service, because the hardness of nitrided parts does not fall until 500°C. is reached, unlike casehardened parts, which start to lose their hardness when a temperature of 200°C. is reached.

Methods in which only the Surface of the Component is Heated

13.50 When these methods are used, the component is made from a steel that can be directly hardened, but, instead, it is hardened by very rapidly heating it to its hardening temperature, and then quenching it before the core reaches the hardening temperature. Two methods which employ local heating are used:

(*a*) Flame Hardening.
(*b*) Induction Hardening.

13.51 Flame Hardening (also called the 'Shorter' process, after its inventor) Steels with a suitably high carbon content can be heated to the hardening temperature by means of an oxy-acetylene flame, and then quenched to pro-

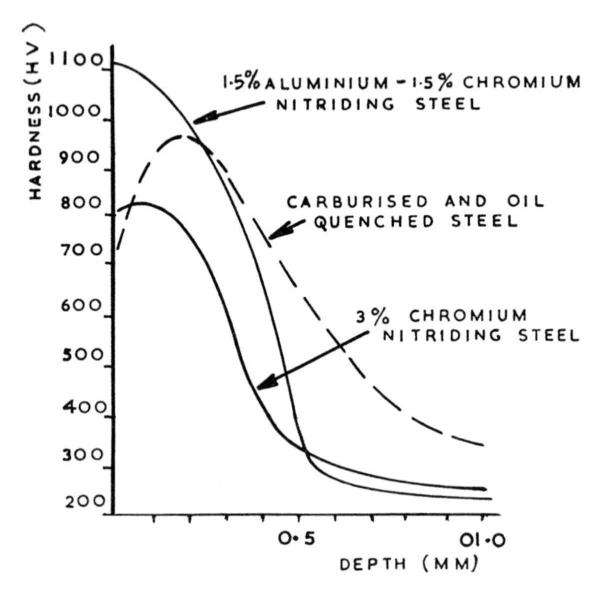

Fig. 13.5 Comparison between Hardness–depth Curves for Nitriding and Casehardening

duce a local surface hardness. This method is suitable for cases of up to 0·8 mm depth; the flame temperature must be above the melting temperature of steel in order to produce the rapid heating necessary in this process, and there is a danger of local melting if greater case depths are attempted.

The steel must have a carbon content of between about 0·4 and 0·7% to respond to this treatment; the hardness obtained will depend upon the composition of the steel, and the treatment conditions.

13.511 Typical flame-hardening techniques are:

(i) Heating the surface locally, and then quenching the component in a separate quenching tank.
(ii) Progressive heating and quenching, in which the flame and the quenching spray are continuously acting whilst they are passed across

the surface to be hardened. The rate at which the unit traverses the surface controls the hardness produced. Progressive heating and quenching can also be done in a booth containing a fixed flame and spray unit through which the parts to be treated are fed on a conveyor moving at about 3 m/s.

(iii) Spinning the component past stationary flames that surround it, and then spraying or immersing it in water to quench it. Long components can be rotated whilst the flame units are reciprocated parallel to the axis of rotation. Components to be treated by this method should be symmetrical about the axis of rotation.

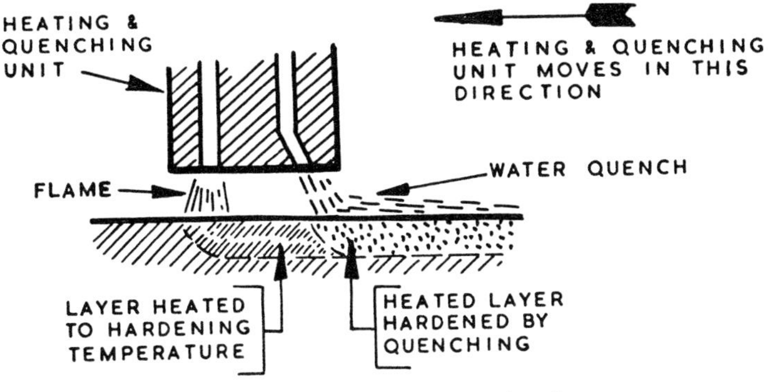

Fig. 13.6 Flame Hardening

13.512 After flame hardening, steel is usually tempered; this can be done by flame heating if necessary.

13.52 Induction Hardening

This is a production method of surface hardening, in which the component to be hardened is placed within an inductor coil through which a high frequency current is passed (see fig. 13.7). The surface of the workpiece is quickly brought to the hardening temperature, and either quenched whilst still within the coil, or dropped from the coil into the quenching bath. It takes about 5 seconds for a case depth of 3 mm to be heated to its hardening temperature.

If a reduced diameter is to be locally treated, the coil can be hinged as shown in fig. 13.8.

Steels with about 0·45% carbon are most suitable for hardening by this method. The temperature produced can be controlled by coil design, and by the distance between the coil and the surface to be hardened.

Applications of Surface-hardening Methods

13.60 CASEHARDENING

This system is used for general work where high temperatures are not expected in service, and where the core is to be tough. Local 'soft' surfaces can

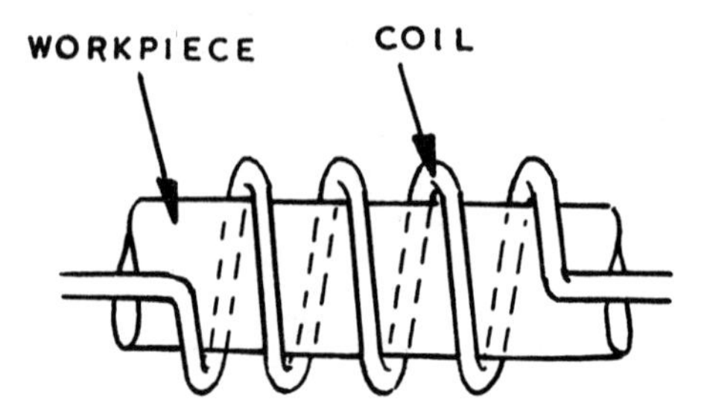

Fig. 13.7 Principle of Induction Hardening

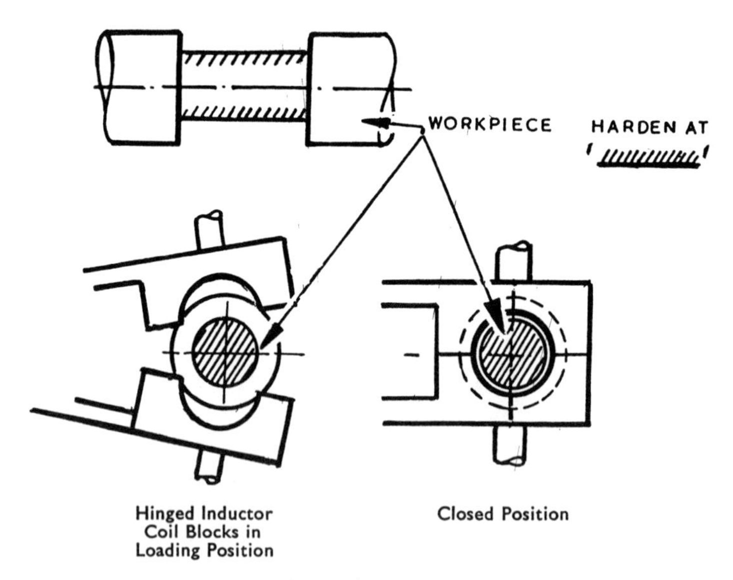

Fig. 13.8 Induction Hardening a Reduced Diameter

be produced easily by this method. Liquid carburising does not give such a good quality case as solid and gaseous carburising media, but it is more rapid.

NITRIDING

A high surface hardness can be produced by this method, but it is less suitable than casehardening if the hardened surfaces are to withstand high pressures (as for example, gear teeth), but hard surfaces so produced resist heat better.

FLAME AND INDUCTION HARDENING

These methods are used when the component is made from a high carbon steel so that the core will have a good strength.

REFERENCES

'Cassel' Manual of Heat Treatment and Casehardening (Imperial Chemical Industries Ltd).
Firth Brown, *Nitriding steels.*

CHAPTER 14

ALLOY STEELS

14.10 An alloy steel can be defined as 'a steel to which one or more alloying elements have been added for the purpose of modifying the properties'; in this definition carbon is not considered to be an alloying element.

Alloy steels are more expensive than carbon steels (steels that contain only iron, carbon, and impurities), because of the cost of the alloying elements and of the alloying process. Alloy steels are often more difficult than carbon steels to manipulate into shapes and to machine; they usually require long and rather complicated heat treatment in order to develop their properties. The main effect of alloying is to make the steel more responsive to heat treatment and it is important that the manufacturers' instructions regarding heat-treatment procedure be followed; an incorrectly heat-treated alloy steel may have properties that are inferior to those produced when a carbon steel is correctly heat treated.

14.20 Alloy steels are used because of the limitations of carbon steels, or when special properties are required.

The limitations of carbon steels may be classified as:

1. Limitations associated with response to heat treatment.
2. Limitations associated with service conditions.

The special properties obtained by alloying include desired electrical and magnetic properties, a specific coefficient of thermal expansion, and the retention of hardness at temperatures associated with metal cutting.

The Effect of Alloying Elements

14.30 It is difficult to state precisely the effect of any one alloying element because the effect depends upon the quantity used, the quantity of other alloying elements used with it, and the carbon content of the steel. The limitations associated with carbon steels and the general effect of some of the principal alloying elements will be considered here, and some representative alloy steels will be considered later in this chapter.

14.31 The Effect of Alloying upon the Response to Heat Treatment

Carbon steels have a high critical cooling rate (see page 98, section 12.313), which means that quenching must be drastic if it is to produce a martensitic structure. Drastic quenching will cause distortion or even cracking (see page 98, section 12.314) but if the critical cooling rate is reduced by making the breakdown of austenite sluggish, a martensitic structure can be produced by oil quenching; if the critical cooling rate is reduced still further, air quenching can be used.

14.311 Mass effect (see page 98, section 12.316) is associated with critical cooling rate; a greater depth of hardness can be produced by lowering the critical cooling rate, and so thicker sections will be of uniform structure when hardened. This is indicated in a materials specification by a larger 'Ruling Section' value. Chromium, manganese, and tungsten are elements that reduce the critical cooling rate.

14.312 When nickel is alloyed with steel, it lowers the temperature at which austenite is formed upon heating and so it lowers the hardening temperature (steel must be heated to a temperature that is high enough to produce austenite during the hardening operation). It will be appreciated that when steel is cooling freely, its cooling rate depends upon its temperature; the lowering of the hardening temperature produced by nickel will, in effect, lower the critical cooling rate. If a suitable hard, but reasonably tough, steel is required, the nickel content must not exceed about 5%.

14.313 If carbide-forming elements such as chromium and molybdenum are added a greater depth of hardness will be produced, and so mass effect will be reduced.

14.32 The Effect of Alloying upon the Properties Required in Service

The behaviour of any steel in service will depend to a large extent upon its response to heat treatment; the effects discussed here are those directly demanded by service conditions, but it will be obvious that most of these effects are only produced as a result of suitable heat treatment.

14.321 Carbon steels have a limited strength and must be of large section to reduce the stresses; when weight or space saving are important considerations it is necessary to use steels with higher strength. The strength of steel can be increased by adding elements such as nickel and manganese in small amounts so that they enter into the ferrite and strengthen it.

14.322 Toughness can be obtained by adding a small quantity of nickel, which will cause the grain to be fine.

14.323 Wear resistance can be obtained by adding a carbide stabiliser, such as chromium; nickel tends to cause the decomposition of carbides and when it is present without chromium to counteract it, the carbon content must be below about 0·4%. An alternative method of producing wear resistance is to add elements such as nickel or manganese in order to lower the transformation temperatures and thereby to cause the retention of austenite upon quenching; these alloy steels are work-hardening steels, and their hardness increases with wear.

14.324 The hardness and strength of carbon steels starts to fall when their temperature reaches about 250°C. Heat resistance can be obtained by raising the transformation temperatures by the addition of chromium or tungsten, or by lowering the transformation temperatures by the addition of nickel to produce an austenitic structure upon quenching; austenitic steels will not undergo any further structural changes upon heating. Grain growth (see page 42, section 5.23) is also associated with heating to high temperatures, but can be offset by the addition of nickel; chromium tends to promote grain growth, and nickel must be introduced when a chromium steel must be heat-resisting. Carbon steels creep when subjected to high temperatures and a small quantity of molybdenum is usually included to improve the resistance to creep.

14.325 Corrosion resistance can be obtained by adding upwards of about 12% chromium, which forms a film of oxide upon the surface of the steel to insulate it against continued corrosion; when better resistance to corrosion, particularly at high temperatures, is required, nickel and chromium are used together to produce an austenitic structure.

Some Examples of Alloy Steels and their Applications

The following alloy steels are representative; for a complete list of alloy steels, their mechanical properties, and the heat-treatment procedure, reference should be made to British Standards, and to manufacturers' data sheets.

14.40 Steels to Suit Special Heat-treatment Techniques

14.41 CASEHARDENING STEELS

Carbon casehardening steels suffer grain growth as a result of the prolonged heating during the carburising process; if the surface pressure in service will be high, the core must be refined to prevent the case from sinking and to give a good strength across the section; the addition of nickel obviates the need for a refining heat treatment, and so distortion is minimised. Slightly higher amounts of nickel will permit oil quenching to be done. When a thick component is to have a good uniform core strength, chromium is also added to offset mass effect; chromium is not used alone, but must be used with nickel to prevent grain growth.

14.411 *Nickel Casehardening Steels.* 0·12% C, 3% Ni, 0·45% Mn. In this steel, the carbon content is low so that the core will not respond to the direct-hardening process. The nickel prevents grain growth during the carburising process, so that when small parts are made from this steel, the refining operation may be omitted; this is a water-quenching steel.

0·12% C, 5% Ni, 0·45% Mn. This steel is similar to the 3% Ni casehardening steel, but the slightly higher nickel content enables it to be oil quenched, making it more suitable for gears and similar heavy duty parts.

14.412 *Nickel-chromium Caseharding Steels.* 0·15% C, 4% Ni, 0·8% Cr, 0·4% Mn. The addition of a small amount of chromium produces a higher hardness and strength as a result of oil quenching.

14.42 NITRIDING STEELS

As explained in Chapter 13, nitriding steels must contain elements that will produce surface hardness. Nitriding steels with about 3% chromium develop a surface hardness of about 850 HV, and steels with about 1·5% aluminium and 1·5% chromium develop about 1100 HV. The carbon content of these steels depends upon the core properties required, but is between about 0·18 and 0·5%.

14.43 AIR-HARDENING STEELS

When sufficient chromium is present, the critical cooling rate is reduced so much that quenching can be done in air. A typical air-hardening steel contains about 2% chromium; the carbon content is about 0·6% so that the hardening temperature, and in effect, the critical cooling rate, is lowered.

14.50 High-tensile Steels

14.51 *Low Manganese Steel.* 0·35% C, 1·5% manganese. This is an inexpensive but good strength steel. It can be oil quenched because the manganese lowers the hardening temperature in addition to strengthening the ferrite.

14.52 *Nickel Steel.* 0·3% C, 3% Ni, 0·6% Mn. This steel has a good strength and hardness, and can be oil quenched because nickel lowers the hardening temperature. It is used for crankshafts and connecting rods and similar applications.

14.53 *Nickel-chromium Steels.* Steels in this group combine the hardness associated with chromium with the toughness associated with nickel.

0·3% C, 3% Ni, 0·8% Cr, 0·6% Mn. This is an oil-quenching steel with good toughness and strength; it is used for connecting rods and similar parts.

0·3% C, 4·25% Ni, 1·25% Cr, 0·5% Mn. The higher nickel and chromium content lowers the critical cooling rate so that quenching can be done in a blast of air, and so distortion is minimised. Although chromium alone will considerably lower the critical cooling rate, it is combined with nickel so that toughness is obtained. Steels of this type are used for crankshafts and connecting rods.

14.531 *Temper-brittleness.* Nickel-chromium steels become brittle if they are tempered at between 250 and 400°C., depending upon their composition; this is known as **temper brittleness** and it can be detected by impact testing. The addition of about 0·3% molybdenum will prevent temper brittleness; molybdenum will also help to reduce mass effect because it is a carbide-forming element.

14.54 *Chromium-vanadium Steels.* The addition of about 0·5% vanadium improves the shock resistance of chromium steels and makes them easier to forge and to stamp. When vanadium replaces nickel, the steel is more prone to mass effect.

14.60 Wear-resisting Steels

14.61 *Austenitic Manganese Steel* (Hadfield's Steel). Steels in this group contain basically 1·2% C, 12·5% Mn, 0·75% silicon; they may also contain carbide-forming elements such as chromium or vanadium to give improved strength. Due to the lowering of the transformation temperature by the manganese, this steel is austenitic if water quenched from about 1050°C.; in this condition it has a hardness of only about 200 HB but an excellent toughness. It cannot be hardened by heat treatment, but when cold worked its surface hardness will increase up to about 550 HB without loss of core toughness. This steel must not be reheated to temperatures higher than 250°C. unless it is water quenched afterwards; heating at intermediate temperatures will cause embrittlement due to precipitation of carbides.

Austenitic manganese steel can be obtained as castings, forgings, and rolled sections, but it is difficult to machine owing to work hardening. This steel is used extensively for rock crusher parts, dredger buckets, and for railway track points and crossings.

14.62 *Chromium Steel.* A typical steel in this group contains 1% C, 1·4 %Cr, 0·45% Mn. The high carbon content of this steel, together with the chromium, produces a high hardness as a result of oil quenching; chromium steels are used for ball, and roller-race parts.

14.70 Corrosion-resisting Steels

Corrosion-resisting, or stainless steels can be classified as:

(*a*) *Ferritic Stainless Steels.* With low carbon content so that most of it is dissolved in the iron. These steels cannot be hardened by heat treatment.

(*b*) *Martensitic Stainless Steels.* These steels have a higher carbon content and can be hardened by heat treatment.

(*c*) *Austenitic Stainless Steels.* Due to the chromium and nickel that is present in these steels, the austenitic structure is retained upon quenching so that these steels cannot be hardened by heat treatment.

14.71 *Ferritic Stainless Steels.* Steels in this group contain up to about 0·04% carbon, and either about 13 or 20% chromium according to the degree of corrosion resistance required. They cannot be hardened by heat treatment, but can be work hardened. These are often called **stainless irons** and are suitable for pressing, deep drawing, and spinning. The 13% chromium steels are used for forks and spoons, and the 20% chromium steels for cathode-ray tubes.

14.72 *Martensitic Stainless Steels.* These steels contain larger amounts of carbon and are affected by hardening and tempering. The following are typical steels in this group:

0·1% C, 13% Cr, 0·5% Mn. This steel can be quenched to improve its strength, but does not develop great hardness; it is often called **stainless iron**, and is used for certain gas turbine parts and for ornamental work.

0·3% C, 13% Cr, 0·5% Mn. Due to the higher carbon content, this steel can be hardened by heat treatment; when used for cutlery it is tempered at about 180°C., and when used for springs it is tempered at about 450°C.

14.73 *Austenitic Stainless Steels.* Austenitic stainless steels contain very high amounts of nickel and chromium; nickel lowers the transformation temperatures and chromium lowers the critical cooling rate, and so between them they produce an austenitic structure at room temperatures. These steels cannot be hardened by heat treatment, but they can be work hardened; work hardening, however, makes them difficult to machine. Like all austenitic steels, they are non-magnetic.

0·15% C, 18% Cr, 8·5% Ni, 0·8% Mn. This steel is suitable for domestic and decorative work.

0·05% C, 18·5% Cr, 10% Ni, 0·8% Mn. The low carbon content makes this steel suitable for deep drawing.

0·3% C, 21% Cr, 9% Ni, 0·7% Mn. Suitable for casting.

Most austenitic stainless steels contain about 18% chromium and 8% nickel; these are generally known as '18/8 stainless steels'. There are a large number of steels in this group with slightly different proportions of nickel and chromium, and with small additions of molybdenum, titanium, and copper to produce special properties. Steels in this group are also used when heat resistance is required.

14.80 Heat-resisting Steels

The main problems associated with high temperature applications are:

(i) Loss of strength.
(ii) Creep.
(iii) Oxidation and chemical attack.

Strength at high temperatures can be improved by raising the transformation temperatures by adding chromium, or by lowering the transformation temperatures by adding nickel, which will produce an austenitic structure. Small amounts of titanium, aluminium, and molybdenum with carbon will increase the strength and improve the creep resistance. Nickel will also help in retaining strength at high temperatures by restraining grain growth. Resistance to oxidation and chemical attack can be improved by adding silicon or chromium.

Heat-resisting steels can be classified as:

(*a*) *Ferritic Heat-resisting Steels.* With low carbon content so that most of it is dissolved in the iron. These steels cannot be hardened by heat treatment.

(*b*) *Martensitic Heat-resisting Steels.* These steels have a higher carbon content so can be hardened by heat treatment.

(*c*) *Austenitic Heat-resisting Steels.* Due to the chromium and nickel that is present in these steels, the austenitic structure is retained upon quenching so these steels cannot be hardened by heat treatment.

It will be seen that the same classification system is used for both stainless and heat-resisting steels.

14.81 *Ferritic Heat-resisting Steels.* 0·06% C, 21% Cr, 0·4% Si, 0·8% Mn. This is a work-hardening steel, and can be used in the temperature range up to 900°C. It is resistant to sulphur gases.

0·1% C, 29% Cr, 1·2% Si, 1·3% Mn. The additional amounts of alloying elements allows this steel to be used up to about 1100°C.

14.82 *Martensitic Heat-resisting Steels.* 0·4% C, 11·5% Cr, 0·3% Si, 0·5% Mn. This steel can be hardened by heat treatment, but can only be used at up to 750°C. It can be machined with ease, but welding is not recommended because it is an air-hardening steel; if welding must be done, it should be followed by suitable heat treatment.

14.83 *Austenitic Heat-resisting Steels.* Steels in this group cannot be hardened by heat treatment, but can be work hardened. They can be welded, but are difficult to machine; they are non-magnetic.

0·12% C, 18·5% Cr, 8·5% Ni, 1·0% Si, 0·7% Mn. Can be used at up to 350°C.

0·2% C, 23% Cr, 11·5% Ni, 1·6% Si, 3% W, 0·4% Mn. Can be used at up to 1105°C.

0·15% C, 13·5% Cr, 63% Ni, 0·8% Si, 1·3% Mn. This steel can be used at up to 1100°C. It has a very low coefficient of thermal expansion.

14.90 Steels for Use at Low Temperatures

Steels for components that are to be used at low temperatures must not only retain their properties when cold, but must also not loose them when they are heated to room temperature. It has been found that steels of the 18/8 type show an improvement in strength with little reduction in ductility and toughness when tested at −183°C.; there is little appreciable change in properties when these steels are at room temperature following refrigeration.

14.91 Spring Steels

Vehicle springs are made from steel that contains up to about 0·8% carbon according to the properties required, and with the addition of up to 0·4% silicon and up to 0·8% manganese; these steels are hardened by water or oil quenching according to their composition.

Valve springs are very critical, and their success depends to a large extent upon the skill of the manufacturer of the springs. Valve springs are made from similar steels to vehicle springs, and also from steels containing 1·5% chromium and 0·17% vanadium in addition to carbon and nickel.

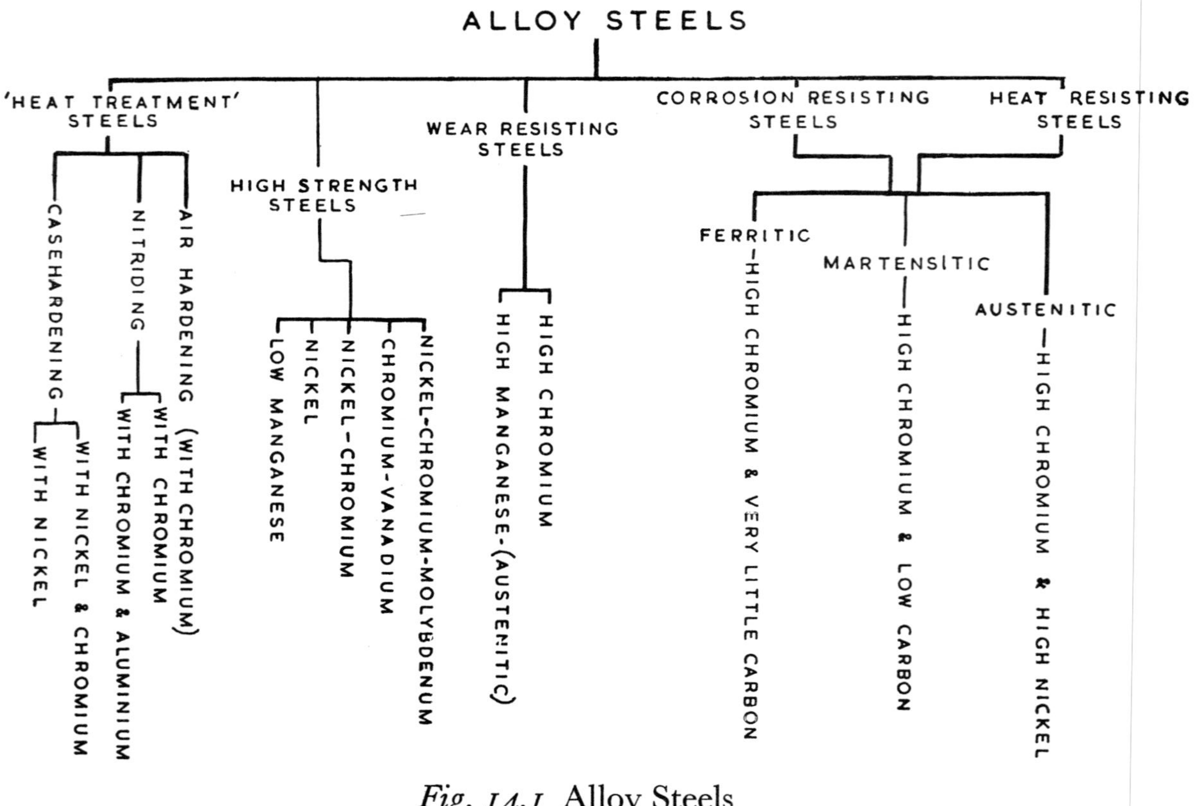

Fig. 14.1 Alloy Steels

14.92 Engine Valve Steels

For low duty, a valve steel with about 0·3% carbon, 3·5% nickel, 0·35% chromium, and 0·35% silicon is used; the silicon and chromium content is increased for heavier duty valves. Aero engine valves are made from austenitic steels with about 10% nickel and 12–16% chromium; exhaust valves are often made hollow and contain sodium for cooling purposes.

14.100 Maraging Steels

(Considered separately because they differ greatly from conventional steels.) The usual way of developing the high strength of steels is by heat-treatment to produce martensite, followed by further heat-treatment to modify the martensite. Although high strength can be produced in this way, it is accompanied by high brittleness caused by the carbon; this method is usually accepted because it is difficult, and therefore expensive, to produce a carbon-free alloy.

Recent experiments have shown that if iron containing the minimum possible amount of carbon is alloyed with between 18% and 25% nickel, a type of martensite is produced even if the alloy is slowly cooled. This martensite is tough, and has a hardness about one half that of untempered carbon-martensite, and is an ideal matrix material for use with other elements dispersed throughout it to increase its strength.

The currently used steels of this type contain iron and 18% nickel, with cobalt, molybdenum and titanium. The properties are developed by a simple ageing process – the name 'maraging' standing for '*mar*tensitic *age*-hardening'.

The martensite developed by initial heating and cooling (solution annealing) is soft enough to allow the steel to be cut, shaped, bent, etc., and a stress-relief heat-treatment can be done if the working is heavy. The hardening is done by heating at 450–500°C for 3 hours, followed by air-cooling; surface-hardening by nitriding can be done during this latter heat-treatment. This heat-treatment is done at a relatively low temperature and does not involve quenching, and so there is no danger of distortion or cracking. The low carbon content eliminates the tendency to scale during heating, and the fact that rapid heating does not cause hardening makes them easier to weld than medium carbon, low alloy steels.

Maraging steels are likely to allow stronger and lighter structures to be produced, but are unlikely to replace 'traditional' steels, because of their high cost.

COMPOSITION AND PROPERTIES OF A TYPICAL MARAGING STEEL

Composition: 18% nickel, 8% cobalt, 5% molybdenum, 0·4% titanium

Mechanical properties	*After solution annealing at 820°C*	*After maraging for 3 hours at 480°C*
Tensile strength	1000–1080 N/mm^2	1600–1820 N/mm^2
Elongation on $5{\cdot}65\sqrt{S_0}$	14–16%	8–10%
Reduction of area	70–75%	35–60%
Hardness	280–320HV	500–560HV

CHAPTER 15

CAST IRON

15.1 Cast iron can be defined as an alloy of iron and more than 1·7% carbon; the carbon content is usually between 2·4 and 4·0%. It is a relatively inexpensive material, and is produced by melting pig iron with scrap iron and/or steel scrap; a large number of iron castings is produced from scrap iron melted with steel scrap. High-duty cast irons are often produced by 'inoculation', in which graphitisers are added in the ladle, or as the cast iron leaves the furnace so that the form taken by the graphite can be controlled. Alloy cast irons are produced by using refined and alloyed pig iron, introducing the elements within the furnace, or by adding the elements to the metal after it has left the furnace. Crankshafts, axles, connecting rods, and similar parts that were previously made from steel forgings are now often made from high-duty or alloy iron castings. Cast shapes can be much more complicated than wrought shapes and where machining is necessary, a much smaller allowance can be made; the equipment required to produce castings is much less massive than that required for forging.

The Production of Cast Iron

15.20 Pig iron is melted in a suitable furnace, where it is modified by the addition of scrap iron and/or steel scrap, before it is cast; the melting methods may be classified as:

1. *The Cupola Furnace.* This furnace is used for general work; it is used during the production of about 90% of all iron castings.
2. *Other Methods.* These methods are used when a special quality cast iron is required; the charge being melted in such a way that the fuel does not come into contact with it. The three principal furnace types in this group are:
   (*a*) The air, or reverberatory furnace.
   (*b*) The rotary furnace.
   (*c*) Electric furnaces.

15.21 THE CUPOLA FURNACE (see fig. 15.2)

The cupola furnace is, in effect, a small-scale blast furnace; it is a continuously operating furnace, but unlike the blast furnace, it operates intermittently, to suit casting requirements; it may be coke-, oil-, or gas-fired. When, for example, a coke-fired cupola furnace is operated, a coke fire is first lit in the furnace, and then alternate layers of broken-up pigs and coke are charged into it; the pigs may be mixed with steel scrap, or scrap iron as required. Some limestone may also be added to flux the coke ash, but the process is not one of refining. The cupola furnace is economical to operate.

15.22 THE AIR, OR REVERBERATORY, FURNACE (see fig. 15.3)

In the furnace the fuel is burned in a grate at the end of the furnace, or pulverised fuel or oil is supplied through a burner, so that the fuel does not

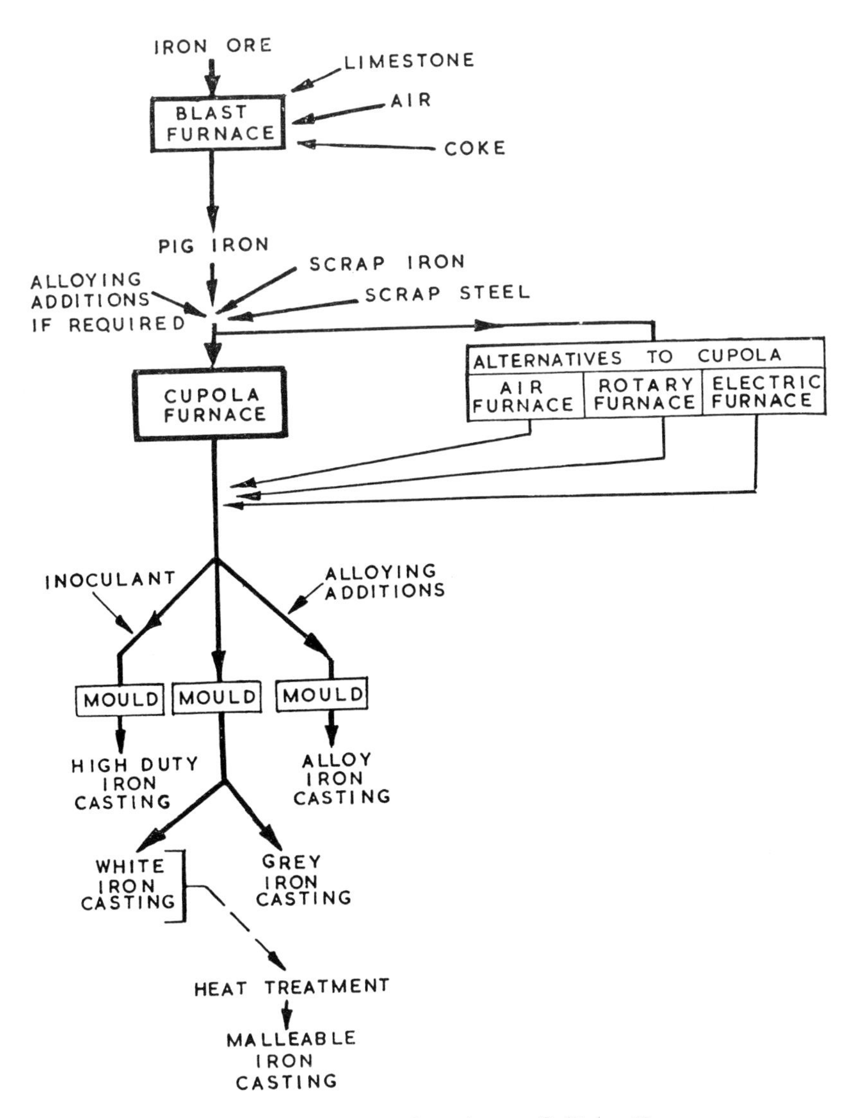

Fig. 15.1 The Production of Cast Iron

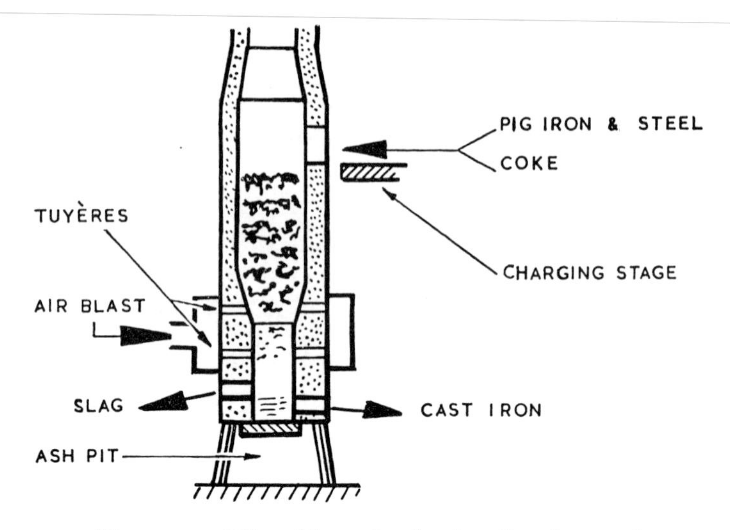

Fig. 15.2 The Cupola (coke-fired type)

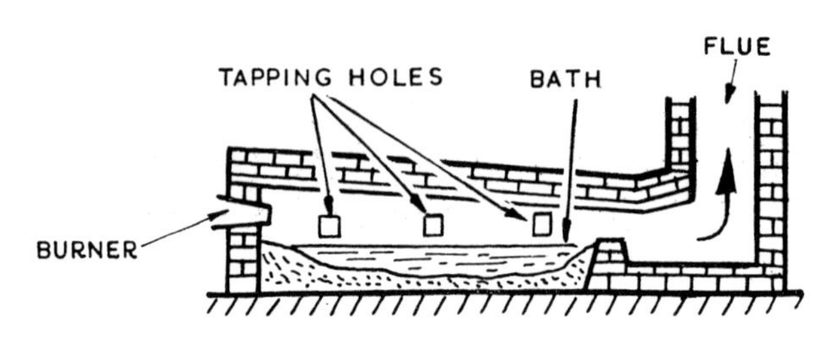

Fig. 15.3 The Air Furnace

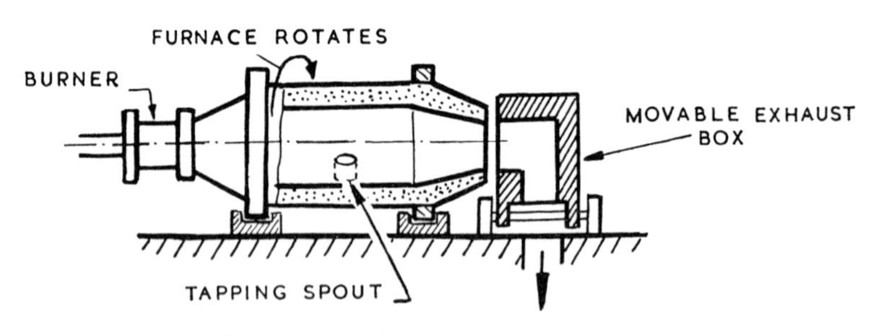

Fig. 15.4 The Rotary Furnace

contact the charge; the heat is reflected from the roof of the furnace on to the charge. This is a batch-melting furnace, and melting is a slow operation; although less economical than the cupola furnace, the air furnace allows a closer control of composition to be exercised.

15.23 THE ROTARY FURNACE (see fig. 15.4)

The rotary furnace is used when a special quality cast iron is required. It is fired using pulverised fuel, oil, or gas; during melting, the furnace is rotated or rocked by chain or friction drive so that the lining is continuously being heated by the gases, and then giving up its heat to the charge to effect the melting.

15.24 ELECTRIC FURNACES

The electric furnaces sometimes used in the production of cast iron are similar in principle to those used in the production of steel (see page 79). The smaller arc furnaces are of the indirect arc type, and the larger ones are of the direct arc type.

COMPARISON BETWEEN INDIRECT AND DIRECT ARC FURNACES

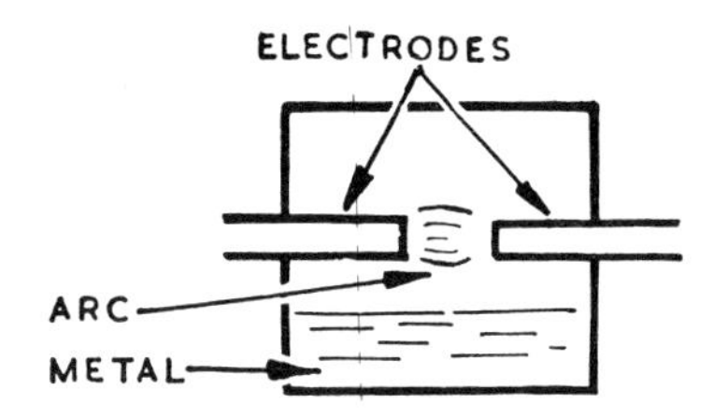

Fig. 15.5 (*a*) Indirect Arc

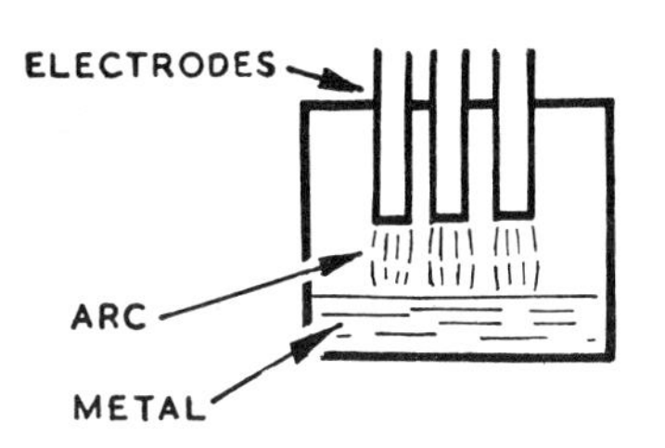

Fig. 15.5 (*b*) Direct Arc

Carbon in Cast Iron

15.30 Carbon may be present in slowly cooled ordinary cast iron in the following forms:

1. In iron, to form the solid solution **ferrite**. Only a small quantity of carbon can be present in this form (see page 74).
2. Combined with iron to form **cementite** (Fe_3C). This will combine with some ferrite to form **pearlite**, but if excess cementite is present this will be in a free form (see page 74).
3. Free carbon (or **graphite**).

15.31 These forms of carbon can exist together, and their proportions will control the mechanical properties of cast iron. When all the carbon is combined, the structure will be steel-like, and the iron is called **white iron**; this type of iron is hard and brittle. When the proportion of free carbon is high, the structure is grey, and the iron is called **grey iron**; grey iron tends to be weak in tension due to the graphite flakes, and so heat treatment, or inoculation, is used to change the form of the graphite and so improve the mechanical properties of this type of iron; grey iron is self-lubricating and will absorb vibrations. Intermediate grades of cast iron are called **mottled irons**. Some typical microstructures are shown on page 134.

15.40 The Control of Structure During Cooling

Directly upon solidification the structure of cast iron consists of austenite and cementite (refer to the iron-carbon equilibrium diagram shown on page 89); as a result of cooling slowly to room temperature, the austenite breaks down to form pearlite (laminated ferrite and cementite), and the cementite breaks down to form graphite and pearlite. If the cooling is fast enough to prevent the breakdown of cementite, a white structure will be obtained. The cooling rate depends to a large extent upon the casting thickness; thin sections of a casting may be white, whilst thicker sections of the same casting may be grey. When a thick section is to have a hard, wear-resisting surface, an iron chill is set into the mould to conduct the heat away and so speed up the cooling at these places. If a casting of non-uniform section is to have a uniform structure, the composition is adjusted so that the thin sections are of the required structure, and the thick sections are chilled to reduce the amount of graphite at these parts of the casting (see fig. 15.6).

Fig. 15.6

15.41 The structure can also be adjusted by chemical composition; silicon promotes graphitisation and when in the correct quantity it will cause thin sections to be grey. Sulphur makes cast iron hard by encouraging it to solidify white. When a complicated shape or thin section is required, the phosphorus content is about 1% to make the iron more fluid; this element is not desirable if strength is required, because it makes the metal brittle.

White Cast Irons and Grey Cast Irons

15.50 WHITE CAST IRONS

White cast irons have a low silicon content so that upon solidification iron carbides are formed instead of graphite in the matrix; if the iron is unalloyed, the matrix will be of pearlite. White irons have a hardness of between about 400 and about 600 HB, and a tensile strength of about 270 N/mm² (this can be raised to about 450 N/mm² if the carbon is kept down to between 2·76 and 2·9%). White irons can only be normally machined by grinding; they are used for grinding mill parts, crusher equipment, furnace components, plough shares, and similar applications. There is no British Standard for White Cast Iron.

15.51 GREY CAST IRONS

Grey cast iron contains graphite in flake form, and is normally readily machined. A range of grey cast irons is covered by British Standards, the irons being distinguished by their tensile strength values. The hardness of grey cast iron ranges from about 155 HB to about 320 HB according to grade. Grey cast irons are used for crankcases, machine tool beds, brake drums, cylinder heads and similar parts.

Grey cast irons can be given stress relief heat treatment to remove stresses that remain after casting; this is done by heating slowly to between 500°C. and 575°C., soaking for about three hours, followed by slow cooling. White iron castings can be annealed at about 850°C. to break down free carbides caused by rapid cooling in the mould; this annealing should be done only as an emergency measure, and the chilling prevented by the use of suitable metal composition and by correct casting design. Annealing can change the structure of grey iron so that machining can be done at high speeds; annealing at about 700°C. for between half an hour and two hours will convert a fully pearlitic structure into one that has mainly a ferritic matrix, so that the hardness is reduced from about 240 HB to about 180 HB.

Malleable Cast Irons

15.60 It has already been stated that grey cast iron is weak in tension owing to the flakes of graphite; this is because the edges of the flakes act as stress raisers, and because the distance between the flakes is comparatively short. Malleabilising aims at changing the size and the shape of the graphite particles and thereby to make the cast iron more ductile and more malleable. The structure of cast iron to be malleabilised must be white because the carbon will be more evenly distributed throughout the structure, and it will be easier to obtain the desired effect.

Malleable cast iron is available in three forms: **Whiteheart**, **Blackheart**, and **Pearlitic**; these names being descriptive of the microstructure.

15.61 WHITEHEART MALLEABLE CAST IRON

Fettled white iron castings are placed in canisters, where they are surrounded with a mixture of unused and partly used haematite ore; the canisters are then packed into a furnace, where the temperature is slowly raised to about 950°C. After a lengthy soaking at this temperature, the furnace is slowly cooled to room temperature, and the canisters removed from the furnace; the castings are taken from the canisters and cleaned ready for machining. This process is, in effect, the reverse of the carburising process used in surface hardening; the carbon will be removed completely from thin sections, but only from the surface of thick sections. The core of thick sections will contain both pearlite and some nodules of carbon. The microstructure of whiteheart malleable iron is shown in fig. 15.10. Whiteheart malleable cast iron is covered by British Standards, which quote two grades distinguished by tensile strength and percentage elongation. The hardness depends upon the distance from the surface, and upon the section thickness; at the surface the hardness is about 120 HB, increasing towards the centre to about 220 HB.

Whiteheart malleable iron is used for motor cycle frame sockets, steering column housings, and wheel hubs; for agricultural machinery, and for forks, brakes, and thread guides, etc., in textile machinery.

15.62 BLACKHEART MALLEABLE CAST IRON

Blackheart malleable cast iron is produced in a similar way to Whiteheart malleable cast iron, but decarburisation during heat treatment is avoided as far as possible by surrounding the castings in the canisters by a neutral packing material to exclude air, and also to provide support for the castings. This process causes the cementite to break down to form 'rosettes' of carbon in a ferritic matrix (see fig. 15.11). Castings to be treated by this process must contain no more than 2·4% carbon, and so special attention must be paid to the composition during melting. British Standards cover three grades, distinguished by tensile strength and percentage elongation. The castability of Blackheart malleable iron is not as good as that of Whiteheart malleable iron because of the lower carbon content. The automobile and commercial vehicle industry uses considerable quantities of Blackheart malleable cast irons for parts where castability, shock resistance, and ease of machining is required, e.g. rear axle housings, wheel hubs, and differential carriers; it is also used for pedals, levers, and similar parts for agricultural machinery, and for brake parts, axleboxes, and coupling parts for railway rolling stock.

15.63 PEARLITIC MALLEABLE CAST IRON

Pearlitic malleable cast iron is produced by heat treating white iron castings in the same manner as for the production of Blackheart cast iron, but the treatment is such that a pearlitic matrix is obtained instead of the ferritic matrix of blackheart malleable iron. The pearlitic matrix can be obtained either by increasing the quantity of manganese to about 1% (manganese is a carbide stabilising element, and so produces pearlite) and subjecting the casting to conventional blackheart malleable iron heat treatment, or by heat treating a ferritic blackheart malleable iron casting (oil or air quench from about 850°C. followed by tempering). As an alternative, white cast iron with a similar composition to that used for the production of Blackheart malleable iron can be heated and quenched in air, and then tempered; in this method there is no malleabilising heat treatment. In all the processes, the object is to produce a steel-like matrix in which the excess carbon is present as temper carbon aggregates; according to the requirements, the matrix can be treated so that its structure will be any desired decomposition product of austenite, and will vary from a structure of lammellar pearlite or spheroidised carbides, to tempered martensite as produced by the heat treatment of steel. British Standards cover two grades of pearlitic malleable cast iron, these being distinguished by tensile strength and percentage elongation. Pearlitic malleable cast iron can be flame or induction hardened, and through hardened to give a wide range of mechanical properties. The use of this cast iron is rapidly increasing, and it is particularly appropriate for applications that require shock resistance; typical applications include axle and differential housings, camshafts and gears.

High Duty Cast Iron

15.70 The properties of ordinary grey cast iron can be improved by using refined pig iron or by introducing a large quantity of steel scrap into the cupola. The shape of the graphite can be altered by a lengthy heat treatment, as described in the previous section, or inoculation can be done as an alternative.

15.71 SPHEROIDAL GRAPHITE CAST IRON (often abbreviated to S.G. Iron)

This is produced by inoculating the iron with magnesium or alternatively with cerium so that the size and shape of the graphite is changed. When cast, S.G. Iron will be mainly pearlitic with spheroids of graphite (see fig. 15.12) and is termed **Pearlitic S.G. Iron**; if this iron is heated to about 900°C., soaked for a few hours and then cooled, the combined carbon will break down so that the microstructure becomes that of spheroidal graphite in a matrix of ferrite; this type of S.G. Iron is called **Ferritic S.G. Iron** (see fig. 15.13).

S.G. Iron has mechanical properties that are intermediate between grey cast iron and steel; but because of the change in the shape of the graphite particles, the damping properties of S.G. Iron is less than that of grey cast iron. S.G. Iron can be worked to a limited extent in both hot and cold conditions, and castings can be bent to remove warpings or distortion. It can be machined wet or dry, welded using normal techniques, and electroplated with copper, nickel or chromium for corrosion or wear resistance. Inoculation can be applied to alloy cast irons.

A range of S.G. Irons is covered by British Standards, and they too are distinguished by tensile strength and percentage elongation. The ferritic S.G. Irons are the more ductile, and the pearlitic S.G. Irons are the stronger. S.G. Irons are used extensively for automobile crankshafts, brake drums, turbine casings, transmission casings, etc.

15.72 PEARLITIC CAST IRON can be produced by inoculation with, for example, calcium silicide. A typical example of this type of iron is produced under the trade name 'Meehanite', the basic structure of which is pearlite with fine flakes of graphite as shown in fig. 15.14. 'Meehanite' is produced to a number of specifications according to the service requirements; for general work the tensile strengths vary from 210 to about 590 N/mm².

Alloy Cast Iron

15.80 When special properties are required, larger amounts of alloying elements are added to cast iron; in general, the effect of these elements is the same as when added to steel, but these effects are modified due to the larger amount of carbon present, and to the effect of thickness and shape of the casting on the cooling rate.

Alloying elements are added to cast iron to give improved strength, hardness, corrosion resistance, response to heat treatment, and special physical properties.

The Effect of Alloying Elements

15.81 NICKEL

Nickel is the most important alloying element used and has a rather complicated effect; for simplicity, the effect of nickel can be considered as follows:

(*a*) It tends to promote graphitisation, and so offsets the effect of chilling due to casting thickness; this graphitisation effect is more pronounced when the iron is white than when it is grey.

(*b*) It lowers the eutectoid temperature (see page 88), and so it enables cast iron to be hardened without cracking. When more than 2% is is present the iron can be hardened by oil quenching, when more than 4% is present the iron can be hardened by air quenching, but when more than about 6% is present, the iron becomes hard as a result of cooling in air after casting and so machining becomes difficult. When the nickel content exceeds about 15% it lowers the eutectoid temperature so much that an austenitic structure is obtained.

(*c*) It promotes uniformity over thick and thin sections and so makes machining easier by preventing hard spots.

15.82 CHROMIUM

This element stabilises carbide and so offsets the effect of silicon; it produces hardness without the brittleness associated with ordinary white cast iron. It is used in conjunction with nickel to produce an austenitic structure.

15.83 MOLYBDENUM

About 1% molybdenum with nickel produces an acicular (needle-like) matrix that has good tensile strength and an improved resistance to impact.

15.84 COPPER

Only a small amount of copper will enter into solid solution in iron, but it is useful when improved resistance to atmospheric corrosion is required.

Some Important Alloy Cast Irons

15.90 HEAT-RESISTING CAST IRONS

When ordinary cast irons are used at high temperatures they tend to scale owing to oxidation, and also suffer 'growth' owing to the breakdown of cementite to form ferrite and graphite which takes up more room than cementite; growth causes warping and cracking to occur.

Silal (developed by the British Cast Iron Research Association). This alloy contains almost 5% silicon, which is a powerful graphitiser, and so the structure consists of fine graphite in a ferrite matrix; therefore there is no cementite to be decomposed at high temperatures and so cause growth. The carbon content is about 2%.

Nicro-silal (B.C.I.R.A.). This is a more expensive alloy cast iron that contains about 4% silicon, 18% nickel, 3% chromium, and only about 2% carbon. Its structure is mainly austenitic, with a small amount of carbide and fine graphite flakes.

Ni-Resist (International Nickel Co. (Mond) Ltd.). This contains about 2% silicon, 14% nickel, 1% chromium, 7% copper, and about 2% carbon; its structure is graphite in an austenitic matrix; it tends to work harden and requires sharp cutting tools. Welding can be done easily provided suitable filler rods are used.

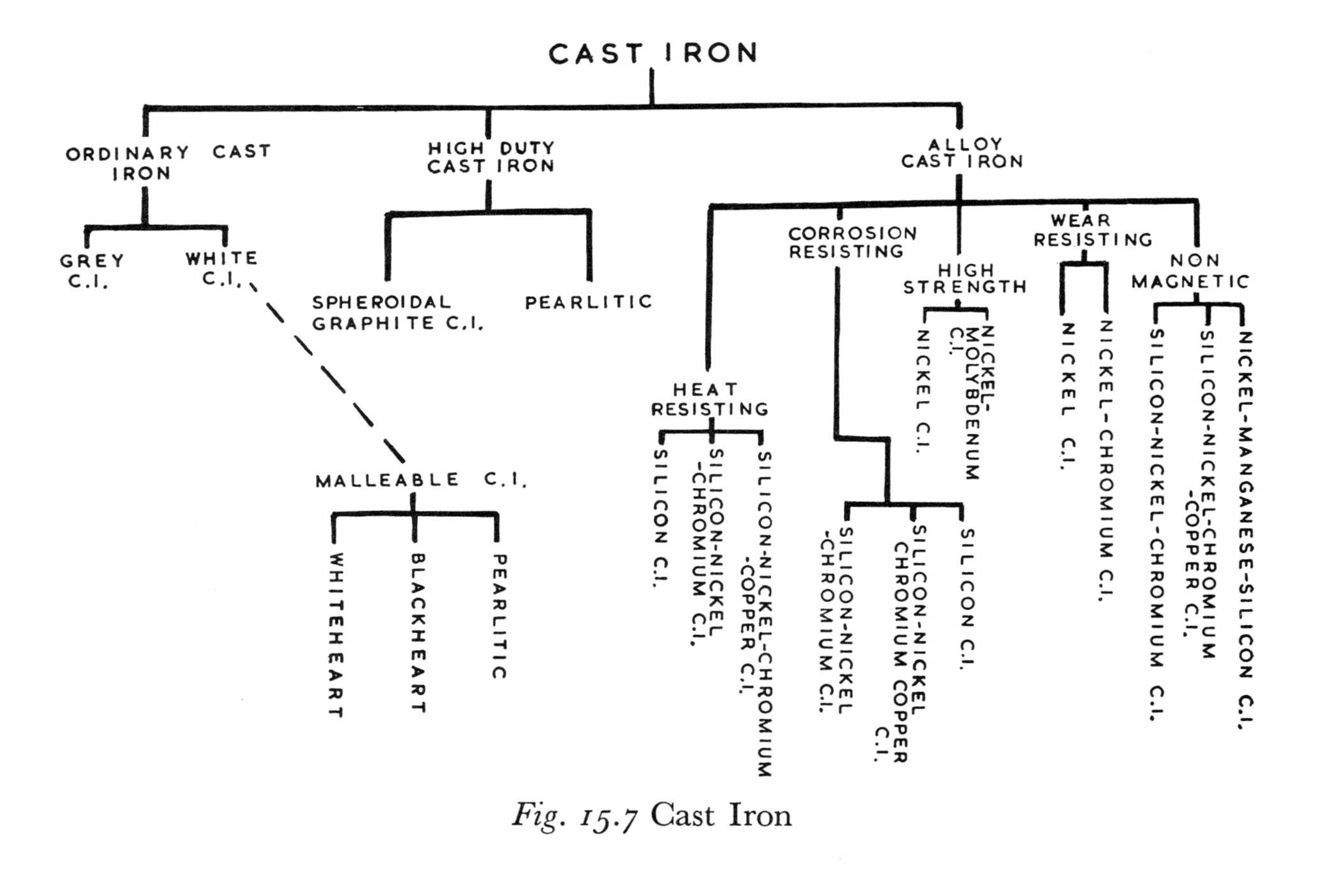

Fig. 15.7 Cast Iron

15·91 CORROSION-RESISTING CAST IRONS

The austenitic cast irons are corrosion resisting; cast irons with about 14% silicon are also good acid-resisting irons, but they are very brittle and are also very difficult to machine.

15·92 HIGH-STRENGTH CAST IRONS

The addition of between about 1 and 1·5% nickel to cast iron will improve its strength. Cast irons with about 2·5% nickel and up to 1% molybdenum and 3% carbon have an acicular matrix and are of higher tensile and impact strengths than pearlitic cast irons. Acicular cast irons are easy to machine and are a useful alternative to steel in applications such as crankshafts and camshafts.

15·93 WEAR-RESISTING CAST IRONS

Hard Grey Iron. This iron contains 2·5% nickel, 3% carbon, and about 1% silicon; it has a good strength and hardness and is moderately easy to machine.

Martensitic Grey Iron. By increasing the nickel content of the above iron to about 5% the structure becomes martensitic, and the hardness is increased; this iron is difficult to machine.

Heat-treatable Cast Iron. This contains about 2·5% nickel, 1·4% silicon, and 3% carbon; it can be hardened by heat treatment to produce a high hardness. Although difficult to machine in the hardened condition, it can be easily rough machined when in the unhardened condition.

Nickel White Iron. This white iron contains 1·8% nickel, 0·8% chromium, 3% carbon, and 0·5% silicon. By minimising the silicon content and adding chromium, a white structure is produced which has a high hardness, but which is difficult to machine.

Ni-Hard (International Nickel Co. (Mond) Ltd.). This cast iron is similar to the white iron described above, but the nickel content is increased to 4·5% and the chromium content increased to 1·5%, so that the structure consists of hard carbide in a martensitic matrix. This is an extremely hard cast iron, and can only be machined by grinding; it can be stress relieved without loss of strength; welding is not recommended, except as a temporary repair, or to weld it to other metals to give a hard facing.

In addition to these hard cast irons, the acicular cast irons described above gives a good hardness combined with strength.

15·94 NON-MAGNETIC CAST IRONS

All the austenitic cast irons are non-magnetic. An alloy cast iron called 'Nomag', developed by Ferranti Limited, is also used extensively in the electrical industry. Nomag contains 11% nickel, 6% manganese, 1·5% silicon, and 3% carbon; manganese acts like nickel and lowers the eutectoid temperature and so with nickel it produces an austenitic structure.

15·941 When the nickel content is increased to between 33 and 38%, low-expansion cast irons are produced similar to 'Invar'. When the nickel content is higher than that needed to produce an austenitic structure, the irons become magnetic again; this is useful in certain applications.

TABLE 15.1

SOME IMPORTANT ALLOY CAST IRONS

Name	*Composition %*					*Tensile strength N/mm²*	*Hardness HB*
	Carbon	*Silicon*	*Nickel*	*Chromium*	*Other elements*		
Silal	2	5				170	
Nicro-silal	1·9	5	18	2 5		185–220 250–280	110–130 320–350
Ni-resist	2·8	1·5	30	2		185–250	170–200
Nickel cast iron	3·2	1·4	1			230–310	200–220
Acicular cast iron	3	2	2·5		0·8% Mo	390–540	260–320
Hard grey cast iron	3·2	1·2	2·5			250–310	240–280
Martensitic grey cast iron	3·2	1·2	5			250–310	350–400
Nickel white cast iron	3	0·5	1·8	0·8		250–310	450–550
Ni-hard	3	0·5	4·5	1·5		250–310	550–800
Nomag	2·8	1·5	11		6% Mn	220–260	200–220
Heat-treatable cast iron	3·2	1·4	2·5			370–470*	250–450*

* After heat treatment.

REFERENCES

Publications from:
The Joint Iron Council.
International Nickel Co. (Mond) Ltd.
British Cast Iron Research Association.
International Meehanite Metal Co. Ltd.

Fig. 15.8

Grey C.I. × 100
Graphite Flakes in a Matrix of Pearlite*

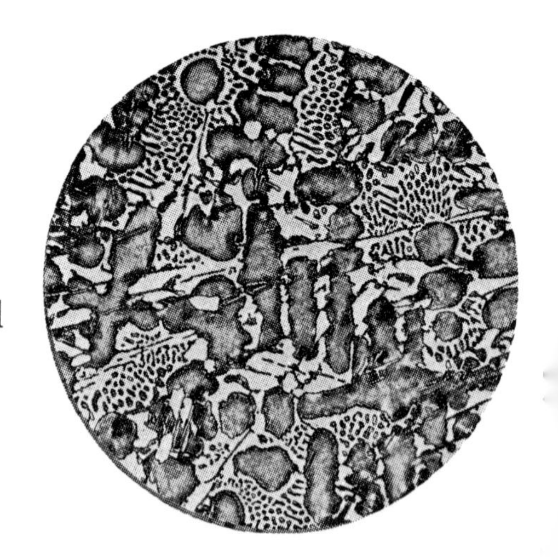

Fig. 15.9

White C.I. × 100
Cementite (white) and Pearlite*

* By courtesy of the British Cast Iron Research Association

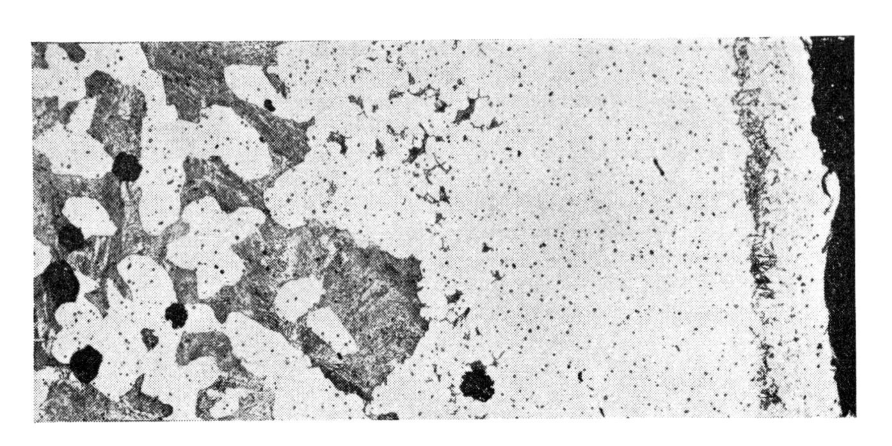

Fig. 15.10 Whiteheart Malleable C.I. × 60
Ferrite (white) and Pearlite*
(note variation in structure with depth; surface on right)

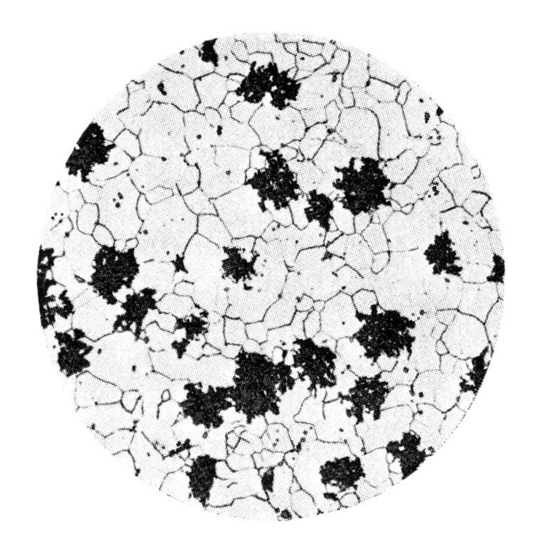

Fig. 15.11

Blackheart Malleable C.I. × 100
Ferrite (white) and Graphite (black)*

* By courtesy of the British Cast Iron Research Association

INOCULATED CAST IRONS

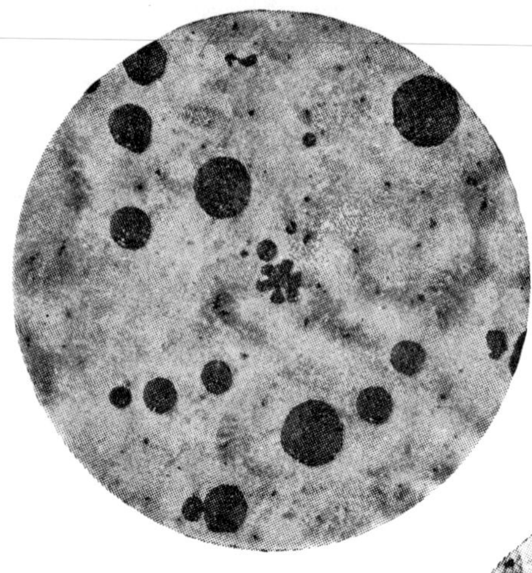

Fig. 15.12

Pearlitic S.G. Iron
× 100
Graphite (black) in
Pearlite Matrix

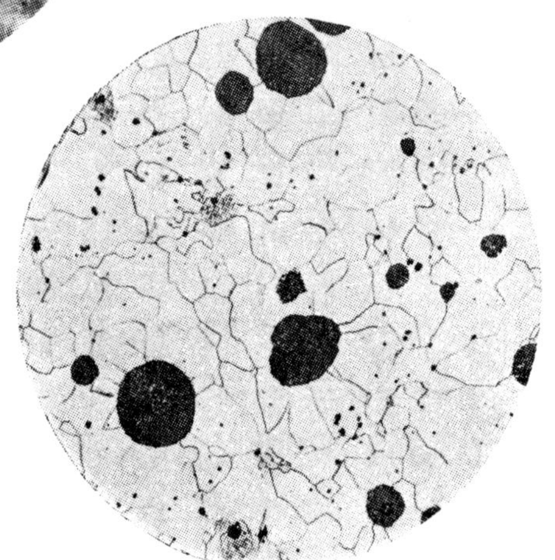

Fig. 15.13

Ferritic S.G. Iron
× 100
Graphite (black) in
Ferrite Matrix

* By courtesy of
the British Cast Iron
Research Association

Fig. 15.14

A Typical Meehanite
× 600
Flakes of Graphite in
Pearlite Matrix

(Courtesy of Messrs.
International Meehanite
Metal Co. Ltd.)

CHAPTER 16

NON-FERROUS METALS

16.10 Non-ferrous metals are used in engineering mainly as alloys, but are used in the unalloyed condition when special properties are required.

Non-ferrous metals may be classified as follows:

1. Metals that are used fairly extensively in the unalloyed condition, or as the base for alloys.
2. Metals that are only used in the unalloyed condition in small amounts, or as alloying elements in small quantities.
3. The so-called 'new metals'.

Metals that are Used Fairly Extensively in the Unalloyed Condition, or as the Base for Alloys

16.20 ALUMINIUM (Al)

Aluminium is a white lustrous metal that is very light, and has a melting point of about 660°C. Aluminium and its alloys are described in Chapter 18.

COPPER (Cu)

Copper is a reddish-brown metal with a melting point of about 1083°C.; it is used unalloyed, with small additions of alloying elements, or as the base for many alloys. Copper and its alloys are described in Chapter 17.

LEAD (Pb)

Lead is very malleable and ductile, but is very weak; it has a silvery-white appearance when it has just been fractured. It is very heavy, resists corrosion, and is a good insulator against nuclear radiation; it melts at 327°C.

Lead is found in the mineral **galena** (PbS) and also in small amounts in a number of rather complicated oxides, from which it is removed by smelting in a blast furnace, followed by melting to remove the oxides and other impurities. It is used as the base for type metals and bearing metals, and it is a major constituent in solders; lead is introduced into steel and non-ferrous metals to produce free-cutting qualities.

MAGNESIUM (Mg)

This is a weak, silvery-white metal that melts at 651°C. It is the lightest engineering metal, and is used as the base for many light alloys as described in Chapter 19.

NICKEL (Ni)

Nickel is a white metal that has properties similar to iron, and melts at 1458°C. Nickel and its alloys are described in Chapter 21.

TIN (Sn)

Tin is a white lustrous metal that is soft and weak, and melts at 232°C. It is extremely corrosion resistant, and is used extensively as a coating for sheet steel (tin-coated steel is known as **tinplate** and is used for foodstuff containers because the tin resists attack by fruit juices). Tin is used as the base for bearing metals, and low melting-point alloys; it is a major constituent in solders, and is alloyed with copper to produce bronzes and gunmetals. It is added in small quantities to copper-zinc alloys (brasses) to give improved corrosion resistance. Tin is found in the mineral **tinstone** (SnO_2) from which it is extracted by smelting, and is then refined by heating to melt the tin away from the impurities that melt at higher temperatures.

TITANIUM (Ti)

Titanium is a greyish-white metal that has strength/weight properties that place it midway between aluminium and steel; it has a melting point of about 1660°C., and is used unalloyed, as the base for a number of alloys, and in small quantities as an alloying element in some non-ferrous alloys. Titanium can be classed as a 'new metal', but it is placed in this group because of its increased use during recent years; titanium and its alloys are described in Chapter 22.

ZINC (Zn)

Zinc is a bluish-white metal that melts at 419°C., is very weak, moderately ductile and malleable, but becomes brittle when worked at temperatures other than between 100°C. and 150°C. (within this range it is easy to work). Zinc is extremely corrosion resistant, and is used as a protective coating for iron and steel; zinc-base alloys are used as die-casting metals. Zinc and zinc-base alloys are described in Chapter 20.

Metals that are Used in the Unalloyed Condition in Small Amounts, or as Small-quantity Alloying Additions

16.30 ANTIMONY (Sb)

This is a bright bluish-white metal with a melting point of 630°C.; it is found in the mineral **stibnite** (Sb_2S_3) and also in **tetrahednite** (Cu_3SbS_3) and **famatinite** (Cu_3SbS_4); some antimony is obtained as a by-product when the latter two minerals are roasted, but because insufficient antimony is produced in this way, it is necessary to extract it also from stibnite. Antimony is used in low melting-point and bearing alloys that contain lead because it acts as a lead-hardener.

BISMUTH (Bi)

Bismuth is a lustrous greyish-white metal that is hard and brittle, neither ductile nor malleable, and melts at 271°C. It is relatively noble, and can be liberated by liquation from the 'alloys' in which it occurs in native condition; the metal so produced is impure, and if a pure metal is required, a complicated treatment is necessary. Bismuth is used in low melting-point alloys.

BORON (B)

Boron melts at about 2300°C.; it is not used as an element, but is used in powder form as a constituent in some of the sintered hard metal alloys, Boron carbide is extremely hard and resists chemical attack; it is used for dies, nozzles for sand-blasting equipment, gauges, pivots, and for bearing surfaces. Boron is a difficult metal to prepare, and for this reason it is sometimes classed as a 'rarer metal'.

CADMIUM (Cd)

Cadmium is a bluish-white metal that is soft and weak, and melts at 321°C. The commercial sources of cadmium are zinc deposits; the cadmium concentrates in certain parts of the zinc-producing plant. Cadmium is used in low-melting-point alloys, in small quantities in copper, and as a protective coating for steel and brass.

CERIUM (Ce)

This is a 'rare earth metal' that melts at 640°C.; it is used as an inoculant in cast iron, for making electrodes for electric arc lamps, and is alloyed with iron to produce lighter flints.

CHROMIUM (Cr)

Chromium is steel-grey in colour, very hard, and melts at 1890°C. It is found in **chromite** ($FeO.Cr_2O$), and in the less important minerals **chromitite** ($Fe_2Cr_2O_6$) and **crocoisite** ($PbCrO_4$). Chromium produces hardness and corrosion resistance when alloyed with steel and cast iron; it is also alloyed with nickel to produce some important heat-resisting alloys. Steel is plated with chromium on a base of nickel plate when corrosion resistance or surface hardness is required.

COBALT (Co)

Cobalt is silvery-white, melts at 1490°C., and is highly magnetic. Cobalt is found with nickel and other elements in certain complex minerals, from which it is obtained as a by-product during the production of nickel. Cobalt is used in both non-ferrous and steel cutting-tool materials (see Chapter 26), in permanent magnet materials, and in nickel-base heat-resisting alloys.

IRIDIUM (Ir)

This steel-white metal of the platinum group melts at 2454°C., and is used mainly for crucibles; it is introduced into platinum alloys to produce hardness and strength, and to raise the melting point.

GERMANIUM (Ge)

Germanium metal is grey-white in colour, and is an important electrical engineering material.

MANGANESE (Mn)

Manganese melts at 1260°C., and is obtained by reduction of its oxide; it is used as a deoxidiser during the production of steel. It is present in all steels and cast iron as a useful impurity because it offsets the ill effects of sulphur;

it is introduced in larger amounts as an alloying element in steel, and also in aluminium, magnesium, and titanium alloys, and in the brasses.

MERCURY (Hg)

This is one of the more noble metals, and is found in native condition with other noble metals, and also as a sulphide (HgS); it can be extracted by simple heating, and then purified by distillation followed if necessary by a further process to remove the last traces of zinc and cadmium. Mercury melts at −38·5°C.; it is used in thermometers and barometers, and in mercury electrical switches.

MOLYBDENUM (Mo)

Molybdenum is a hard, silvery-white metal with a melting point of 2620°C.; it occurs as a sulphide, and also as an oxide with other metals. Molybdenum is used in small quantities in alloy steels and cast iron.

PLATINUM (Pt)

This is a heavy, bright greyish-white metal with a melting point of 1773°C.; it is malleable and ductile, soft, and does not oxidise or tarnish in the air. It is usually alloyed with iridium to produce increased hardness. Platinum occurs mainly as a native metal alloyed with other noble metals, and also in nickel-copper deposits; it is obtained during the extraction of gold, and of nickel. Platinum is used as an electrical contact metal, for resistance pyrometer wire, and for thermocouple wire.

PALLADIUM (Pd)

This is a rare metal of the platinum group that is white, slightly ductile and malleable, resists oxidation, and melts at 1555°C. It is alloyed with silver when an electrical contact material is required that is harder and more corrosion resistant than silver.

RHODIUM (Rh)

Rhodium is another rare metal of the platinum group; it melts at 1985°C. and resists acid attack. It is used mainly as a plating metal, but is also used alloyed with platinum as thermocouple wire metal.

SILVER (Ag)

Silver is a noble metal that melts at 960°C.; it occurs native and also in an alloy containing copper and gold. It has the highest electrical conductivity of any metal, and is used for electrical contacts; it is also used in silver solders, and as a plating metal.

SELENIUM (Se)

Selenium melts at 220°C.; it is usually obtained as a by-product during the extraction and refining of various metals, including copper. The electrical conductivity of selenium changes when it is exposed to light, and it is used in the photocell; it is also used in small amounts to improve the machinability of copper and copper alloys.

TANTALUM (Ta)

This metal is silvery-white in colour, heavy, and can be cold worked; if hot worked it becomes extremely hard. Its melting point is about 3207°C. It is used in cemented carbide cutting-tool material, and in small amounts as an alloying addition in non-ferrous alloys.

TELLURIUM (Te)

Tellurium melts at 452°C.; it is used in small quantities to strengthen lead, and is introduced in small quantities in copper to produce free-cutting properties.

THORIUM (Th)

Thorium is a soft, lead-like metal that melts at 1827°C. It is used as an alloying element with tungsten to produce superior filament wire, and in magnesium alloys to produce creep resistance.

TUNGSTEN (W)

Tungsten melts at 3410°C., is grey in colour, very hard, brittle at room temperatures, but malleable and ductile at high temperatures. It is found in several oxide minerals, from which it is obtained by reduction. Tungsten is used as a filament wire for radio valves and for lamps. It is also used as an alloying element in high speed steel, magnet steels, and in carbide form in sintered cutting-tool materials.

VANADIUM (V)

This metal melts at 1900°C., is white, and very hard. It is alloyed with steel in small quantities to produce toughness.

16.40 The so-called 'New Metals'

16.41 BERYLLIUM (Be)

Beryllium is a hard, steel-grey metal that melts at 1285°C., is lighter than aluminium, has a very low neutron absorption cross section (that is, it does not react to any marked degree with neutrons which pass through it), has a good thermal conductivity, good strength at high temperatures, but has a poor ductility. The ductility can only be improved by powder metallurgy techniques during the early stages of processing. Beryllium is obtained from the aluminium beryllium silicate **beryl**, which yields only about 3½% beryllium; the extraction of the metal from its ore is a costly process, and special techniques are necessary to overcome the technical difficulties and to eliminate the toxic hazard which powdered beryllium and its salts may present.

16.411 Beryllium has been used for some time in small amounts as an alloying element in copper, but is now in demand in pure condition in wrought forms as a structural material; due to its low weight and high modulus of elasticity, it is likely to be used in high speed aircraft and guided missiles.

16.412 Beryllium can be cast into an ingot which, if less than about 150 mm diameter, will be sound enough to be fabricated by hot rolling or extrusion;

the alternative, and more successful, method is to machine the ingot, mill the swarf to powder form, and then to sinter it. The sintered block can be worked; the tensile strength of the sintered block is of the order of 310 N/mm^2 with an elongation of 1–3%, and this is improved to about 620 N/mm^2 with an elongation of about 10% as a result of rolling.

16.413 Sintered beryllium can be easily machined using carbide-tipped tools, and it behaves rather like fine grey cast iron. It can be joined to other metals by brazing, and beryllium-to-beryllium joints can be made by electric arc, resistance, or spot welding.

16.42 HAFNIUM (Hf)

This metal is very similar to zirconium; it is heavy, has a tensile strength of 340 N/mm^2, a hardness value of 180 HV, and it melts at 2130°C. It can be processed and fabricated fairly easily provided the recommended techniques are used; hafnium can be machined satisfactorily if heavy cuts and slow speeds are used; it can be welded provided that suitably high currents are used.

Hafnium is used as a control rod material for pressurised water-cooled reactors because it has a good strength and corrosion resistance, high neutron absorption properties, and freedom from irradiation damage.

16.43 NIOBIUM (Nb)

This silvery-white metal is extremely ductile and soft, has a tensile strength of about 280 N/mm^2, and melts at 2468°C. Its ductility is affected by small amounts of oxygen and carbon impurities, and hot working and heating in air should be avoided. Thin sheets of niobium can be welded by resistance welding, but sheets that are thicker than 0·5 mm must be welded by argon-arc, or argon-arc spot welding methods. Niobium is being developed as a nuclear engineering material and as a gas turbine blade material.

16.44 ZIRCONIUM (Zr)

Zirconium is an abundant metal, but it is difficult to separate from its ore (the silicate **zircon**). It is silvery-white in colour, melts at 1852°C., has a tensile strength of 420 N/mm^2, and a hardness of 140 HV; zirconium and its alloys have excellent corrosion resistance. Zirconium is very similar to titanium, but it is about one and a half times as heavy. It can be machined using similar practices to those used for aluminium, but with very low cutting speeds; it can be fabricated with comparative ease, but care must be taken to prevent contamination by oxygen, nitrogen, and hydrogen during heating. Zirconium has been used for some time as an alloying element in magnesium alloys, but is now being developed as a nuclear engineering material on account of its low neutron absorption cross section, its good strength at room and moderately elevated temperatures, and its resistance in alloy form to corrosion by water, steam, and other reactor coolants.

16.441 Zirconium is alloyed with tin, iron, chromium, and nickel, and also with copper and molybdenum; zirconium and its alloys are available in the usual wrought forms.

16·45 Aluminium, magnesium, and vanadium are also being developed as nuclear engineering materials.

REFERENCES

'*New*' *Metals:* Publications issued by Imperial Chemical Industries Limited.

CHAPTER 17

COPPER AND COPPER-BASE ALLOYS

Copper

17.1 Copper is used extensively in engineering in both alloyed and unalloyed conditions. It has a tensile strength of about 150 N/mm² as cast, which can be raised to about 390 N/mm² by cold working; the hardness as cast is only about 45 HB, but this can be raised to about 90 HB by cold working. Cold working reduces the ductility of copper, but this can be increased, at the expense of hardness and strength, by annealing. A range of so-called 'tempers' can be obtained by controlling the extent of working after annealing.

The electrical and thermal conductivities of copper are second only to silver; copper for electrical applications is generally of highest purity (about 99·9% pure). Copper has an extremely good resistance to atmospheric corrosion, and to attack by corrosive media; it can be easily joined by soldering, brazing, and welding.

The Production of Copper

17.2 Copper is found in small quantities (no more than about 4%) in its ores, which are crushed and ground to a fine powder so that the copper-bearing grains can be separated by flotation from the useless grains. The grains are then heated in a reverberatory furnace to remove the gangue and leave a mixture (or matte) of copper and iron sulphides. This matte is heated in a converter, like a Bessemer converter, to remove the iron and the sulphur; the copper so produced is finally refined by fire refining or by electrolytic refining.

In the **fire refining** system the impure copper is melted and oxidised to remove some of the impurities. When the slag so produced has been removed, poles of green hardwood are thrust into the bath to remove the oxygen by combustion; after this **poling** operation. the copper is poured into moulds.

Very pure copper is produced by **electrolytic refining** in which thick slabs (or anodes) of impure copper are suspended in warm diluted sulphuric acid and copper sulphate, and interleaved with thin sheets of pure copper to act as cathodes. As a result of the electrolytic action, copper from the anodes is deposited at the cathodes, and the impurities are deposited at the bottom of the bath.

17.3 THE GRADES OF COPPER

Cathode Copper. This grade is produced as a result of electrolytic refining and is used as the raw material for production of high conductivity and alloy coppers, and is also used as a casting material.

Electrolytic Tough Pitch High Conductivity Copper. Cathode copper is melted and cast into billets and other suitable shapes for working; the oxygen content, or **pitch**, is carefully controlled to reduce the ill effects of some of the impurities.

Fire Refined Tough Pitch High Conductivity Copper. The conductivity of this grade is almost as good as that of electrolytic tough pitch copper but it contains small quantities of impurities that cannot be removed by the fire refining.

Ordinary Tough Pitch Copper. Coppers of this type are not of a specified conductivity, and contain larger amounts of oxygen and other impurities; they are, however, quite satisfactory for general use.

Oxygen-free High Conductivity Copper (O.F.H.C.). This is produced by remelting cathode copper and casting it in such a way as to prevent absorbtion of oxygen; it is more suitable for flame welding and brazing, impact extrusion, and for severe spinning.

Arsenical Copper. The tensile strength of copper can be increased by the addition of up to 0·5% arsenic, which also enables copper to be used at up to about 300°C. without loss of tensile strength. The resistance to atmospheric corrosion is improved by the arsenic, but it produces poor thermal and electrical conductivities.

17.31 THE WORKING AND MACHINING OF COPPER

Copper can be hot worked by rolling, extrusion, and forging over a wide temperature range, but these operations are preferably done at between 800 and 900°C. Cold working can be easily done, but when an excessive amount of cold working is required, copper should be annealed at about 500°C.; the cooling rate from this temperature is not critical, but quenching in water causes dirt and scale to be removed and so simplifies pickling and cleaning. When machining copper, the cutting tools should have a large rake, the cutting speeds should be high, and the cuts light.

Copper-base Alloys

17.40 A large number of copper-base alloys are used in engineering; the advantages claimed for the use of copper-base alloys are as follows:

1. They have good mechanical properties, high electrical and thermal conductivities, and are very resistant to corrosion and to wear.
2. They can be easily machined.
3. They can be easily formed.
4. They can be easily joined by soldering, brazing, and welding.
5. They can be easily polished and plated if desired.
6. The pressing and forging temperatures are lower than is the case with ferrous materials.

Copper-base alloys can be classified as follows:

1. Alloys of copper and very small amounts of other metals. This group includes silver copper, chromium copper, cadmium copper, tellurium copper, beryllium copper, and copper-nickel-silicon alloys.
2. Alloys of copper and larger amounts of other metals. This group includes the brasses and the bronzes.

17.41 Alloys of Copper and Small Amounts of Other Metals

17.411 *Silver Copper.* The softening temperature of copper can be increased from about 200°C. to about 350°C. by the addition of about 0·08% silver so that its hardness and strength will not be reduced by soldering, tinning, or low-temperature heating. The addition of this small amount of silver will have only a negligible effect upon the conductivity of copper. Silver copper is used for commutator segments, radiator parts, and similar applications in which the strength or hardness of copper parts must not be reduced by heat involved during their joining or assembly. Silver also increases the creep resistance of copper because it raises its softening temperature.

17.412 *Cadmium Copper.* When 1% cadmium is added to copper, the softening temperature is raised, and the strength, toughness, and fatigue resistance is also improved. Cadmium copper is used for long-span overhead line conductors, contact wires for electric traction and for resistance welding electrodes. Soft cadmium copper wire has been advocated for electrical wiring of aircraft because it combines flexibility with resistance to the ill effects of vibration. The addition of a small amount of cadmium will have only a slight detrimental effect upon the conductivity of copper.

17.413 *Chromium Copper.* The addition of about 0·5% chromium to copper will have little effect upon conductivity, but will improve the strength and hardness by producing an alloy that responds to heat treatment. The portion of the copper-chromium-equilibrium diagram illustrated (fig. 17.1) indicates that only a small quantity of chromium can be contained in copper to form a solid solution. The solid solubility of chromium in copper increases with temperature, and almost all the chromium present in this alloy will enter into solid solution at about 1000°C. If the alloy is quenched from this temperature, that is, **solution treated**, all the excess chromium will be retained in solid solution to produce softness and ductility. When the material has been worked, it is given **precipitation treatment** to restore equilibrium and to improve the mechanical properties; this precipitation treatment consists of reheating the material to about 500°C., soaking for at least 2 hours and then cooling it. The principle of this kind of heat treatment is explained in Chapter 5. The conductivity of the solution treated alloy is low, but it is improved by the precipitation treatment.

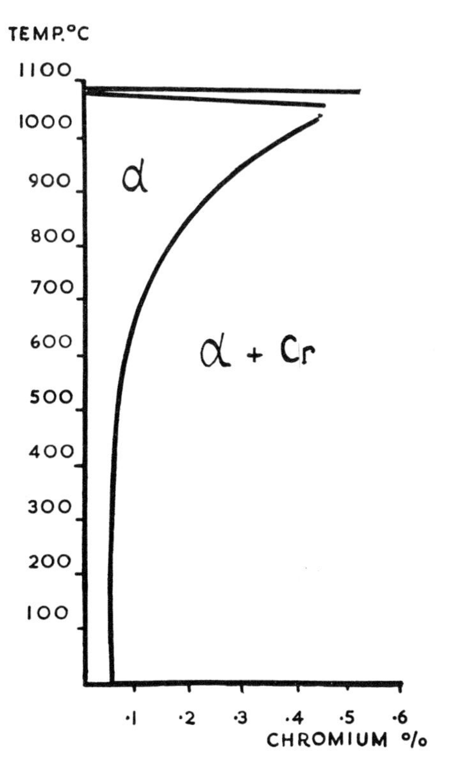

Fig. 17.1 Part of the Copper-chromium Equilibrium Diagram

17.414 *Tellurium Copper.* When a high conductivity copper is to be easily machined about 0·5% tellurium is added. Tellurium is insoluble in copper, and so will be dispersed throughout the copper when the alloy is molten, and remain in fine particles when the alloy is solid, so that it breaks up the chips during machining to make cutting easier.

17.415 *Beryllium Copper.* Beryllium is alloyed with copper when strength is more important than conductivity. It will be seen from the portion of the copper-beryllium-equilibrium diagram illustrated (fig. 17.2) that only a very small amount of beryllium will enter into solid solution with copper, and that the excess beryllium will form a constituent (indicated by γ) with the copper when at room temperatures. The solid solubility of beryllium in copper is

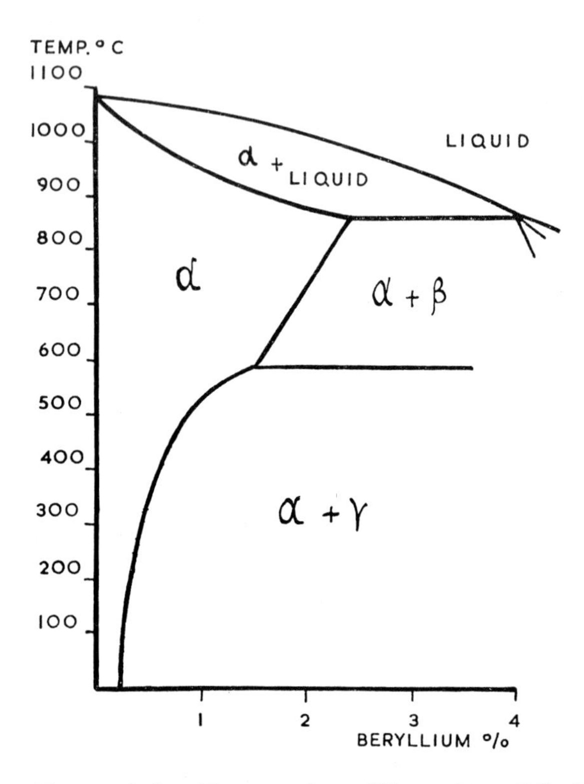

Fig. 17.2 Part of the Copper-beryllium Equilibrium Diagram

increased by heating to a sufficient extent to make this alloy respond to precipitation heat treatment. This treatment consists of heating the alloy to about 800°C. and quenching from that temperature to produce a soft and ductile structure; after working, the strength and hardness is restored by precipitation treatment at about 320°C.

Two beryllium-copper alloys are of industrial importance; the stronger and harder alloy contains 2% beryllium, but the alloy containing 0·4% beryllium and 2·6% cobalt is less expensive.

Beryllium copper is used for corrugated diaphragms, flexible bellows, and for bourdon tubes; it is also used for cold chisels and for hacksaw blades when the 'sparking' associated with steel hand tools would cause explosion.

17.416 *Copper-Nickel-Silicon Alloys.* When nickel and silicon in the proportion of four parts of nickel to one part of silicon are alloyed in copper at high temperatures they form nickel silicide (Ni_2Si) which is more soluble in copper at high temperatures than when at lower temperatures; alloys of this type are suitable for precipitation heat treatment. The solution treatment is done by quenching from about 700°C. to produce softness and ductility, and after working, precipitation treatment at about 450°C. will increase the hardness and strength. The total nickel and silicon content depends upon the application of the alloy, but it is usually between 1 and 3%. These alloys have good thermal and electrical conductivities, and good resistance to scaling and to oxidation at high temperatures; they also retain their mechanical properties at fairly high temperatures.

Alloys of Copper and Larger Amounts of Other Metals

17.50 THE BRASSES

The brasses are alloys of copper and up to 50% zinc; they may also contain small quantities of tin, manganese, lead, nickel, aluminium, and silicon.

The portion of the copper-zinc equilibrium diagram illustrated (fig. 17.3) shows that up to 37% zinc can be accepted into copper to form a solid solution (called the α phase); the solid solubility of zinc in copper does not increase with temperature, and so the brasses are not precipitation-treatment alloys. Brasses with up to 37% zinc are called 'α brasses', and are cold working alloys because they are of solid solution structure; the strength of 'α brasses' increases with increase in zinc content because the latter causes distortion of the copper 'lattice'. Brasses in this group are unsuitable for hot working because the α phase is hot short.

17.501 When the zinc content exceeds 37% a second phase (called the β' phase) is present with the α phase; these brasses are called '$\alpha + \beta'$ brasses', and are reasonably ductile at room temperatures because the ductility of the α crystals offsets the brittleness of the β' crystals. Brasses in this group are hot working brasses because the atoms of the β' phase become disordered at high temperatures to form the ductile β phase; at the same time the α crystals, brittle at high temperatures, become dissolved in the β phase, and so the alloy becomes ductile at these higher temperatures.

17.502 Brasses with more than 45% zinc consist of all β' crystals, and are too brittle at room temperatures to be used structurally; it will be seen from the equilibrium diagram that the melting point of these high zinc alloys is low compared with the low zinc brasses. The high zinc content brasses are used as brazing spelter because of their low melting point; the high zinc content of the spelter will not cause the joint to be brittle, because some of the zinc will be lost during the joining operation due to its volatility, and some of it will be diffused into the brass being joined.

17.51 *The Cold Working* (α) *Brasses.* These brasses are usually annealed before working and are given a stress relief annealing treatment at 250°C. after working to prevent a failure known as **season cracking**. Season cracking is

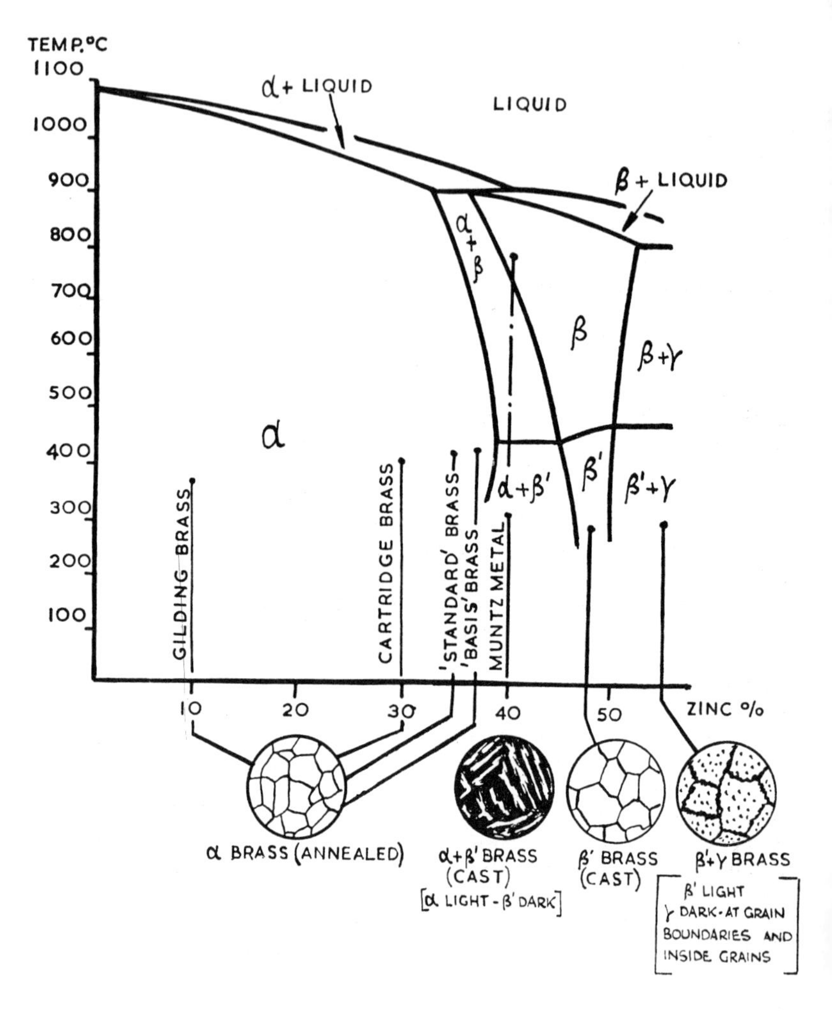

Fig. 17.3 Part of the Copper-zinc Equilibrium Diagram and Microstructure of Some Brasses

the name given to cracks which develop between the crystals some time after working, and without the application of any additional loading.

The following are the important cold working brasses:

17.511 *Cap Copper.* This is copper deoxidised with zinc and with about 3% zinc remaining; it is very soft and ductile and has a good conductivity. It is called 'cap copper' because it is used mainly for the containers of priming caps of ammunition.

17.512 *Gilding Brass.* Brasses of this type contain about 10% zinc, and can be heavily worked; they are less prone to 'season cracking' than brasses with higher zinc content. These brasses are used for jewellery and similar decorative work.

17.513 *Cartridge Brass.* Brass with about 30% zinc is called 'cartridge brass' because it is associated with cartridge and shell cases. It is the most ductile of the cold working brasses and has a good tensile strength.

17.514 *'Standard Brass'.* Although slightly less ductile than cartridge brass, this alloy is rather cheaper because it contains less copper. It is slightly harder than other cold working brasses and must be annealed if it is to be greatly deformed during forming.

17.515 *Basis Brass.* This brass contains between about 36 and 38% zinc, and so may have a small amount of the β' phase present; it is used where a relatively cheap brass suitable for presswork is required. When its mechanical properties are not guaranteed, it is known as **common brass.**

17.516 Small additions of other elements are often made to the above brasses, the following are the more important of the alloys:

17.517 *Admiralty Brass.* The addition of up to 1% tin to 'cartridge brass' improves its resistance to many forms of corrosion. It is used for condenser tubes and similar parts that are cooled by fresh water.

17.518 *Aluminium Brass.* Brass containing 76% copper, 22% zinc, and 2% aluminium has a good corrosion resistance and is used extensively for marine condenser tubes.

17.519 *Clock Brass and Engraving Brass.* About 1% lead can be added to basis brass or to standard brass in order to improve its machinability. Lead is almost insoluble in brass in the liquid state, and so remains in minute particles throughout the structure to break up the chips and to assist in lubrication during cutting. Lead also assists in lubrication in service and this is particularly useful if the assembly presents lubrication difficulties.

17.52 *The Hot Working* ($\alpha + \beta'$) *Brasses.* The group of brasses includes muntz metal, muntz metal with small additions, and high tensile brasses.

17.521 *Muntz Metal* (also called 'Yellow Metal'). This is the principal straight hot working brass, and contains 40% zinc; it is used as hot rolled plate, rod that is often later forged, and for extrusions. It is also used for casting, and as a brazing alloy for steels.

17.522 *Leaded* 60:40 *Brass, or Turning Brass.* Between 0·5 and 3·5% lead is added to muntz metal to improve its machinability; lead does not reduce the tensile strength, but impairs the ductility and impact value, and so if the brass is to be hot forged, the lead content should be low.

17.523 *Naval Brass.* About 1% tin is added to muntz metal to improve its corrosion resistance and to slightly increase its strength. This alloy is then called 'naval brass', and is suitable for hot rolling, forging, and for casting by sand, or die-casting methods. Between 0·5 and 2·0% lead can be added to naval brass to improve its machinability, but should be kept to a minimum if the material is to be forged.

17.524 *High Tensile Brasses.* Small amounts of manganese, iron, nickel, tin, and aluminium (up to about 7% total) can be added to muntz metal to give improved mechanical properties; these alloys are collectively classed as 'high tensile brasses'.

17.60 THE BRONZES AND GUNMETALS

The true bronzes are alloys of copper and tin, with small quantities of other elements such as nickel and lead; there is a tendency to call all alloys of copper and elements other than zinc, 'bronze'; alloys of copper and tin are often called 'tin bronzes'. Tin bronzes that contain zinc are called 'Gun Metals'.

Bronzes are used where ease of casting, good corrosion resistance, and good wearing qualities are important.

17.61 *Tin Bronzes and Gunmetals.* The copper end of a simplified copper-tin-equilibrium diagram is shown in fig. 17.4. It will be seen that alloys with up to 14% tin are classed as solid solution (α) alloys; if these alloys are cooled extremely slowly, the solid solubility of tin in copper will fall as indicated by the broken line on the equilibrium diagram, so that particles of a hard and brittle phase (the δ phase) will be present in the solid solution. This only occurs in practice when an alloy containing more than about 10% tin is cast, but the δ phase can be broken down, and the excess tin made to enter into the solid solution if the alloy is annealed for about 1000 hours at 300°C.

17.611 If the alloy contains between 14 and 32% tin, the structure will consist of both the hard δ phase and the softer α phase, and so combine hardness with toughness; these alloys are good casting alloys because of their lower melting temperatures.

17.612 It will be seen from the equilibrium diagram that bronzes have a large solidification range (indicated by the distance between the liquidus and the solidus lines); these alloys tend to be of a 'cored' structure as cast. An alloy is said to be cored when the centre of each grain is rich in the constituent with the higher melting point, and the outside of each grain is richer in the constituent with the lower melting point; the composition of each grain can be made uniform by annealing.

Tin bronzes can be classed as (i) wrought bronzes and (ii) cast bronzes.

17.62 *Wrought Bronzes (the α bronzes).* Bronzes that contain up to about 8% tin are working bronzes, and can be cold rolled or drawn; they can be given a range of mechanical properties according to the extent of the cold working after annealing.

About 0·3% phosphorus is often alloyed with these bronzes to produce 'wrought phosphor bronzes'; these bronzes are used for springs, springy electrical contacts, and for the suspension for coils of moving coil instruments.

Wrought bronzes with more than 8% tin are made suitable for cold working by a lengthy annealing at about 700°C.; these bronzes have a very good corrosion resistance.

17.63 *Casting Bronzes (the $\alpha + \delta$ bronzes).* Casting bronzes contain between about 10 and 18% tin, and are of a complex structure; they usually contain other elements in addition to copper and tin.

17.631 *Casting Phosphor Bronze.* This is an important casting bronze containing

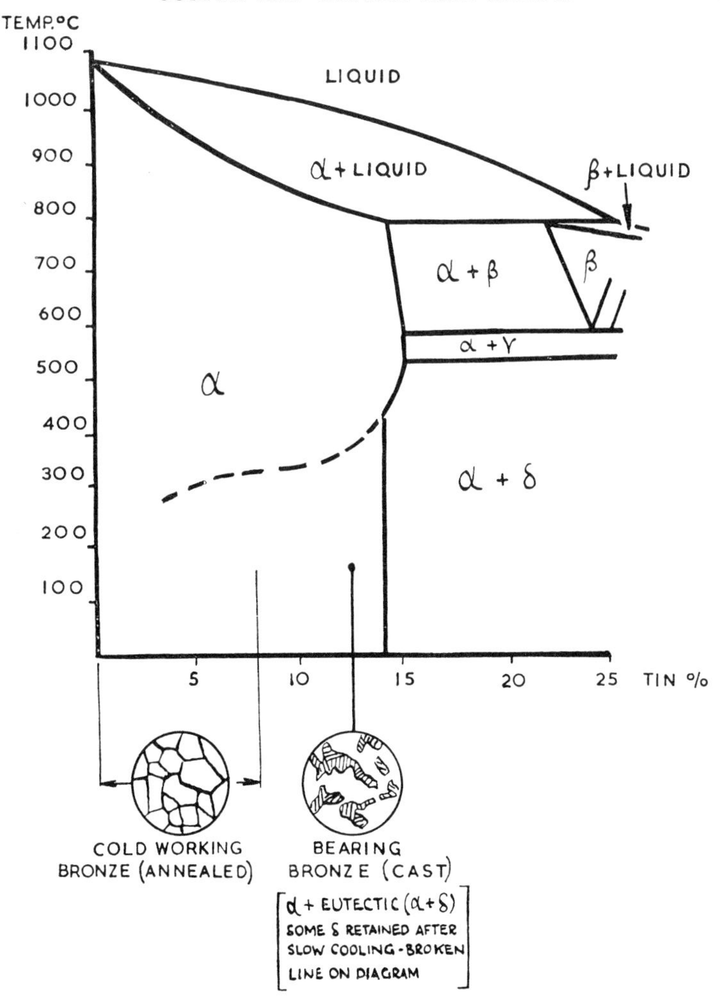

Fig. 17.4 Part of the Copper-tin Equilibrium Diagram and Typical Microstructures

10% tin and 0·05% phosphorus. It is a very good bearing material because it combines hardness and toughness; if the bearing is to be subjected to heavy loads, the phosphorus content can be increased to up to 0·5% but alloys with this increased phosphorus content have a rather poor ductility.

17.632 *Bell Metal.* Bells are usually cast in a bronze containing more than 20% tin because, although brittle, bells cast in this alloy give a sonorous note when struck.

17.633 *Speculum Metal.* Bronzes containing between 30 and 40% tin are hard and brittle but take a high polish. These alloys are called 'speculum metals' because they were used for mirrors; they are now used for diffraction gratings, and for other optical instrument parts. Speculum metal can also be used as an electroplating metal.

17.634 *Leaded Bronzes.* Small quantities of lead are added to bronzes to improve their machinability; 5% lead is often added to a 10% tin bronze to give improved bearing properties.

17.64 *Gunmetals.* Casting bronzes that contain zinc are called 'gunmetals'; the zinc gives better casting properties.

Admiralty Gunmetal. This alloy contains about 88% copper, 10% tin, and 2% zinc; it is used for naval components and for valves and similar steam plant parts.

Leaded Gunmetals. Up to about 5% lead is added to gunmetals to improve their castability and machinability.

17.65 *Nickel Bronzes.* Small amounts of nickel are often added to tin bronzes to give better mechanical properties and quality to castings; nickel is usually added in conjunction with zinc and so these alloys are strictly 'nickel gunmetals'. Although up to 1·5% nickel will produce the effects described, between 3 and 5% nickel is added to alloys containing between 5 and 10% tin and 2% zinc because castings with this higher nickel content can be solution treated by quenching from 760°C., and then given precipitation treatment for several hours at about 300°C. to improve their strength and hardness. Nickel bronzes resist wear and corrosion, and also retain their strength at elevated temperatures; they are used for valves and pump parts for boiler feed water.

17.7 *Aluminium Bronze.* The copper-rich end of the copper-aluminium-equilibrium diagram is shown in fig. 17.5. This diagram indicates that up to 9·4% aluminium will enter into solid solution in copper at room temperature, but that the solid solubility does not increase with temperature; in fact it falls when the temperature exceeds 565°C. When the aluminium content is greater than about 7·5% and the temperature more than 565°C., a second phase (the β phase) will be present; when the aluminium content is greater than 9·4%, slow cooling will cause a breakdown of the β phase so that the structure will consist of the brittle γ_2 phase, with the solid solution (the $\alpha + \gamma_2$ phase). If the alloy is cooled less slowly, for example by knocking it from the mould as soon as it has solidified, this breakdown of the β phase will not occur and a better structure will be produced; a small amount of iron will retard the breakdown of the β phase and give a similar result.

The equilibrium diagram also indicates that the temperature at which the β phase breaks down depends upon the aluminium content and that it reaches a minimum value when the aluminium content is 11·8%; this part of the copper-aluminium equilibrium diagram resembles the steel part of the iron-carbon equilibrium diagram (see page 87, fig. 11.6), and alloys with these higher aluminium contents can be quenched to produce a structure that resembles martensite and which is hard and brittle. These alloys also resemble steels in that after hardening, they can be tempered so that the desired intermediate properties can be obtained.

17.71 *The α Aluminium Bronzes.* Alloys in this group usually contain between 4 and 7% aluminium, and can be annealed to make them soft and ductile, and then hardened and strengthened by cold working.

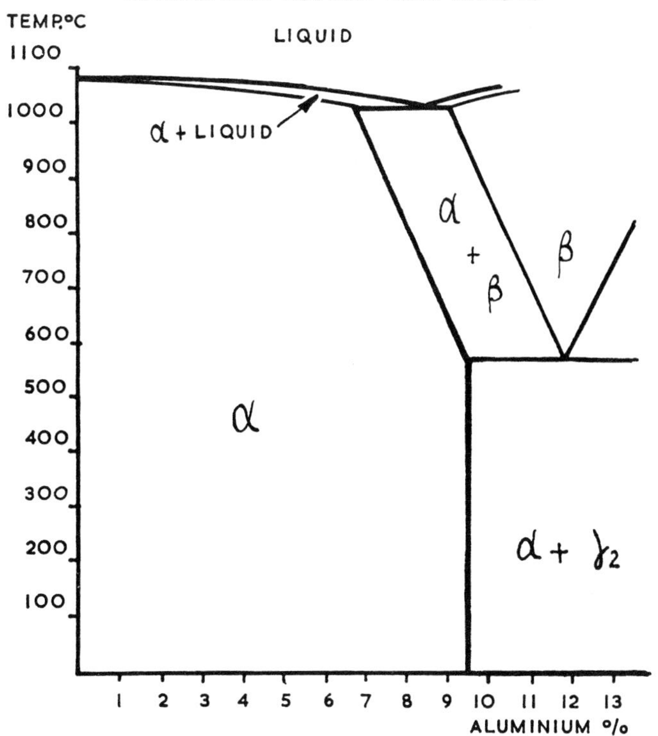

Fig. 17.5 Part of the Copper-aluminium Equilibrium Diagram

17.72 *The Duplex Aluminium Bronzes.* These alloys usually contain between 9 and 10% aluminium with about 2% iron to retard the breakdown of the β phase. Alloys in this group lend themselves to both sand casting and to gravity die-casting; they are not suitable for pressure die-casting because of their small solidification range. Aluminium bronze castings are used for pump casings, valve parts, gears, and racks.

In general, aluminium bronzes have a good corrosion resistance due to the alumina film produced on the surface by the aluminium, and they also retain their mechanical properties at reasonably high temperatures.

17.80 ALLOYS OF COPPER AND NICKEL

Alloys of copper and nickel can be grouped as follows:

(i) Cupro-nickels, which are alloys of copper and nickel.
(ii) Nickel silvers, which are alloys of copper, nickel, and zinc.

17.81 *Cupro-nickels.* The copper-nickel-equilibrium diagram (fig. 17.6) indicates that these elements will form a solid solution in all proportions; all the alloys so produced are useful and are suitable for both hot and for cold working.

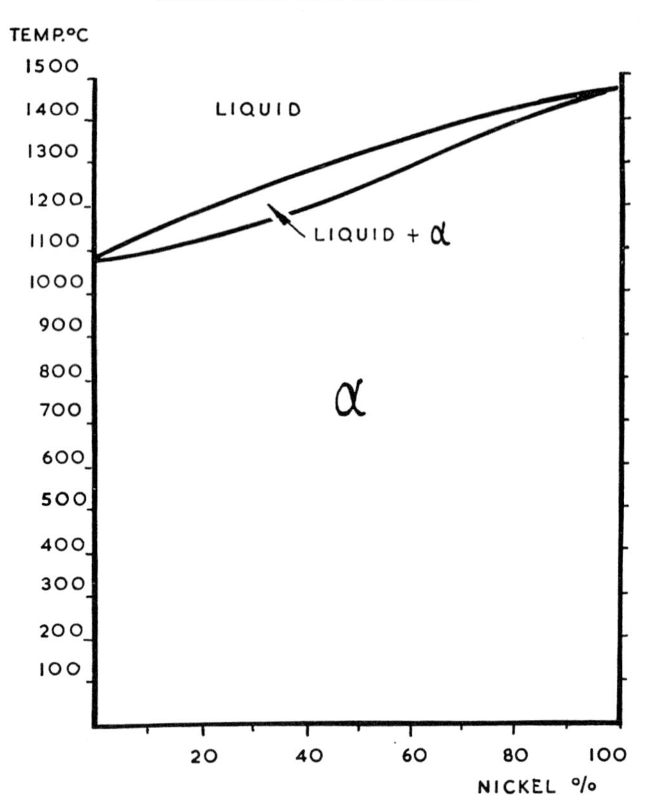

Fig. 17.6 The Copper-nickel Equilibrium Diagram

The nickel content is usually between 15 and 68%; the tensile strength, ductility, and hardness increases with nickel content. The alloy with 20% nickel is the best in this group for severe cold working, and that with 25% nickel is used for British 'silver' coinage; an important alloy in this group is known as **Monel**, and contains about 68% nickel. **Monel** has an extremely good corrosion resistance, and retains its mechanical properties at the high temperatures associated with steam turbines (this alloy is also described in Chapter 21).

17.82 *Nickel Silvers.* These alloys do not contain silver, but are so called because of their silvery appearance; they contain copper, nickel, and zinc. Since each commercial nickel silver is a solid solution, all of these can be cold worked; if the impurities are kept to a minimum, they can be hot worked also. The copper content is between 55 and 63%, and the nickel content between 10 and 30%. Nickel silvers are used for spoons and forks, and usually silver plated (E.P.N.S.); one grade, with 18% nickel, is used for spring contacts for electrical equipment.

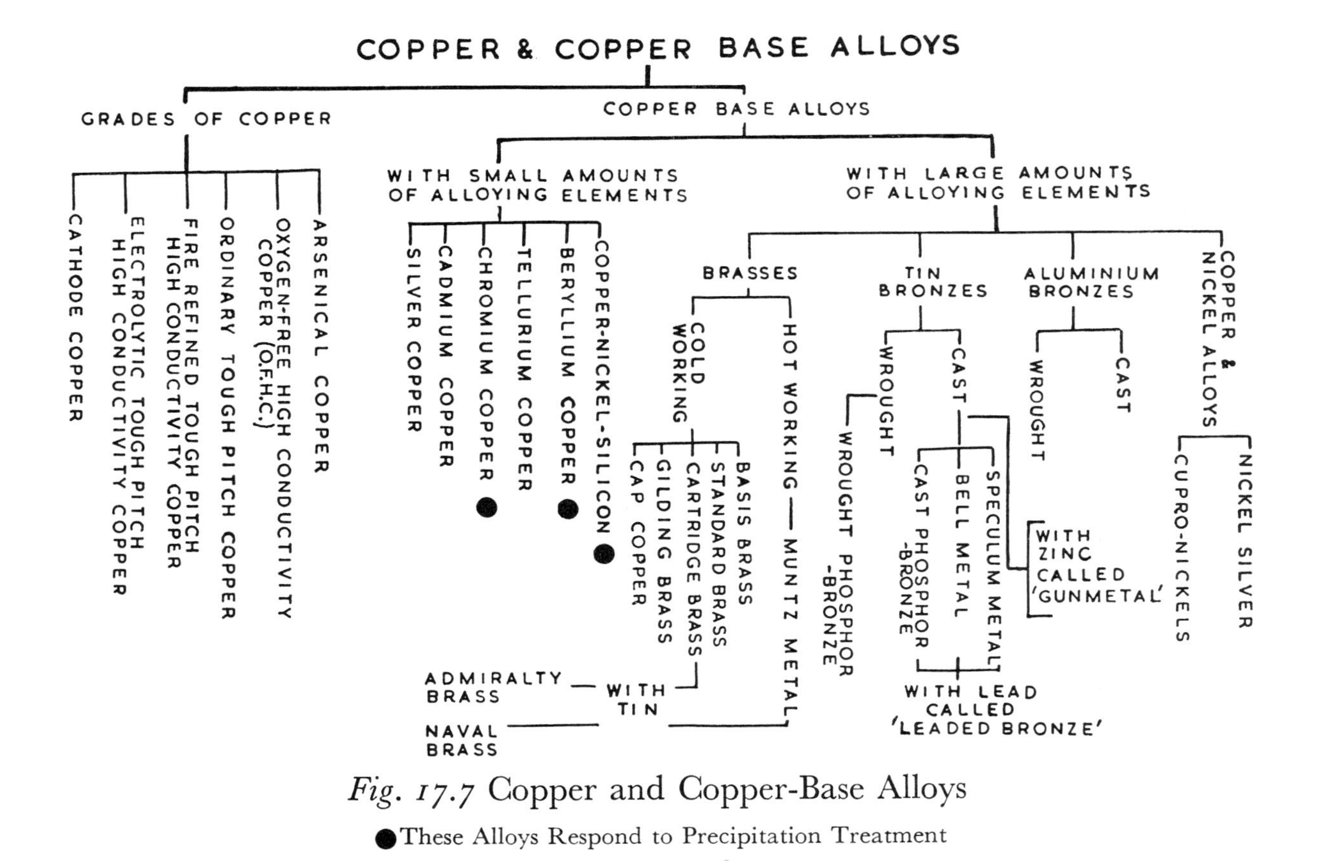

Fig. 17.7 Copper and Copper-Base Alloys

● These Alloys Respond to Precipitation Treatment

TABLE 17.1

MECHANICAL PROPERTIES OF SOME COPPER ALLOYS WITH SMALL AMOUNTS OF ALLOYING ADDITIONS

Description	*Composition %*		*Mechanical properties*					
	Copper	*Other elements*	*Condition*	*Limit of proportionality (N/mm²)*	*0·1% Proof stress (N/mm²)*	*Tensile strength (N/mm²)*	*Percentage elongation on $5{\cdot}65\sqrt{S_0}$*	*Hardness (HV)*
Silver copper	99·9 +	0·06–0·1 silver	annealed	15	62	220	35	45
			hard	190	320	380	3	115
Cadmium copper	99	0·6–1·0 cadmium	annealed	31	62	280	32	60
			hard	230	460	540	1	140
Chromium copper	99–99·5	0·5–1·0 chromium	solution treated	31	46	230	35	65
			solution treated and prec. hard.	250	310	450	16	130
			solution treated, cold worked, and prec. hard.	310	430	510	7	150
Copper-nickel-silicon	98–99	0·5–1·0 nickel 0·5–1·0 silicon	as received	31	77	250	18	60
			heat treated	200	270	370	39	110
Beryllium copper	97	1·75–2·5 beryllium with up to 0·5 cobalt or nickel	solution treated	60–120	120–180	470–540	28–35	100–120
			solution treated and prec. hard.	470–620	620–930	1200–1280	3–5	320–380
			solution treated, cold worked, and prec. hard.	540–770	770–1200	1280–1400	1–3	360–420
	97	2·6 cobalt 0·4 beryllium	solution treated	—	—	310	23	80
			solution treated and prec. hard.	—	—	590	11	200
			solution treated, cold worked, and prec. hard.	—	—	740	10	230

Note: 'prec. hard.' = 'precipitation hardened'.

TABLE 17.2

MECHANICAL PROPERTIES OF SOME TYPICAL BRASSES

Description (nearest B.S. or other standard in brackets)	Composition %			Mechanical properties					
	Copper	Zinc	Other elements	Condition	Limit of proportionality (N/mm^2)	0·1% Proof stress (N/mm^2)	Tensile strength (N/mm^2)	Percentage elongation on $5{\cdot}65\sqrt{S_0}$	Hardness (HV)
Cap copper (STA.17)	97	3	—	annealed	15	62	230	35	55
				hard	190	340	430	3	130
Gilding brass (713)	90	10	—	annealed	31	78	280	38	60
				hard	230	460	510	3	150
Cartridge brass (267)	70	30	—	annealed	54	78	320	50	65
				hard	280	510	700	4	185
'Standard' brass (266)	65	35	—	annealed	62	93	320	47	65
				hard	280	510	700	3	185
Basis brass (265)	63	37	—	annealed	62	93	340	38	65
				hard	280	540	730	3	185
Muntz metal (1541)	60	40	—		62	110	370	28	75
Admiralty brass	70	29	1% tin		47	78	360	50	70
Naval brass (1541)	62	37	1% tin		78	124	390	28	80
Aluminium brass	76	22	2% aluminium		47	62	360	46	70
Clock brass	58–60	Bal.	1·5–2·5% lead	annealed	47	93	370	33	75
				hard	290	470	620	3	190
High tensile (medium strength) (1400–HTB1–C)	55–63	Bal.	0·5–2·5% Fe 3% max. Mn 5% max. Al 2% max. Ni	Cast	—	260–340	580–700	10–14	120–200
High tensile (high strength) (1400–HTB3–C)	55–70	Bal.	1–2·5% Fe 4% max. Mn 3–6% Al 1% max Ni	Cast	—	400–540	720–830	8–14	150–230

TABLE 17.3

MECHANICAL PROPERTIES OF SOME TYPICAL BRONZES

Description (nearest B.S. or other standard in brackets)	*Composition %*				*Mechanical properties*				
	Copper	*Tin*	*Zinc*	*Other elements*	*Condition*	*0·1% Proof stress (N/mm²)*	*Tensile strength (N/mm²)*	*Percentage elongation on 5·65 √S₀*	*Hardness (HV)*
Wrought phosphor bronze (384)	Bal.	5	—	0·02–0·4% phosphorus	annealed	120	360	43	—
					hard	770	930	3	—
Cast phosphor bronze (1400–PB3–C)	Bal.	10	—	0·03–0·25% phosphorus	—	120	250–310	7–14	80–100
Admiralty gunmetal (1400–G1–C)	88	10	2	—	—	120	250–340	8–14	70–100
Nickel gunmetal	88	5	2	5% nickel	as cast	—	320	32	90
					heat treated	—	550	70	155
Wrought aluminium bronze (378)	4–7% aluminium. Up to 4% Mn and/or Ni. Balance copper				annealed	120	390	50	80
					hard	590	770	3	220
Cast aluminium bronze (1400–AB1–C)	9·5% Al, 2·5 Fe Up to 1% Ni and Mn. Balance copper				—	170–220	500–590	14–28	90–140

TABLE 17.4

MECHANICAL PROPERTIES OF SOME TYPICAL NICKEL SILVERS

Description (nearest B.S. or other standard in brackets)	*Composition %*			*Mechanical properties*					
	Copper	*Nickel*	*Zinc*	*Condition*	*Limit of proportionality (N/mm²)*	*0·1% Proof stress (N/mm²)*	*Tensile strength (N/mm²)*	*Percentage elongation on 5·65 √S₀*	*Hardness (HV)*
10% Nickel silver (790)	63	10	27	annealed	60	110	340	46	65
				hard	310	590	700	3	220
18% Nickel silver (790)	62	18	20	annealed	80	120	370	37	75
				hard	340	620	700	3	220

BRASSES

Fig. 17.8
Cartridge (70/30)
Brass × 200
α Crystals

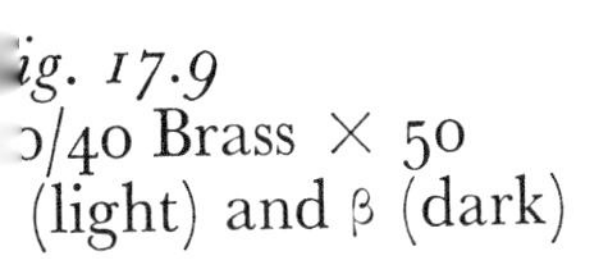

ig. 17.9
ɔ/40 Brass × 50
(light) and β (dark)

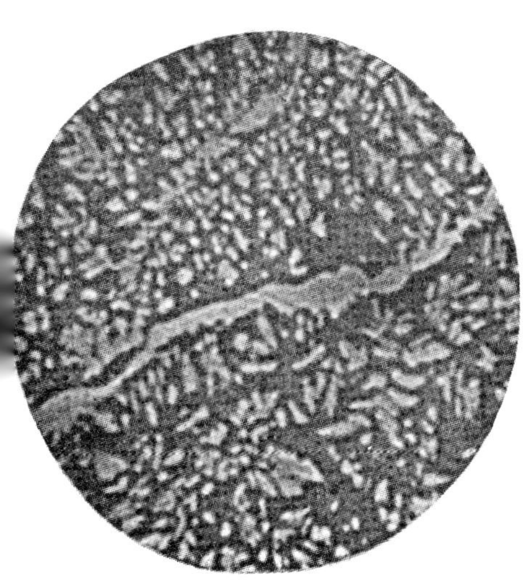

Fig. 17.10
50/50 Brass × 50
γ (light) at Boundaries
and within the β (dark)
Crystals

17.90 *Copper Alloys Containing Silicon.* A small quantity of silicon improves both the strength and the corrosion resistance of copper; it also makes copper easier to join because it deoxidises the weld metal when fusion welding is done, and produces a moderately high resistance that is an advantage when resistance welding is done. About 3% is the maximum amount of silicon added to a wrought bronze, but up to 5% is used in a casting bronze in order to increase the fluidity and so make it possible to cast intricate shapes.

17.91 *Copper Alloys Containing Manganese.* Manganese is added to copper with either aluminium or with nickel, to give specific electrical properties. These alloys are easier to work into complicated shapes than are steels, and are of good corrosion resistance.

REFERENCES

Publications issued by the Copper Development Association.

CHAPTER 18

ALUMINIUM AND ALUMINIUM-BASE ALLOYS

18.10 Aluminium is an important engineering material because it is extremely light, and because it resists atmospheric attack. It has high electrical and thermal conductivities, it can be polished to reflect both light and heat, it has a high coefficient of thermal expansion, and is non-magnetic. Commercially pure aluminium is available in a range of purities from about 99·9% down to 99%. The tensile strength of the unalloyed metal is only about 60 N/mm^2 but it can be cold worked to increase its strength to about 140 N/mm^2; the actual tensile strength so obtained depends upon the extent of the cold working.

The resistance of aluminium to atmospheric attack is due to the oxide film that is set up very rapidly on its surface upon exposure to air; this film is only about 13×10^{-6} mm thick, and it adheres to the surface so that the aluminium becomes insulated against further attack. The presence of this film does not spoil the appearance of the metal, or alter the reflective qualities of aluminium that had been polished before exposure to air.

Alloying elements are added to aluminium when a stronger material is required or if its casting properties are to be improved; copper, manganese, magnesium, zinc, nickel, and silicon are the most important alloying elements used.

Aluminium-base Alloys

18.20 Aluminium-base alloys can be classified as:

1. Wrought aluminium alloys.
2. Cast aluminium alloys.

The alloys in each of these two classes are further classified according to whether they respond to heat treatment or not; in this classification, the term 'heat treatment' refers to a strengthening heat treatment, and so does not include annealing, which is a softening heat treatment.

18.21 THE WROUGHT ALUMINIUM ALLOYS

Aluminium alloys in this group are manufactured in the form of sheet, tube, forgings, wire, and extruded sections; as stated above, these alloys are divided into two groups according to their response to heat treatment of the strengthening type.

18.211 WORK-HARDENING ALLOYS

Alloys in this group will not respond to heat treatment, but a range of so-called 'tempers' can be produced by controlling the extent of cold working done after the final annealing; it must be appreciated that when the desired thickness has been obtained, the tensile strength of the material cannot be increased without making the material undersized. The annealing of aluminium alloys is dealt with later in this chapter.

The principal work-hardening aluminium alloys are:

(i) Alloys of aluminium and up to about 1% total of alloying additions such as silicon, iron, manganese, and zinc, according to the properties required; the maximum tensile strength obtained by cold working increases with increase in the amount of alloying additions made, but does so at the expense of ductility.

(ii) Alloys of aluminium and up to about 2·4% total additions that include about 1·25% manganese.

(iii) Alloys of aluminium that include various amounts of magnesium up to about 7%, according to the required strength.

Most of the alloys in the above groups are of a solid solution structure, and the others are of solid solution structure with small amounts of a second phase also present. The aluminium-magnesium Equilibrium diagram (fig. 18.1) shows that only a small amount of the β phase will be present; although this diagram indicates that the solubility of magnesium in aluminium increases with temperature; these alloys are not subjected to precipitation treatment because this will produce only a slight increase in strength. Due to their solid solution structure, these alloys are soft and of very good corrosion resistance.

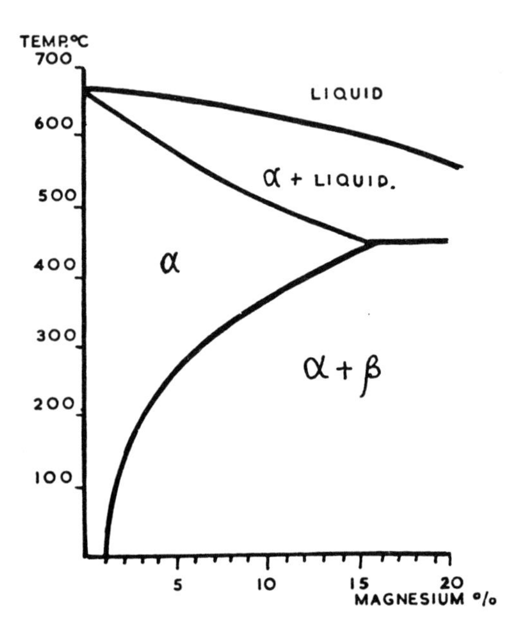

Fig. 18.1 Part of the Aluminium-magnesium Equilibrium Diagram

18.212 *Heat-treatable Wrought Aluminium Alloys.* Heat-treatable wrought aluminium alloys can be strengthened by precipitation heat treatment; the principle of this type of heat treatment is dealt with in Chapter 5, and the heat treatment of aluminium alloys is dealt with later in this chapter.

Aluminium alloys in this group can be considered as:

(i) Alloys with up to about 4% copper; the compound $CuAl_2$ is the hardening medium in these alloys.

(ii) Alloys with up to about 2% total amount of silicon and magnesium; here, the hardening medium is Mg_2Si.

(iii) Alloys with various amounts of copper, silicon, and magnesium; these alloys have both $CuAl_2$ and Mg_2Si as the hardening media.

The heat-treatable aluminium alloys fall into two classes; some of them become harder spontaneously after solution treatment, and others require a further heat treatment, called '**precipitation treatment**', to develop their full properties (see page 46).

In addition to the hardening element, other strengthening elements, such as iron and zinc, may be present; when an aluminium alloy is to be used at high temperatures, it may also contain a small amount of nickel.

18.22 THE CAST ALUMINIUM ALLOYS

When high ductility and corrosion resistance is required, commercially pure

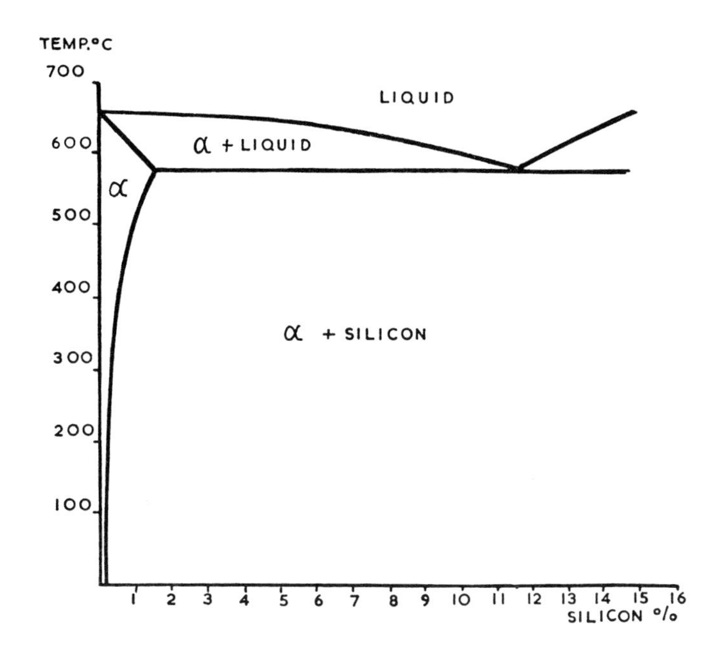

Fig. 18.2 Part of the Aluminium-silicon Equilibrium Diagram

aluminium is used with the addition of a small amount of silicon or magnesium; when stronger and harder materials are required, a complex alloy is used. When a very fluid alloy is required, more than 5% silicon is employed; the aluminium-silicon-equilibrium diagram indicates that the eutectic composition is about 11·6% Si. The cast aluminium alloys are suitable for sand casting, most of them are suitable for gravity die-casting, only a few of them are suitable for pressure die-casting, and these are only suitable for casting by the cold chamber system of pressure die-casting.

Cast aluminium alloys can be grouped according to their response to heat treatment of the strengthening type.

18.221 *'As Cast' Aluminium Alloys.* These alloys derive no benefit from heat treatment. Three main groups of 'as cast' alloys are used:

(i) Alloys of aluminium and between 9 and 13% silicon; these alloys can be die-cast.

(ii) Alloys of aluminium, about 1·6% copper and about 10% silicon; these alloys have only a moderate strength, but can be pressure die-cast.

(iii) Alloys of aluminium, 4·5% magnesium, and 0·5% manganese. Although these alloys are of only moderate strength, they have good corrosion resistance. They are suitable for sand casting and for gravity die-casting.

18.222 *Heat-treatable Casting Aluminium Alloys.* In addition to silicon and small amounts of other elements, these alloys contain elements that act as hardening media. A large number of these alloys contain 4% copper and a small amount of magnesium; some of them contain up to about 3% nickel to combine with the aluminium to form the hardening medium $NiAl_3$.

The Heat Treatment of Aluminium Alloys

18.30 STRENGTHENING HEAT TREATMENT

Aluminium alloys of a suitable composition can be subjected to strengthening heat treatment consisting of solution treatment followed by precipitation. In order to respond to this type of heat treatment, an alloy must contain an element that has a limited solid solubility in the solvent metal at room temperature, but which increases with increase in temperature.

Copper behaves in this manner when alloyed with aluminium, and this is illustrated by part of the aluminium-copper equilibrium diagram (fig. 18.3). Only about 0·2% copper can be contained in solid solution at room temperature, and copper in excess of this quantity will, with some of the aluminium, form the intermetallic compound $CuAl_2$. The solid solubility of copper in aluminium rises with temperature, to reach a maximum of 5·7% at a temperature of 584°C; and so if the copper content is less than 5·7%, it will all enter into solid solution if the temperature is high enough. If the alloy is allowed to attain equilibrium by slow cooling as, for example, after casting, the excess copper will gradually be precipitated from the solid solution to form the hard and brittle compound, $CuAl_2$, which collects at the grain boundaries.

18.31 SOLUTION TREATMENT

If the slowly cooled alloy is reheated to produce a complete solid solution, and then quenched in water or oil, precipitation will not occur, and a supersaturated solid solution will be produced. The temperature and duration of this **solution treatment** depends upon the composition of the alloy, previous treatment, and its thickness. At the end of this stage of the heat treatment, the alloy is soft and weak, and this is a convenient stage at which to do cold working. Aluminium alloys that contain magnesium and silicon (which form the compound Mg_2Si) and those that contain nickel (which, with aluminium forms with compound $NiAl_3$) will also respond to the heat treatment being discussed here.

18.32 PRECIPITATION TREATMENT

The supersaturated solid solution produced by solution treatment is only stable at lower temperatures, and if the alloy is given a further heat treatment, called **precipitation treatment**, precipitation will start; provided the temperature is not too high, the copper (or the other alloying additions) will not leave the solid solution, but will form regions of 'high population' within it, so strength-

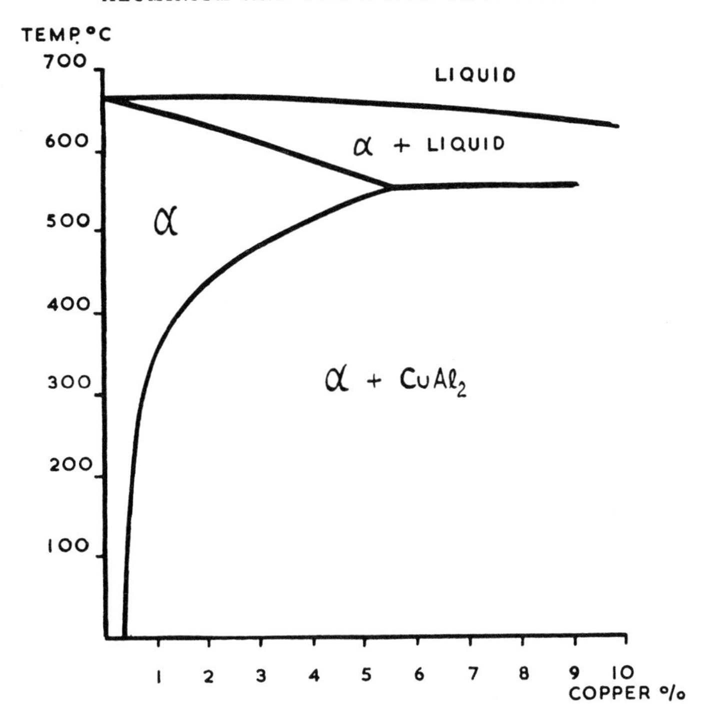

Fig. 18.3 Part of the Aluminium-copper Equilibrium Diagram

ening the alloy. The temperature to which the alloy is heated depends upon its composition, and the duration of the treatment depends upon its composition and thickness; the temperature is usually between 100 and 200°C., and the duration between 2 and 30 hours. Manufacturer's instructions should be followed regarding the treatment because the strength of the alloy will be reduced if the temperature is too high, or if the alloy is heated for too long.

18.33 NATURAL AGEING

In the case of some alloys, room temperature is high enough to cause precipitation to occur. These alloys are given solution treatment, and held at room temperature, when precipitation will start within 30 minutes, and be completed in about 4 days, when the maximum strength will be reached. A wrought aluminium alloy containing about 4% copper (usually known as 'Dulalumin') is a typical **natural ageing** alloy. If a natural ageing alloy is to be cold worked, it must be done within about 2 hours after quenching because after this time the precipitation will have advanced so far that it will be difficult to cold work. Precipitation can be delayed for about 4 days by refrigeration at between −6 to −10°C., so that batches of material can be solution treated and stored until required for working; aluminium rivets made from natural ageing aluminium alloys are stored in this way.

18.40 ANNEALING

Annealing is applied to all wrought alloys so that they can be cold worked. The annealing temperature depends upon the recrystallisation temperature of the alloy and may be between 340 and 450°C.; the duration of the soaking will be between 20 minutes and 2 hours according to the composition and the thickness of the material. Care must be taken not to overheat the material because this will cause grain growth and so reduce the mechanical properties finally produced.

18.50 STABILISING TREATMENT

Very often castings are heat treated to release internal stresses set up during cooling in the mould; this treatment is also applied to large extruded sections and to large forgings. The temperature of this treatment is about 200°C. and the duration is about 5 hours, according to the section thickness.

18.60 EQUIPMENT

The heating furnaces used are either air circulating furnaces or salt baths; either type can be used for solution treatment, but the air-circulating furnace is recommended for annealing and precipitation treatment. When a salt bath is used the material must be degreased and dried before placing in the bath, and be washed in clean water after the treatment to remove all traces of the salt, otherwise the aluminium may suffer chemical attack.

18.70 The Fabrication of Aluminium and Aluminium Alloys

Commercially pure and wrought aluminium alloys can be manipulated into shape by rolling, deep drawing and pressing, stretch forming, stamping, extrusion and impact extrusion, and by bending. The casting alloys can be sand cast, some of them gravity die-cast, and a few of them can be pressure die-cast provided that the cold chamber system is used.

Aluminium alloys can be machined with ease but high cutting speeds should be used and the tool cutting angles should be suitable.

Aluminium and its alloys can be joined by welding provided that active fluxes are used to remove the oxide film that forms readily upon the surface; soldering and brazing can be applied to pure aluminium and certain aluminium alloys. Mechanical joining can be done by riveting and by bolting.

Aluminium and its alloys can be surface finished by polishing and by burnishing, by chemical finishing or anodising to thicken up the oxide film, by painting after chemical or anodic finishing, or by electroplating after suitable surface preparation.

The corrosion resistance of sheet aluminium alloy can be improved by rolling a thin layer of pure aluminium on to each side of the alloy to produce a 'three-ply' effect; clad aluminium alloy is marketed under the name 'Alclad'.

18.8 Nomenclature used in British Standards for Aluminium Alloys

This system indicates the form of the material (plate, strip, extruded section, casting, etc.), the composition of the material, and also the treatment that it has received or will respond to.

The specification reference includes a letter to indicate if the material will respond to heat treatment.

For example, alloy NS3, covered by BS 1470, is for strip (shown by letter S) and will not respond to strengthening heat treatment (shown by letter N).

Alloy HF30, covered by BS 1472, is a forging alloy (shown by letter F), which will respond to strengthening heat treatment (shown by letter H).

The condition of the material, or the heat treatment it has received is indicated by symbol:

Symbols and Definitions

M	As manufactured. Material which acquires some temper from shaping processes in which there is no special control over thermal treatment or amount of strain hardening.
O	Annealed (wrought material). Material which is fully annealed to obtain the lowest strength condition.
H1, H2 H3, H4 H5, H6 H7, H8	Strain hardened (wrought material). Material subjected to the application of cold work after annealing (or hot forming) or to a combination of cold work and partial annealing/stabilising in order to secure the specified mechanical properties. The designations are in ascending order of tensile strength.
TB	Solution heat treated and naturally aged. Material which receives no cold work after solution heat treatment except as may be required to flatten or straighten it. Properties of some alloys in this temper are unstable.
TB7	Solution treated and stabilised (cast material).
TD	Solution heat treated, cold worked and naturally aged.
TE	Cooled from an elevated temperature shaping process and precipitation treated.
TF	Solution heat treated and precipitation treated.
TF7	Fully heat treated and stabilised (cast material).
TH	Solution heat treated, cold worked and then precipitation treated.
TS	Material which is thermally treated to improve dimensional stability (cast material).

REFERENCES

Publications issued by the Aluminium Development Association.

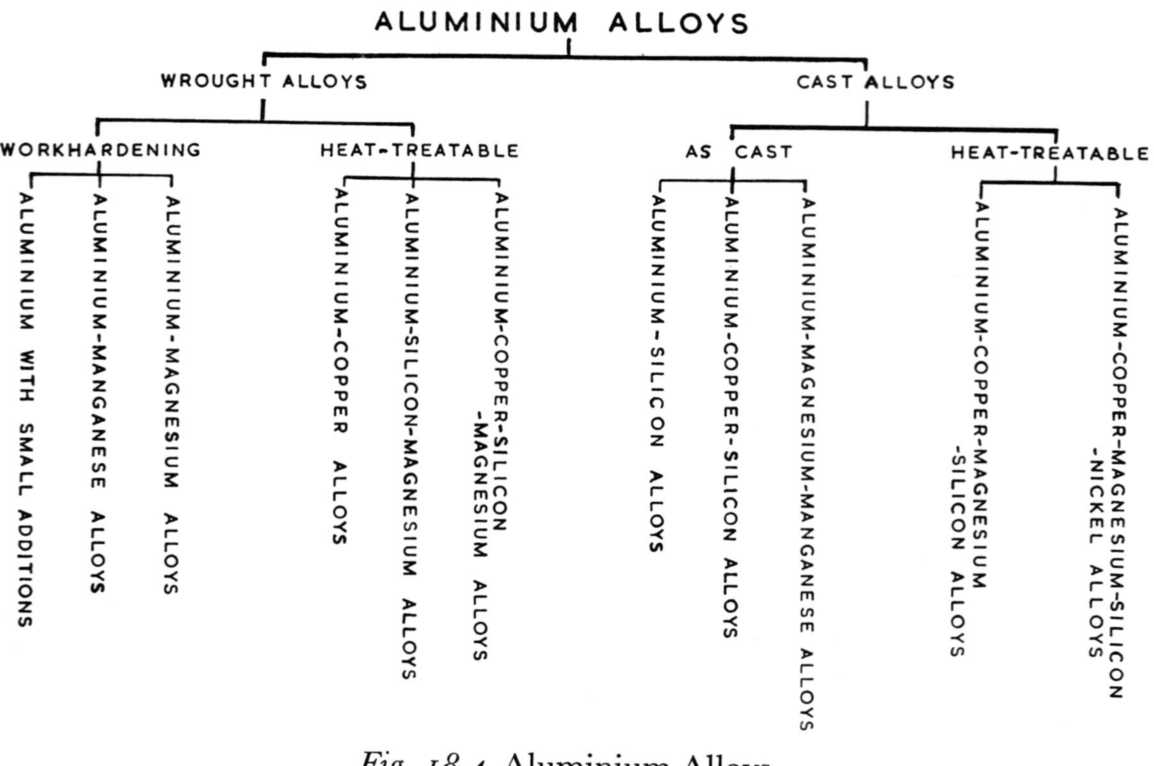

Fig. 18.4 Aluminium Alloys

TABLE 18.1

THE MECHANICAL PROPERTIES OF SOME TYPICAL WROUGHT ALUMINIUM ALLOYS

Type			*Composition %*	*Condition*	0·2% *Proof stress* *(N/mm²) min*	*Tensile strength* *(N/mm²)*	*Elongation on* 5·65 $\sqrt{S_0}$
'Work-hardening' Alloys	BS 1470 Sheet and Strip	NS 3	Copper 0·1 Magnesium 0·1 Silicon 0·6 Iron 0·7 Manganese 0·8–1·5 Zinc 0·2 Aluminium Rem.	O	—	130 max	—
				H4	—	175 max	—
				H8	—	175 min	—
		NS 4	Copper 0·1 Magnesium 1·7–2·4 Silicon 0·5 Iron 0·5 Manganese 0·5 Zinc 0·2 Chromium 0·25 Aluminium Rem.	M	—	—	—
				O	60	200 max	—
				H3	130	240 max	—
				H6	175	275 max	—
		NS 8	Copper 0·1 Magnesium 4·0–4·9 Silicon 0·4 Iron 0·4 Manganese 0·5–1·0 Zinc 0·2 Chromium 0·25 Aluminium Rem.	M	—	—	—
				O	125	350 min	14 min
				H2	235	375 min	—
				H4	270	405 min	—
'Heat-treatable' Alloys	BS 1470 Sheet and Strip	HS 15	Copper 3·9–5·0 Magnesium 0·2–0·8 Silicon 0·5–1·0 Iron 0·7 Manganese 0·4–1·2 Zinc 0·2 Chromium 0·1 Aluminium Rem.	TB	245	385 min	10 min
				TF	380	440 min	6 min
	BS 1472 Forgings	HF 30	Copper 0·1 Magnesium 0·5–1·2 Silicon 0·7–1·3 Iron 0·5 Manganese 0·4–1·0 Zinc 0·2 Chromium 0·25 Titanium 0·2 Aluminium Rem.	TB	120	185 min	16 min
				TF	255	295 min	8 min
		HF 12	Copper 1·8–2·8 Magnesium 0·6–1·2 Silicon 0·5–1·3 Iron 0·6–1·2 Manganese 0·5 Nickel 0·6–1·4 Zinc 0·2 Titanium and other elements 0·2 Aluminium Rem.	TB	160	310 min	13 min
				TF	300	385 min	6 min

TABLE 18.2

THE MECHANICAL PROPERTIES OF SOME TYPICAL CAST ALUMINIUM ALLOYS (BS 1490)

Type	*Composition %*	*Condition*	*Mechanical properties*			
			Tensile strength (N/mm^2)		*Elongation % on $5{\cdot}65\sqrt{S_0}$*	
			Sand Cast	*Chill Cast*	*Sand Cast*	*Chill Cast*
'As Cast' Alloys	Copper 0·1 Magnesium 3·0–6·0 Silicon 10·0–13·0 Iron 0·6 Manganese 0·5 Nickel 0·1 Zinc 0·1 Tin 0·05 Lead 0·1 Aluminium Balance	M	160	185	4	5
'As Cast' Alloys	Copper 0·7–2·5 Magnesium 0·3 Silicon 9·0–11·5 Iron 1·0 Manganese 0·5 Nickel 1·0 Zinc 1·2 Small amounts of titanium, tin, and lead Aluminium Balance	M	125	145	—	—
'As Cast' Alloys	Copper 0·1 Magnesium 3·0–6·0 Silicon 0·3 Iron 0·6 Manganese 0·3–0·7 Nickel 0·1 Zinc 0·1 Small amounts of tin, lead, titanium, and niobium Aluminium Balance	M	140	170	2	4
'Heat-treatable' Alloys	Copper 4·0–5·0 Magnesium 0·1 Silicon 0·25 Iron 0·25 Manganese 0·1 Nickel 0·1 Zinc 0·1 Small amounts of lead, tin, titanium, and niobium Aluminium Balance	Solution treated	220	260	5	9
		TF	280	310	3	7
'Heat-treatable' Alloys	Copper 0·5–1·3 Magnesium 0·8–1·5 Silicon 11·0–13·0 Iron 0·8 Nickel 2·0–3·0 Zinc 0·1 Small amounts of tin, lead, titanium, and niobium Aluminium Balance	TF	170	250	—	—

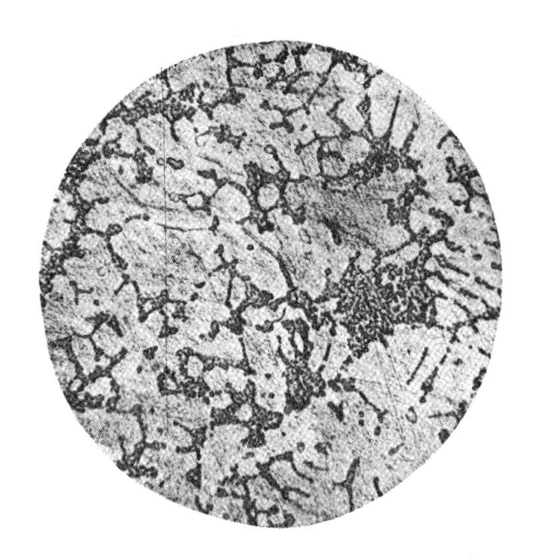

Fig. 18.5 Aluminium-copper Alloy with about 3.5% Copper as Cast × 50
$CuAl_2$ (dark) and solid solution (light)

Fig. 18.6 Aluminium-silicon Alloy with 10–13% Silicon as Cast, Showing Eutectic Structure

CHAPTER 19

MAGNESIUM AND MAGNESIUM-BASE ALLOYS

19.10 Magnesium is the lightest engineering metal, and it has similar characteristics to aluminium; it has only a slightly lower melting point than aluminium, and like aluminium, it combines readily with oxygen. Unlike aluminium, it forms a porous oxide on its surface when attacked by air; this oxide is sufficient protection against corrosion when in dry air, but if the air is humid, and if it contains traces of salts, the corrosion resistance of this oxide is low, and so when magnesium is to be subjected to these conditions, it must be protected by paint or by lacquer.

Pure magnesium has a tensile strength of about 110 N/mm^2 as cast, but this can be improved to about 200 N/mm^2 by working; it is soft, and has a low modulus of elasticity.

Magnesium differs from most of the commoner metals, such as aluminium, iron, copper, and nickel, in that it has a hexagonal lattice structure; this arrangement does not allow 'slip' to occur easily, and therefore magnesium cannot be easily cold worked (its elongation is only about 5%); it can be hot worked fairly easily.

The Production of Magnesium

19.20 Magnesium is found in the ores **magnesite** ($MgCO_3$) and **dolomite** ($(CaMg)CO_3$), and also in sea water as magnesium chloride. Magnesium can be extracted by electrolysis, in a similar way to aluminium, or by fire reduction using coke. If the latter method is used, the elemental magnesium vapour and carbon oxides produced must be cooled quickly to prevent the oxygen and magnesium from combining during the cooling.

19.30 Magnesium Alloys

Magnesium is not strong enough to be used structurally without alloying. The strength of a metal can be increased by the addition of elements that enter into solid solution with it, elements that will form strengthening compounds, or elements that cause the alloy to respond to strengthening heat treatment. Due to the more unusual lattice structure of magnesium, only a few metals will form a solid solution with it; these include manganese and zinc, which can only enter into the solid solution in very small quantities, and aluminium and silver, which can be present in solid solution in slightly larger quantities. Figure 19.1 illustrates a portion of the magnesium-aluminium equilibrium diagram, and fig. 19.2 illustrates a portion of the magnesium-zinc equilibrium diagram; it will be seen that the solid solubility of zinc in magnesium and of aluminium in magnesium increases with temperature; when suitable amounts of these elements are present, the alloy will respond to strengthening heat treatment of the precipitation type. A small amount of 'rare earth metals' has a similar effect, but silver is often introduced with them to speed up the ageing.

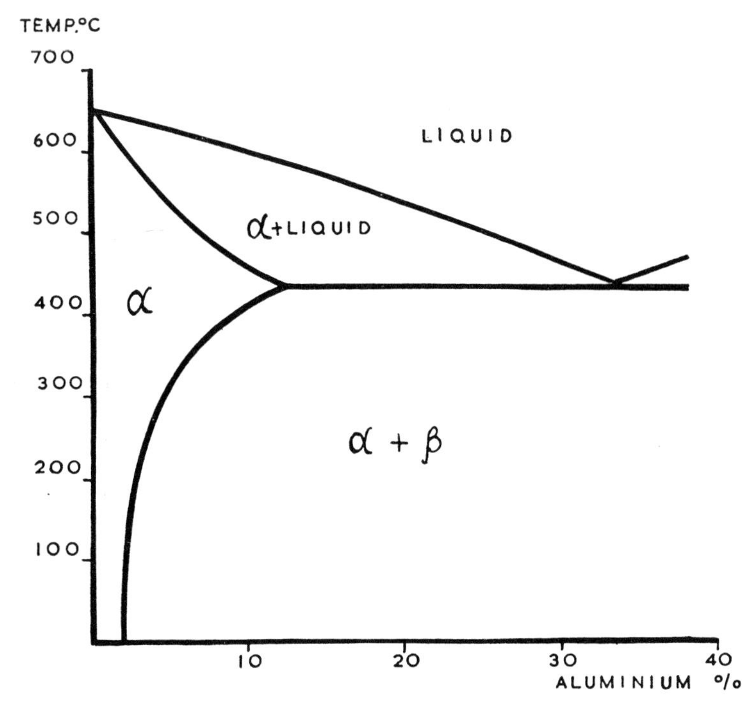

Fig. 19.1 Part of the Magnesium-aluminium Equilibrium Diagram

19.301 About 0·6% zirconium is included in many of the magnesium alloys to give a refined grain without the need for special heat treatment; up to about 3% thorium is introduced when improved creep resistance is required.
19.302 Magnesium-base alloys can be classed as **wrought alloys**, and **cast alloys**; some of these alloys will respond to heat treatment.

19.31 WROUGHT ALLOYS

These alloys can be grouped as follows:

1. Alloys with about 1·5% manganese.
2. Alloys with aluminium, zinc, and manganese.
3. Alloys with zinc and zirconium (alloys in this group with larger amounts of zinc can be heat treated).
4. Alloys with zinc, zirconium, and thorium (these are creep-resisting alloys).

19.32 CAST ALLOYS

These alloys can be grouped as follows:

1. Alloys with aluminium, zinc, and manganese (the cast alloys with these alloying elements are heat-treatable alloys).

2. Alloys with zirconium, zinc, and thorium } these alloys are heat-treatable and are creep-resisting.
   Alloys with zirconium and thorium
3. Alloys with zirconium, rare earth metals, and silver (these alloys can be heat treated).
4. Alloys with zinc and zirconium (some of these alloys can be heat treated).

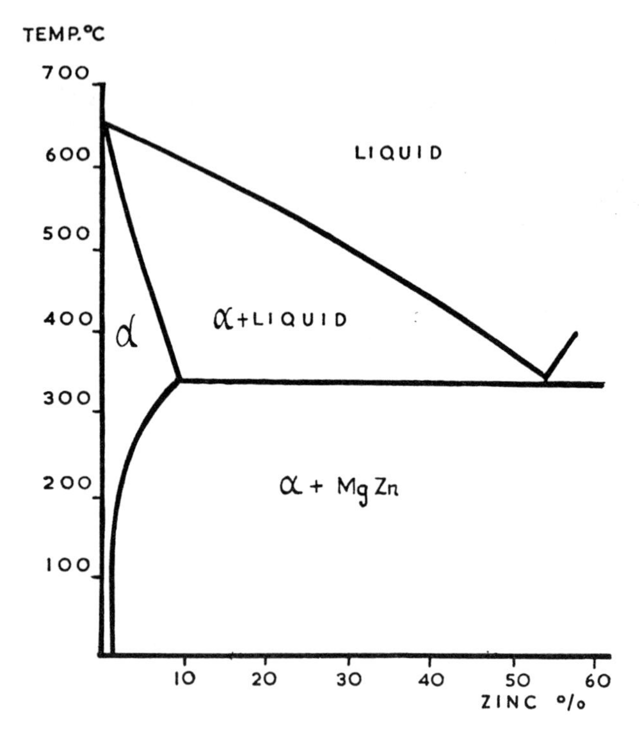

Fig. 19.2 Part of the Magnesium-zinc Equilibrium Diagram

19.40 The Heat Treatment of Magnesium Alloys

It has already been stated that magnesium alloys with a suitable amount of aluminium, zinc, or rare earth metals can be heat treated to improve their strength. The precise heat-treatment technique must be as specified by the material manufacturer, but it is similar to that done to the heat-treatable aluminium alloys. The treatment may be solution treatment followed by natural ageing, solution treatment followed by precipitation treatment, or it may be precipitation treatment without previous solution treatment. The material will be either air-cooled, or quenched after solution treatment, according to the manufacturers' instructions.

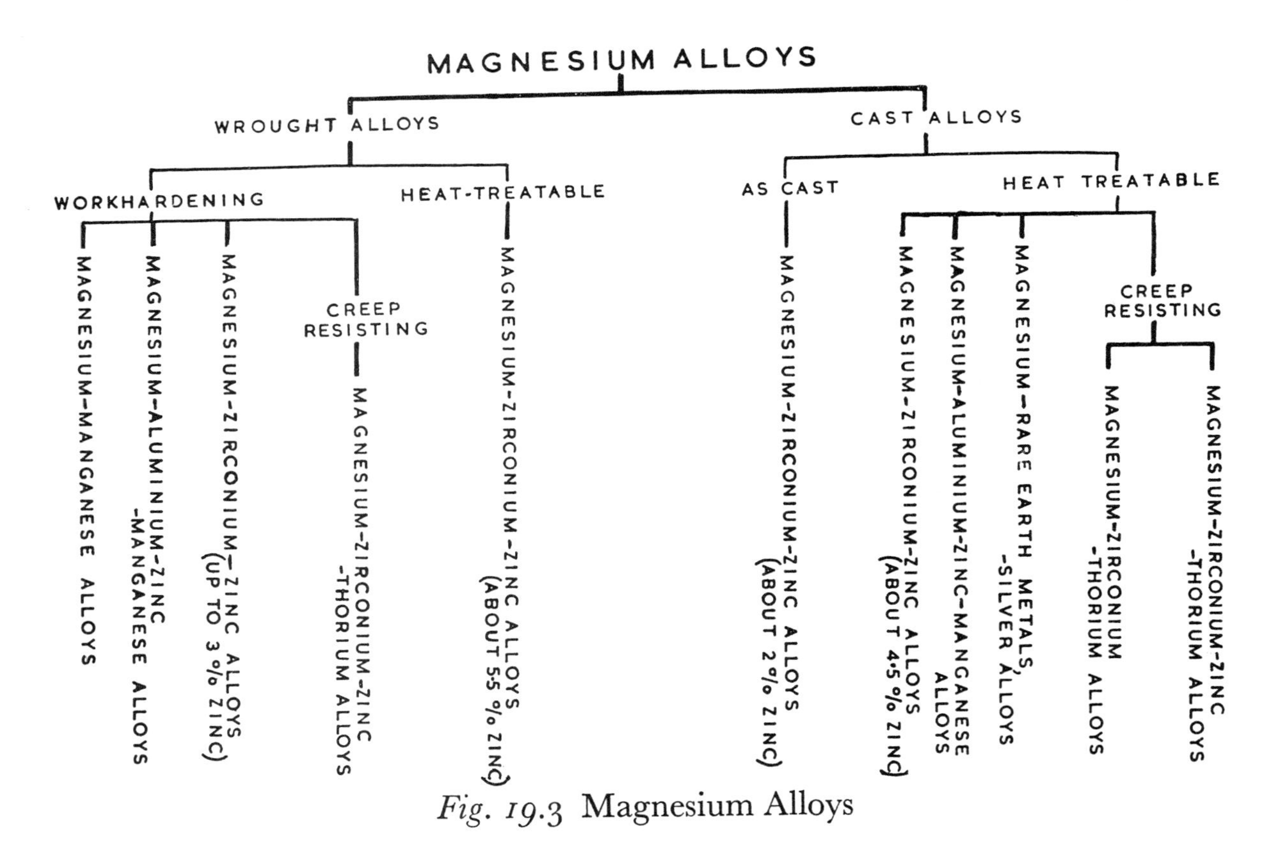

Fig. 19.3 Magnesium Alloys

19.50 The Fabrication of Magnesium Alloys

Magnesium alloys are available for casting by sand, gravity die-casting, and pressure die-casting; similarly, wrought alloys are available for rolling, forging, and extruding. In rolled material there is a difference between the properties obtained in the longitudinal and in the transverse directions; the tensile strength, proof stress and the percentage elongation being higher in the transverse direction.

19.51 These alloys can be cut at high speeds, but the tools should be sharp and the workpiece firmly clamped and supported to ensure a good finish. Magnesium alloys are normally machined dry, but if a coolant must be used, it must not be a water-base coolant. When magnesium is in a finely divided form it is inflammable, and so special precautions must be taken when machining; in addition to maintaining sharp cutting tools, these precautions include prevention of rubbing during the machining, frequent removal of swarf from the machine and surrounding floor, and installation of suitable dry fire-extinguisher agents.

19.52 Magnesium alloys can be joined by bolting or riveting, or by welding by argon-arc, oxy-acetylene, or electric resistance methods.

19.53 The surface of magnesium alloys can be protected against corrosion by painting; the surface must be degreased before painting, and for best results the surface should be chromated (see Chapter 28) so that it will retain its condition unchanged over a reasonable period. To avoid galvanic corrosion of magnesium alloys when in contact with other metals in the presence of an electrolyte such as moisture, the contact surfaces must be insulated; paint or jointing compound will suffice if the potential difference is small, as between magnesium and some aluminium alloys, but when magnesium is attached to steel, etc., a non-conducting gasket that projects beyond the area of contact must be used.

19.60 Some Applications of Magnesium Alloys

Cast magnesium alloys are sand cast for engine casing, and pressure die-cast for domestic and office equipment parts. Wrought magnesium alloys are extruded and used for step ladders and railings, and are forged for levers and brackets.

19.61 Magnesium alloys have been used more recently in nuclear engineering as a canning material for uranium because of their a low neutron absorption cross section (that is, they do not react to any marked degree with neutrons which pass through them).

REFERENCES

Publications issued by the Magnesium Industry Council, and by Magnesium Electron Ltd.

TABLE 19.1

THE MECHANICAL PROPERTIES OF SOME TYPICAL WROUGHT MAGNESIUM ALLOYS

Composition %	*Condition*	*Mechanical properties*			
		Tensile			*Hardness (HB)*
		0·1% *Proof stress* (N/mm^2)	*Tensile strength* (N/mm^2)	*Elongation% on* $5{\cdot}65\sqrt{S_0}$	
Manganese 1·5 Magnesium Balance (1353)	Plate	62	200–280	4–10	35–45
Aluminium 6·0 Zinc 1·0 Manganese 0·3	Forging	155–200	280–310	6–10	60–70
Zinc 5·5 Zirconium 0·6	Extrusions as extruded	200	300	7	65–80
	Extruded and heat-treated	220	310	6	65–80
Zinc 0·5 Zirconium 0·6 Thorium 0·75	Forging	125	230	6	50–65

TABLE 19.2

THE MECHANICAL PROPERTIES OF SOME TYPICAL CAST MAGNESIUM ALLOYS

Composition %	*Condition*	*Mechanical properties*			
		Tensile			*Hardness (HB)*
		0·1% *Proof stress* (N/mm^2)	*Tensile strength* (N/mm^2)	*Elongation% on* $5{\cdot}65\sqrt{S_0}$	
Aluminium 7·5–9·5 Zinc 0·3–1·5 Manganese 0·15 min Magnesium Balance	As cast	62–85	125–170	1–4	50–60
	Solution treated	62–85	190–250	3–7	50–60
	Fully heat-treated	77–115	190–250	1–2	70–80
Zinc 2·2 Zirconium 0·7 Thorium 3·0 Magnesium Balance	Fully heat-treated	77–93	190–220	4–7	50–60
Zirconium 0·6 Rare earth metals 2·5 Silver 2·5	Fully heat-treated	155	240	3	70–90

CHAPTER 20

ZINC AND ZINC-BASE ALLOYS

20.10 Although zinc is a weak metal it is used extensively in engineering in the form of die castings. The effect of corrosion is resisted by a dense layer of corrosion product that is formed on its surface, so that it is insulated against continued corrosion. It is used in the form of rolled sheets for roofing and battery containers; it is also used for transportation case lining because it can be made water- and air-tight, and is proof against insects and rodents.

Parts to be rendered corrosion resistant can be treated with zinc by plating, dipping, spraying, or by sherardising (see Chapter 28); underground pipe lines can be protected against the corrosive action of the soil by connecting them with insulated wires to zinc anodes that are buried nearby.

Zinc is also used as an alloy addition to strengthen other non-ferrous metals.

The Production of Zinc

20.20 Zinc ores are sulphides and carbonates; they are nearly always found with lead, and sometimes with silver, and so must be concentrated either by gravity or by flotation methods. The first step towards the production of zinc from the concentrated ores is a roasting process to form zinc oxide; sulphuric acid is a by-product when this is applied to the sulphide ores.

The oxide is then treated to produce the metallic zinc. The oldest process used is a thermal one in which the metallic zinc is produced as a vapour and then condensed; the metal so produced contains between 1 and 2% lead and is known as 'spelter'. A much purer zinc (about 99·99% pure) is produced by electrolysis, in which the roasted ore is dissolved in sulphuric acid which is purified and then subjected to electroysis. When an extremely pure zinc is required, a newer process is used, in which the roasted ore is mixed with carbon and briquetted before being heated in a continuously operating vertical retort. By fractionating, a zinc that is claimed to be one of the purest commercial metals is obtained.

Zinc Die-casting Alloys

20.30 Die casting is a rapid casting method that produces accurate and intricate castings that require little or no machining, and which enables studs and inserts to be cast in position. The success of die casting depends to a large extent upon the design of the part to be cast, so that a sound casting is produced with a maximum die life. Zinc alloys are good die-casting metals because they have a low melting temperature, and can be pressure die-cast by the hot-chamber system, which is the most rapid method; zinc alloys can be finished by painting or by electroplating. Die castings are used extensively in domestic appliances, optical instrument casings, television and sound-reproducing instrument parts, lightly stressed car parts, and for toys.

20.31 Zinc die-casting alloys contain a small amount of aluminium which strengthens the alloy and lowers its melting temperature. The portion of the zinc-aluminium equilibrium diagram shown in fig. 20.1 indicates that a small quantity of aluminium will enter into solid solution in zinc, and that the eutectic is produced when the aluminium content is about 5%. Zinc, like many cast alloys, undergoes **ageing**, which is aggravated by the rapid solidification associated with pressure die casting. As a result of ageing, the

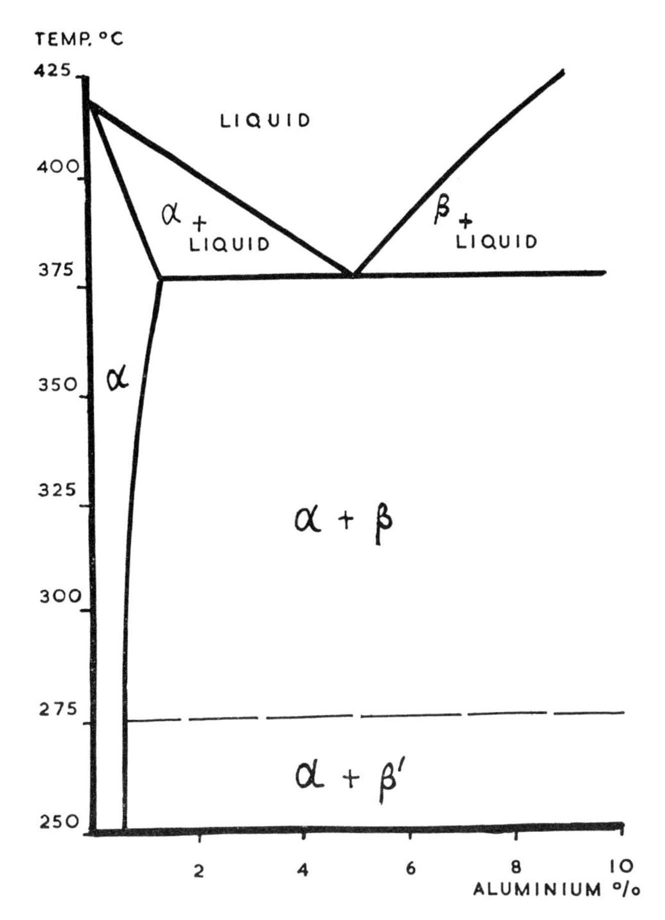

Fig. 20.1 Part of the Zinc-aluminium Equilibrium Diagram

tensile strength, hardness and impact strength falls, and the ductility rises; the actual properties after ageing depend upon the duration and the conditions during the ageing. It is customary to determine the mechanical properties of zinc die-casting alloys five weeks after casting; the properties so determined are called **original** properties. During ageing, die-cast parts will shrink, but after eight years this is less than 0·0015 mm/mm, which can be reduced if necessary by stabilising for a few hours at up to 100°C. before machining.

20.32 Two zinc-base die-casting alloys are covered by British Standards; these are known as Alloy 'A' and Alloy 'B'. An indication of the composition and the 'original' properties of these alloys is given in the following tables, but the manufacturers' specifications should be consulted if full details are required.

Alloy 'A'

Composition	4·1% aluminium; 0·05% magnesium: balance zinc
Tensile strength	285 N/mm²
Impact strength	57 J/cm² (Izod)
Percentage elongation	10·8% on $5{\cdot}65\sqrt{S_0}$
Brinell hardness	83

Alloy 'B'

Composition	4·1% aluminium; 1·0% copper: 0·05% magnesium
Tensile strength	330 N/mm²
Impact strength	58 J/cm² (Izod)
Percentage elongation	6·5% on $5{\cdot}65\sqrt{S_0}$
Brinell hardness	92

In both these alloys the zinc purity is at least 99·99%.

20.321 *Comparison Between Alloy 'A' and Alloy 'B'*. Alloy 'A' is the more satisfactory alloy for general purpose, and little use is made of Alloy 'B'. Alloy 'A' is the more ductile, but Alloy 'B' is stronger and harder. Alloy 'A' is the more dimensionally stable and will not suffer drop in impact strength or change of dimensions where the casting is subjected to heat when in service; Alloy 'B' is slightly easier to cast.

The temperature of the metal and of the die during casting will influence the properties of the casting, and manufacturers' instructions regarding casting conditions should be followed.

20.33 Fabrication of Zinc Die-casting Alloys

Zinc die-casting alloys can be machined by the normal techniques, and can be punched, bent, swaged, and spun. The ability of these alloys to be worked slightly is useful because shapes that are difficult to cast can often be produced by a final setting of the casting provided the section is thin enough.

Zinc alloy die castings cannot easily be soldered because of the aluminium content; castings have been soldered by plating the casting, and soldering on to the plated casting. Welding is not recommended except when a part cannot be replaced, or as an emergency repair; when welding is done, the filler rod must be of the same composition as the casting and a slightly reducing oxy-acetylene flame used.

REFERENCES

Publications issued by the Zinc Development Association and by the Zinc Die-Casters Association.

CHAPTER 21

NICKEL AND NICKEL ALLOYS

21.10 Nickel is a common constituent of the earth's crust, but it is only found in a few workable deposits, where it is mixed with copper ores; a complicated process is used to separate these two ores.

In many ways nickel is similar to iron. It has a slightly lower melting point, and is slightly stronger and harder; it is magnetic, but is more resistant than iron to corrosion and to loss of strength due to heating.

Nickel plating is used as an underplating before chromium plating to give protection against corrosion; it is the basis of many heat-resisting, and corrosion-resisting alloys. As stated in Chapters 14 and 15, nickel is alloyed with steel and cast iron to produce special properties.

The Production of Nickel

21.20 Nickel-bearing ores contain only about 2·5% nickel, together with large quantities of iron and silica, about 4% copper, and small amounts of cobalt, selenium, tellurium, silver, platinum, and gold; the nickel, copper, and iron are present in the ore as sulphides.

After mining, the ore is crushed, and the sulphides separated from the other rocks by flotation; the nickel sulphides and the copper sulphides are roughly separated by a further flotation process.

The nickel sulphides are roasted to remove a proportion of the sulphur and then tipped into a vessel that is similar to a Bessemer converter, where a considerable proportion of the impurities is removed by oxidation.

After the oxidation process, the product, consisting of about 48% nickel and 27% copper, is heated with sodium sulphate and coke to produce a mixture of molten copper, nickel, and iron sulphides, which are poured into large pots to solidify. During cooling, the copper and sodium sulphides rise to the top; when solid, the nickel and the copper can be separated by blows from a heavy hammer.

The nickel sulphide is sintered to produce an oxide that can be subjected to final refining by electrolysis, or by the 'carbonyl process'. The electrolytic refining process is employed when ample electric power is available, and is similar to that used in the production of copper. In the carbonyl process, the raw material is crushed, then roasted to remove the remaining sulphur and metals, and then reduced using hydrogen so that the metal oxide is removed in the form of steam; the reduced material is passed to the volatisers, where it is converted into gaseous nickel carbonyl by a stream of carbon monoxide. After passing through a series of volatisers, the gas is decomposed in a tower by percolating it through nickel pellets so that it deposits its nickel on the pellets as a series of coatings.

21.30 THE PRINCIPAL USES OF COMMERCIALLY PURE NICKEL

Commercially pure nickel is used for anodes, cathodes, and support wires in radio valves; it is also used in chemical- and food-processing plant. Nickel-clad steel is often used in chemical and petroleum industries when both strength and corrosion resistance is required; steel clad with nickel of 10–20% of the total thickness gives the advantages of both materials at a compromise cost.

21.31 Nickel can be hot or cold worked, and is suitable for forging, cupping, drawing, spinning, swaging, bending, and forming. It may be softened by annealing, and it can be joined by soft soldering, brazing, and welding by gas, arc, and resistance methods. Nickel must be machined by high speed steel tools ground with sharp cutting edges; the cutting speeds and feeds must not be excessive, and the work must be flooded with cutting compound during the machining operation.

Nickel Alloys

(The trade names quoted are those of Messrs. Henry Wiggin & Co. Ltd.)

21.40 NICKEL-IRON ALLOYS

Alloys of nickel and iron are used where controlled low and intermediate coefficients of thermal expansion are required, as in precision machines, glass-to-metal seals, and thermostats. A range of nickel-iron alloys are marketed under the trade name **Nilo.**

21.41 *Alloys of Iron and between* 36 *and* 50% *Nickel.* **Nilo 36**, containing 36% nickel, has an almost negligible coefficient of expansion at normal atmospheric temperature, and is used for length standards, measuring tapes, pendulum rods, and precision machine parts. It is used in thermostats operating up to 100°C. **Nilo 40** and **Nilo 42**, containing 40 and 42% nickel respectively, are used in thermostats for electric and gas cooker ovens; **Nilo 42** forms the core of copper-clad wires used for sealing into the glass envelopes of electric lamp bulbs, radio valves, and television tubes.

21.42 **Nilo 48** and **Nilo 50**, with 48 and 50% of nickel respectively are used mainly for sealing into the soft glasses used in radio valves and electronic equipment.

21.43 *Alloy of Iron, with* 29% *Nickel and* 17% *Cobalt* (**Nilo K**). The expansion of this alloy is very similar to that of medium-hard glasses of the borosilicate type used for envelopes for special high-power valves; it is used for glass-to-metal seals on X-ray tubes and numerous electronic components.

21.5 NICKEL-MOLYBDENUM ALLOYS

The corrosion resistance of nickel, and nickel containing a small percentage of iron, can be improved by the addition of molybdenum. The alloy **Corronel B** is a typical wrought alloy of this type, and contains 66% nickel, 28% molybdenum, and 6% iron; its properties can be controlled by the extent of cold working, but the high strength (930 N/mm^2) and hardness (250 HV) of the annealed alloy is usually high enough. If an improved hardness and strength is required, it can be hardened after annealing by a prolonged heating at 750°C. to develop about 350 HV; this treatment is usually unnecessary. **Corronel B** can be forged, machined at low cutting speeds, and is readily welded.

21.60 NICKEL-COPPER ALLOYS

Nickel and copper form a solid solution in all proportions (see the nickel-copper equilibrium diagram on page 154), and so they produce a wrought alloy. A range of copper-nickel alloys are available in the form of castings, sheet, strip, tube, wire, rods, and sections.

21.61 Monel is an alloy that contains about 66% nickel and 33% copper with up to about 2% manganese. It is a wrought alloy with a tensile strength of up to about 840 N/mm² and a hardness of about 200 HV, depending upon the extent and the method of working employed. Casting **Monel** alloys contain up to 4% silicon; the strength of these casting alloys increases with the silicon content, and can be as high as 700 N/mm² with a hardness of about 260 HV.

Ordinary wrought and cast nickel-copper alloys are not heat-treatable, but the addition of between 2 and 4% aluminium to the wrought alloys enables them to respond to solution treatment followed by precipitation treatment; the tensile strength of a fully heat-treated alloy of this type can be as high as 1500 N/mm² and its hardness about 340 HV. These alloys are marketed under the trade name **K Monel**.

21.62 Monel resists attack by acids and alkalis, gases, and sea water; it also retains its strength at high temperatures. It is used for pump parts, steam turbine blades, motor boat propellor shafts, food-handling equipment, laundry equipment, and for surgical apparatus. Due to its excellent corrosion and heat resistance it is used for electrical terminal nuts and bolts, and for electrical water heater parts.

21.63 These alloys can be fabricated by the usual methods, and machined and joined easily, provided the recommended techniques are used. Steel can be clad with **Monel** when high strength and good corrosion resistance is required.

21.70 NICKEL-CHROMIUM ALLOYS

These alloys are used when resistance to high temperature oxidation is required; they are based on an 80/20 nickel-chromium solution.

21.71 INCONEL

This is an alloy of 76% nickel and 15% chromium with the balance mainly iron; it resists corrosion by many inorganic and organic compounds, and also resists attack by oxidising atmospheres at high temperatures. It has a tensile strength of about 1080 N/mm² and can be hot or cold worked; with care it can be cast, and in cast form it has a tensile strength of about 500 N/mm². It can be joined by the normal methods.

Inconel is used in food, chemical, and textile-processing plant, and also for heat-treatment equipment and for steam turbine parts.

21.72 BRIGHTRAY

Alloys in this group are used for electrical furnace-heating elements.

21.73 THE NIMONIC SERIES

This range of basically 80/20 nickel-chromium alloys was developed originally for use in gas turbine engines, where high strength at high temperatures and resistance to oxidation and to creep is required. These alloys can be formed by spinning, rolling, and pressing; they can be joined by argon-arc and by electrical resistance welding. The **Nimonic** alloys are tough and work harden easily, and so cutting tools must be sharp, with smooth cutting surfaces, and must cut at a slow speed with small feed rate, and be well lubricated; the tool and the workpiece must both be rigid.

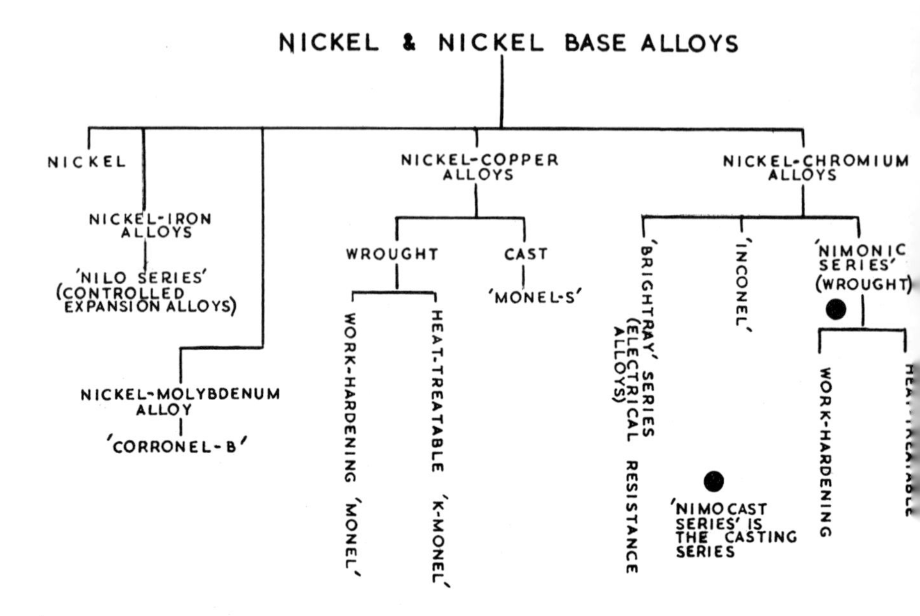

Fig. 21.1 Nickel and Nickel-base Alloys

The heat-treatment of suitable alloys consists of solution-treatment followed by precipitation-treatment. The solution-treatment involves heating to about 1100°C, depending on the alloy, and either free cooling or quenching, again depending upon the alloy. The precipitation-treatment is usually at a high temperature, but the temperature and cooling depends upon the alloy. The manufacturer's instructions must be followed regarding both the temperatures and cooling rate.

The Nimocast Series of alloys is the casting equivalent of the Nimonic Series. Some Nimocast alloys are suitable for air-casting but many of them are intended for vacuum melting. Most of the alloys are used in the 'as cast' condition, but some of them can be strengthened by a similar heat-treatment to that applied to the Nimonic alloys.

REFERENCES

Publications issued by Messrs. Henry Wiggin & Co. Ltd. and by the International Nickel Co. (Mond) Ltd.

TABLE 21.1

TYPICAL NIMONIC ALLOYS

Alloy	*Composition*	*Approx tensile strength (N/mm^2)*	*Applications*
Nimonic 75	Contains 75% nickel, 20% chromium, 4% iron, with small quantity of carbon and titanium. This is a work-hardening alloy.	750	A high temperature alloy for sheet metal work in gas turbines, heat-treament equipment and nuclear engineering.
Nimonic 80A	Similar to Nimonic 75, but with 2·4% titanium and 1·4% aluminium to enable it to respond to precipitation treatment.	1200 after heat-treatment	Creep resisting, for service up to about 815°C. For gas turbine blades etc. and i.c. engine exhaust valves.
Nimonic 81	Similar to Nimonic 80A, but with 66% nickel and 30% chromium. Chromium increased to give improved corrosion resistance.	1200 after heat-treatment	For gas turbine blades and i.c. engine exhaust valves.
Nimonic 90	Developed from Nimonic 80A by reducing the nickel content to 59% and introducing 16·5% cobalt to strengthen the alloy by entering the nickel-chromium solid solution.	1200 after heat-treatment	Creep resisting, for service up to 920°C. For gas turbine blades etc.
Nimonic 105	Developed from Nimonic 80A and 90 by reducing the chromium content to about 15% to allow more titanium and aluminium to enter the solid solution.	1200 after heat-treatment	Creep resisting, for service up to 940°C. For gas turbine blades, discs and shafts.
Nimonic 115	Similar to Nimonic 105 but with more titanium and aluminium.	1300 after heat-treatment	Creep resisting, for service up to 980°C. For gas turbine blades.
Nimonic 263	Developed by Rolls-Royce to meet creep criteria. It is a nickel-chromium-cobalt alloy containing 6% molybdenum, 2% titanium and 0·4% aluminium. This alloy has a good formability.	1000 after heat-treatment	For creep resistance at up to 850°C. Used for gas turbine rings and sheet metal components.

CHAPTER 22

TITANIUM AND TITANIUM-BASE ALLOYS

22.10 Titanium is the fourth most abundant structural metal in the earth's crust but although first detected in 1789, it was not produced in economic quantities until 1949, because special techniques had to be developed for its extraction due to the great affinity of titanium for oxygen.

Titanium has a tensile strength of about 470 N/mm², and a density about 56% that of steel; this excellent strength/weight ratio, combined with very good corrosion resistance, makes it a very useful structural metal. The strength of titanium falls with temperature, and its effective temperature limit is about 500°C.; titanium is much better than other light alloys in this respect.

The Production of Titanium

22.20 Most titanium is found as an oxide, or as an oxide combined with the oxides of other elements such as iron and silicon. The great affinity of titanium for oxygen has already been noted; this, together with the effect of oxygen upon the properties of titanium, makes it impossible for titanium to be extracted directly from its oxide. Titanium tetrachloride is first produced by heating titanium oxide with carbon and chlorine, and this is reduced either by magnesium or by sodium at about 800–900°C. The product of this reduction is titanium mixed with magnesium chloride or with sodium chloride, according to the process used; the chloride is removed by a further process.

The melting and casting of titanium into ingots requires special techniques because it attacks refractory oxides, and because it must be melted out of contact with air. Titanium is melted using a consumable electrode of raw titanium mixed with the alloying elements and compacted into shape. The electrode so produced is suspended from the top of the furnace; when the furnace has been evacuated, the arc is struck between this electrode and powdered titanium in a water-cooled crucible at the bottom of the furnace, where the titanium collects. An argon atmosphere can be used as an alternative to vacuum melting.

The ingots produced by this method weigh 1 or 2 tonnes, and are heated in an electric furnace before being forged into shape ready for rolling, drawing, or extrusion.

The Grades of Commercially Pure Titanium

22.30 Small amounts of oxygen and nitrogen will enter into titanium to form a solid solution; the strength and hardness of commercially pure titanium increases with increase in the quantity of these elements present, so that a range of grades of commercially pure titanium can be produced with tensile strengths from 400 N/mm² up to about 770 N/mm²; the ductility of these grades falls as the purity is reduced.

Titanium-base Alloys

22.40 Aluminium, copper, manganese, molybdenum, tin, vanadium, and zirconium can be alloyed with titanium to give improved strength and to produce other effects. The following titanium alloys are currently in use:

22.41 *Titanium Alloy Containing 2% Copper.* This is a ductile heat-treatable alloy that can be solution treated for between 30 minutes and 1 hour at 790°C. to develop a tensile strength of 500–700 N/mm². It can then be given precipitation treatment at 400°C. to develop a tensile strength of 700–820 N/mm²; this precipitation treatment is slow, and it may take 7 days. This alloy is usually used in sheet form but can be forged if necessary.

22.42 *Titanium Alloy Containing 2% Aluminium and 2% Manganese.* This alloy combines strength and malleability and can be readily forged at between 700 and 900°C. Its tensile strength is 630–800 N/mm², and it is usually used in the annealed condition; annealing is done at about 700°C. and takes about 30 minutes.

22.43 *Titanium Alloy Containing 4% Aluminium and 4% Manganese.* This is a stronger version of the above alloy with a tensile strength of about 950 N/mm²; this can be increased to about 1260 N/mm² by solution treatment followed by precipitation treatment.

22.44 *Titanium Alloy Containing 5% Aluminium and 2½% Tin.* This alloy has a tensile strength of about 770 N/mm², and is used when an easily formed and welded alloy is required, but where the strength must be higher than that of a commercially pure titanium.

22.45 *Titanium Alloy Containing 6% Aluminium and 4% Vanadium.* This has a tensile strength of about 950 N/mm², which can be raised to about 1100 N/mm² by water quenching from about 925°C., followed by 2 hours' ageing at 480°C. This treatment also improves the creep resistance, and this can be improved further by special cooling techniques.

22.46 *Titanium Alloy Containing Tin, Zirconium, Aluminium, Molybdenum, and Silicon.* This is a creep-resisting alloy with a tensile strength of 1000 N/mm². It can be forged with care, and can be heat-treated by a short duration solution treatment followed by a lengthy ageing treatment.

22.47 The cooling of the above alloys after solution treatment and precipitation treatment is done in air; the manufacturer's instructions for both this heat treatment and for annealing should be followed.

22.50 The Fabrication of Titanium-base Alloys

Forging. Titanium alloys can be forged in the same way as low carbon steels, except that they must be held at high temperatures for only a short time to minimise surface contamination.

Forming. These alloys can be formed by pressing, stretch forming, and spinning. During the annealing prior to these operations, care must be taken to avoid scaling, and an electric furnace should be used for this heating.

Machining. This offers no special problems, but the cutting tool and the workpiece must be rigid, and low cutting speeds and coarse feeds should be used.

Welding, Brazing, and Soldering. Fusion welding can be done, but it is necessary to use the argon-arc process to avoid scaling of the surface; resistance welding does not normally require a shielding gas because of the short duration of the heating. The brazing of titanium alloys does not present any special problems provided that suitable filler rods are used so that the base metal is not attacked. Very little soldering of titanium alloys has yet been done, other than using electrochemical deposition of silver, copper or tin, and then soldering on to the surface so produced.

Surface Treatment. The scaling caused by heating titanium and titanium-base alloys in air can be removed by a modified caustic soda, by pickling, or by grit blasting. These materials can be electroplated, but the adhesion is not as good as in the case of steel. Titanium can be anodised, but anodised titanium shows no affinity for dyestuffs; anodising can be done to protect the surface from contamination during the heating that preceeds hot working.

REFERENCES

Publications issued by Imperial Chemical Industries Ltd.

CHAPTER 23

NON-METALLIC MATERIALS

ABRASIVES

Abrasives are usually classified as (i) natural abrasives and (ii) manufactured abrasives.

The natural abrasives include the mineral **corundum** (Al_2O_3), **emery** (a mixture of corundum and the iron oxide **magnetite**), **garnet** (a common garnet is **almandine** ($Fe_3Al_2(SiO_4)_3$)), and **sand** (SiO_2).

The principal manufactured abrasives are **aluminium oxide** and **silicon carbide**. The aluminium oxide used in grinding wheels is a pure form of the natural mineral corundum; silicon carbide (SiC) does not exist naturally, and is produced by heating sand and coke in an electric furnace.

Abrasives are used in suspension in paraffin or water for lapping and polishing, as coated cloth, or bonded to form abrasive slips and grinding wheels. The pieces of abrasive material are crushed and ground into smaller pieces or grains; these grains are graded according to size. They are bonded with a suitable agent that holds each grain in place until it has become too blunt for efficient cutting.

ASBESTOS

This term is applied to a group of minerals that can be separated easily into fibres and spun or woven into fabrics. Asbestos is fire-resisting, has a low heat conductivity and high electrical resistance, is chemically inert, and free from decay. It is used in roofing cements and tiles, fireproof paints, and building sheets; it is also used as an insulating material, and reinforced with brass threads for brake linings and clutch facings (the brass threads also conduct away the heat generated).

CERAMICS

Ceramics are used as cutting tool materials (see page 216, section 26.80), as extrusion dies, and as a refractory coating applied to materials used for rocket casings.

CONCRETE

Concrete is made by mixing cement, aggregates, and water to produce an artificial stone.

Cement. Two main types of cement are used; these are Portland cement and high alumina cement. Portland cement is composed of chemical compounds formed by mixing substances that contain calcium carbonate (for example, chalk) with substances containing silica, alumina, and iron oxide (for example, clay); the mix is heated and the clinker is ground to form a powder. Portland cement is available in a number of grades to cover a range of applications. High alumina cement sets slowly but it hardens rapidly;

it is more resistant than Portland cement to the action of chemicals such as sulphates.

Aggregates. This term is used to describe the gravels, stones, and sand which are mixed with cement and water to form concrete; about 75% of the volume of concrete is aggregate. Aggregates should be at least as hard as the hardened cement, should be durable, and also be clean; the maximum size of aggregate depends upon the type of work to be done. The proportion of the mix depends upon the application; a typical mix contains 1 cement: 2 fine aggregate: 4 coarse aggregate by volume.

Reinforced Concrete. Concrete is good in compression but poor in tension; steel reinforcing bars are introduced to take the tensile loading and to assist in carrying the compressive loads.

Pre-stressed Concrete is used for such structures as bridges and reservoirs; and for pre-cast products such as railway sleepers, telegraph poles, and floor beams. The two main methods of stressing are **pre-tensioning** and **post-tensioning**. In pre-tensioning, the high-tensile steel is stretched and secured, the concrete cast in place and allowed to harden, and the steel released so that the stresses are transferred from the reinforcement wires to the concrete. In post-tensioning, the wire is coated so that it can move in the concrete which is cast around it; the wire is stretched when the concrete is set. Post-tensioning is used for bridges and other large work.

DIAMOND

Diamond is the purest form of crystallised carbon, and is the hardest known material. It is used as a cutting tool material (see page 216, section 26.70), as a spindle bearing material, and as a stylus material for sound reproduction.

GLASS

Glass is produced by heating silica (sand) with carbonate of potash or soda, lime, and other substances; these fuse together at about 1500°C. to form glass.

The properties of glass can be controlled by composition. Flint glass and Crown glass are two grades of optical glass. Flint glass is optically dense and contains lead; it has a high refractive index and a low dispersive power. Crown glass has a low dispersive power; the dispersive power can be taken as the ability to break up white light to produce a spectrum. Lenses of crown glass and lenses of flint glass are cemented together to form an **achromatic doublet** to minimise the coloured fringes seen around the image of a bright object.

Glass is hard and brittle; when a safety glass is required, a glass that has been toughened by heat treatment or a glass that is laminated with sheets of a plastics material is used. Glass can be blown into bottle-like shapes, or cast and rolled into shape; fibre glass is produced by spinning glass into fine fibres so that it can be woven into shape by textile techniques, and laminated by impregnating each sheet with a thermosetting plastics material and building up to the required thickness before curing the plastics material (see page 193).

PLASTICS—see Chapter 24.

OILS

Oils are used in engineering for lubrication, corrosion prevention, as the operating medium in hydraulic systems, for heat-treatment quenching baths, and as an electrical insulation material (oil-impregnated silk and paper is also used for electrical insulation).

RUBBER

Both natural and synthetic rubbers are used in engineering; the latter are produced to a range of special properties. Both natural and synthetic raw rubbers are composed of long molecules that are kinked and coiled when unstressed, but which can be straightened out under tension. Sulphur is the usual agent used in the vulcanising process, in which raw rubber is mixed with the agent and other ingredients, and then heated under pressure to produce a cross-linking of the molecules (similar to the curing of thermosetting plastics—para 24.30). A range of properties can be obtained depending upon the ingredients and the vulcanising process. Rubber is used for resilient mountings because of its ability to stretch and recover, for packing and sealing because it retains elastic pressure over long periods, and for transmission belting and tyres because it has good frictional grip. It has a high abrasion resistance, and is a good electrical insulator.

TIMBER

Constructional timber is classed as **soft wood** and **hard wood**. The soft woods are obtained from coniferous trees; typical soft woods are pine, spruce, larch, and lime. The hard woods are obtained from non-coniferous trees; typical hard woods are oak, teak, ash, beech, mahogany, lignum vitae, and elm.

Timber is used for foundry patterns, tool handles, railway sleepers, etc.

Cermets

Cermets are a class of materials that are a mixture of both metals and ceramics to combine the high temperature strength of ceramics with the ductility and toughness of metals. The ceramics include oxides, carbides and nitrides, and the metal can be any pure metal or an alloy; the ceramic to metal ratio depends upon the properties required. Titanium carbide base and aluminium oxide base are the more important cermets; the sintered carbides used as cutting tool materials can be included by definition.

Cermets must be produced by powder metallurgy (para. 4.40); some roughing can be done prior to the final sintering operation, greater accuracy and finish can be obtained by final grinding, and very fine finishes by lapping and polishing. Titanium carbide cermets can be joined by silver soldering, but aluminium oxide cermets should be mechanically joined. Cermets are produced in standard rods, tubes, plates, etc., but complicated non-standard shapes can also be produced. These materials are currently being developed for certain turbine parts and for bearings, but they are not as good in impact as high temperature alloys.

CHAPTER 24

PLASTICS IN ENGINEERING

24.10 A plastics material can be defined as '*an organic material which at some time in its history is capable of flow, and which, upon the application of adequate heat and pressure, can be caused to flow, and to take up a desired shape, which will be retained when the applied heat and pressure are withdrawn.* Plastics materials are composed of long molecular chains which produce many of the properties associated with these materials.

24.20 THERMOPLASTIC PLASTCIS MATERIALS

Plastics of this type can be softened and resoftened indefinitely by the application of heat and pressure, but the temperature must not be too high otherwise decomposition will take place.

The following diagram represents the structure of a thermosoftening plastics material.

—M—M—M—M—M—M—M—M—

—M—M—M—M—M—M—M—M—

—M—M—M—M—M—M—M—M—

Fig. 24.1

In this diagram 'M' represents a molecule, or a so-called '**monomer**'. A monomer is a substance that is capable of joining up with other monomers to form chains of great length. In the case of '**co-polymers**', there may be two or three different monomers in each chain; these may be distributed along the chains at random, or in blocks of a similar kind. In actual materials, these chains will be tangled.

When these materials are heated, the chains move apart, and under pressure slide past each other to take up new positions, which are retained when the heat and pressure are removed.

Plastics materials of this type are of varying rigidity, depending upon the structure of the basic material (called the **binder**) and the other materials that are added. These other materials include a large quantity of **filler**, to produce strength; they also include very small amounts of colouring matter and plasticiser. The plasticiser is a softening agent that acts as an internal lubricant to allow the chains to move more freely.

Thermoplastic plastics materials reach the manipulator in the form of sheets, films (thin sheets), rods, tubes, and moulding materials; they can be formed or shaped at temperatures slightly higher than that of boiling water, and require very little force to change their shape; they can be joined by using a suitable solvent, or in some cases by the application of heat and suitable pressure.

These materials do not melt, but flow at suitable temperatures and pressures; they are particularly suitable for injection moulding and extrusion.

They behave like glass when blown, and can be formed into bottle and dome-like shapes by pressure or vacuum techniques.

24.30 THERMOSETTING (OR THERMOHARDENING) MATERIALS

These materials undergo a chemical change when they are subjected to the action of heat and pressure, after which they cannot be changed by the application of further heating and pressure.

The following diagram represents the structure of a thermosetting plastics material.

```
 |  |  |  |  |  |  |  |  |  |
—M—M—M—M—M—M—M—M—M—M—
 |  |  |  |  |  |  |  |  |  |
—M—M—M—M—M—M—M—M—M—M—
 |  |  |  |  |  |  |  |  |  |
—M—M—M—M—M—M—M—M—M—M—
 |  |  |  |  |  |  |  |  |  |
—M—M—M—M—M—M—M—M—M—M—
 |  |  |  |  |  |  |  |  |  |
```

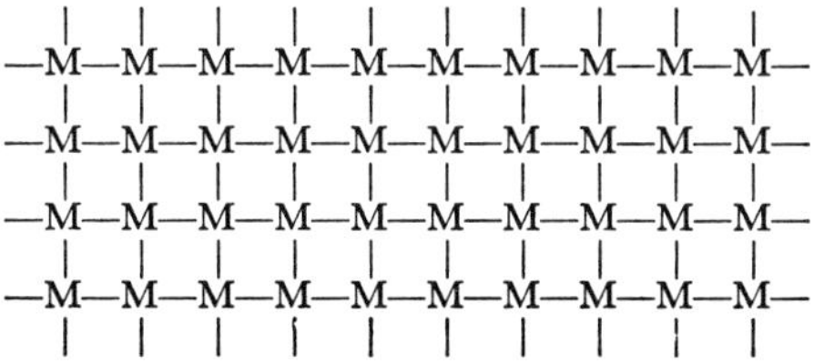

Fig. 24.2

During the production of these materials they are partly changed and reach the manipulator in a thermosoftening condition; as a result of further heating and pressure, the cross links are produced so that definite distances are maintained between the chains, and they are prevented from sliding past each other. Thermosetting plastics materials are therefore rigid and are insoluble because it is virtually impossible for a solvent to enter between the chains to disperse them. In actual materials, the chains will be tangled as well as cross-linked; the heating process that develops the cross-linking is sometimes called **'curing'**.

Thermosetting plastics materials reach the manipulator as moulding powders, resins for casting or for use in a lay-up process, or as paper or cloth that has been impregnated with resin.

These materials include, in addition to the basic material, a **filler, colouring matter**, a **plasticiser**, a **hardening agent** (to produce the cross-linking), and an **accelerator** (to speed up the action of the hardening agent).

The Characteristics, Structure and Manufacture of Some Typical Plastics Materials

24.40 The first step towards the production of a plastics material is to produce a suitable unit from which to build the long chains. The unit is known as the monomer; monomers can be joined by **polymerisation** (to produce a polymer), or by **condensation**, depending upon the material. Alternatively a natural longchain molecule material such as cellulose can be used.

The monomer can be produced in many ways, depending upon the raw material that is available and the monomer required.

In this section, the structure and the *construction* of some typical plastics materials is illustrated, and the characteristics and applications of the common plastics materials are listed.

24.41 THERMOPLASTIC PLASTICS MATERIALS

Polythene is an example of a simple plastics material; it is produced by the polymerisation of ethylene. Ethylene is produced from petroleum, from coal gas, or by fermentation of molasses. The actual polymer contains over 1000 ethylene units. The following diagrams illustrate the 'construction' of polythene from ethylene.

```
H  H        H  H  H  H  H  H  H  H  H
|  |        |  |  |  |  |  |  |  |  |
C=C   →   —C—C—C—C—C—C—C—C—C—
|  |        |  |  |  |  |  |  |  |  |
H  H        H  H  H  H  H  H  H  H  H
ethylene              polythene
```

This material is available as low-density polythene, high-density polythene, and high-molecular-weight polythene. Low-density polythene is used for thin-walled flexible tubing, piping-cable insulation, thin extruded films, and blown forms such as bottles. The high-density polythene has a higher softening-point, and is stronger and more rigid; it is used where hot liquids and steam must be resisted. Typical applications of high-density polythene are test tubes and similar laboratory ware, bowls and jugs, valves and taps for petrol and paraffin containers, shockproof housings for power tools and appliances, and lighting fittings. The high-molecular-weight polythene is tough and hard, and has high electrical resistance; it is used in papermaking gears, which are lubricated with oil and water emulsion.

Polyvinyl Chloride (p.v.c. polymer) illustrates the formation of a double-bonded monomer which is in turn polymerised.

```
H  H              H  Cl         H  Cl H  Cl H  Cl H  Cl
|  | + Cl         |  |          |  |  |  |  |  |  |  |
C=C          →    C=C     →   —C—C—C—C—C—C—C—C—
|  |              |  |          |  |  |  |  |  |  |  |
H  H              H  H          H  H  H  H  H  H  H  H
ethylene       chloro-ethylene        polymer chloride
+ chlorine     (or vinyl chloride     (p.v.c. polymer)
               monomer)
```

This plastics material is available in a range of grades, controlled by the method of manufacture, and by the addition of ingredients such as plasticisers, lubricants, etc. It can be extruded into bottle-like shapes, and rolled into thin sheets, which can be embossed to produce leather substitute. It is used for such widely ranging applications as insulation for electrical wiring, window curtain material, motor-car lining and upholstery, flooring material, toys, pipes, and gutterings.

Polystyrene is an example of a plastics material, the long chain molecules of which includes groups. This material is produced by joining phenyl (C_6H_5) to ethylene, to produce the monomer 'styrene'; styrene is then made into polystyrene by polymerisation.

```
H  H               H  H            H  H      H  H      H  H      H
|  | + C6H5        |  |            |  |      |  |      |  |      |
C=C           →    C=C       →   —C—C——C—C——C—C——C—
|  |               |  |            |  |      |  |      |  |      |
H  H               H  C6H5         H  C6H5 H  C6H5 H  C6H5 H
ethylene           styrene                  polystyrene
+ phenyl
```

Polytetrafluoroethylene (PTFE) is a similar material to polythene, but it consists entirely of carbon and fluorine atoms.

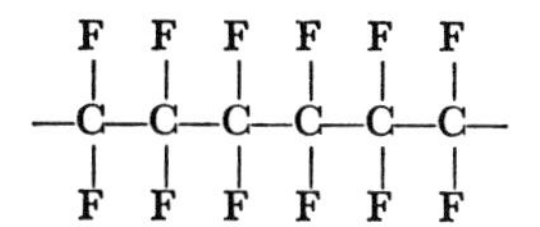

It is non-inflammable, has a high softening-point, a good resistance to chemical or solvent action, and a very low frictional resistance. It is used for acid-plant gaskets, ignition-cable sheathing, bearings, and cathode-ray tube holders.

Polymethyl methacrylate. This is available as sheets (perspex) and moulding powder (diakon). It has good light transmission, good weather-resistance, and is fairly tough. It is used as a substitute for glass, where the latter cannot be used. In sheet form, it is used for machine guards, windshields, and display fittings, and is moulded into brush handles, hair-dryer casings, telephone cases, and radio dials and panels.

24.42 CONDENSATION POLYMERS, INCLUDING POLYESTERS

Condensation polymerisation implies that a chain is produced by 'dove-tailing' dissimilar molecules by means of a chemical change, which usually eliminates a third product that is not part of the final product. These plastics are thermosoftening if cross-links are not developed, and thermohardening if cross-links are developed.

Polyamides (the 'nylon' materials). These are so named because the polymer consists of short carbon chains that are linked by amide groups. (Amide groups contain nitrogen, hydrogen, carbon, and oxygen.) The various 'nylons' are designated by numbers that indicate the number of carbon atoms in the 'starting materials'. Nylon is used in monofilament form for brushes; and as mouldings for gears, self-locking nuts, door mechanisms, fuel-tank caps and floats, and bearings.

Polyesters (N.B. acid + alcohol → ester + water). Polyethylene terephthalate, Terylene, can be treated during its manufacture to produce a tough material that can be extruded as film, or treated to make it very strong, and suitable for use in capacitors, printed circuits, magnetic recording tape, and typewriter ribbons.

24.43 THERMOSETTING PLASTICS MATERIALS

Phenolic plastics. These are produced from phenol and formaldehyde, in the presence of an acid, if the product is to be suitable as a moulding powder that develops cross-links when combined with a hardener. When produced from phenol and formaldehyde in the presence of an alkaline catalyst, the product is a resin that easily cures without a hardener when finally heated. By variation of procedure and of filler material, a range of phenolic plastics can be produced. Typical applications are distributor caps, electric plugs, and door handles.

Aminoplastics ('amino'—from ammonia—refers to the chemical nature of these plastics). Urea formaldehyde is used in the production of thin-walled articles such as cups and tumblers, and for tough electrical fittings. Melamine formaldehyde is harder and stronger, and is used for the moulding of plates and dishes.

Polyurethanes (these contain the 'urethane link'). Materials in this group are used as foam for seats and arm rests, and as a hard, tough, and high chemical-resistance coating material that can be pigmented.

Epoxy resins. In these materials, an ether with an 'epoxy' ending, that can be used at a later stage to produce the linking, is produced. These resins are used in laminating, and in glass-reinforced plastics.

Laminates. In the high-pressure laminates, the sheets are fibrous or porous materials, and are bonded into a solid mass by using an impregnating resin. The resin is applied in liquid form, and the crosslinking is obtained by heating. Phenol formaldehyde, urea formaldehyde, and melamine formaldehyde are the usual resins. The first of these is dark, and used mainly for industrial laminates, but the latter two are clear, and used to laminate and cover decorative material.

Low-pressure laminates are produced by 'laying up' the reinforcing materials with liquid polyester or epoxy resins, and then subjecting the assembly to low pressures: this process is usually applied to glass fibre reinforcement.

24.50 THE MANIPULATION OF PLASTICS MATERIALS

Plastics materials can be manipulated by moulding, casting calendering, and forming by pressure or vacuum techniques; they can also be reinforced by lamination techniques.

24.51 MOULDING METHODS

Compression Moulding. This is the most common method used for the shaping of thermosetting moulding materials; although this method can be applied to thermoplastic material, it is only employed when the parts being produced are too large for them to be made by the injection moulding method. The equipment consists of a press with two heated platens which carry the punch and the die units; when these are in the closed position, the cavity between them is the same size and shape as the finished part plus shrinkage allowance. When a **positive mould** is used the thickness of the moulding depends upon the amount of moulding material placed in the die before the mould is closed, and it is necessary that the exact amount of moulding powder is used; this type of mould is shown in fig. 24.4. The **flash** or **semi-positive** mould (fig. 24.5) incorporates a flash gutter between the punch and die contact faces; a little more powder than is necessary to exactly fill the mould cavity is placed in the die, and the excess material is squeezed out leaving a 'fin' or 'flash' that must be removed after completion of the moulding. This method allows a complete filling of the mould cavity without accurate measuring of the quantity of moulding powder required for each component, and if the part is carefully designed the flash removal can be done easily. When the mould cavity is filled, the pressure and temperature is held for about six minutes to 'cure' the material, after this, the mould is opened and the moulding ejected.

If the moulding must not have a flash, or if it is delicate or intricate, the **transfer moulding** method is used (as illustrated in fig. 24.6). In this method the mould is closed and the moulding material is heated in a separate chamber and forced into the mould cavity through small channels; when the mould had been filled, the pressure and temperature is held to effect the 'curing' process.

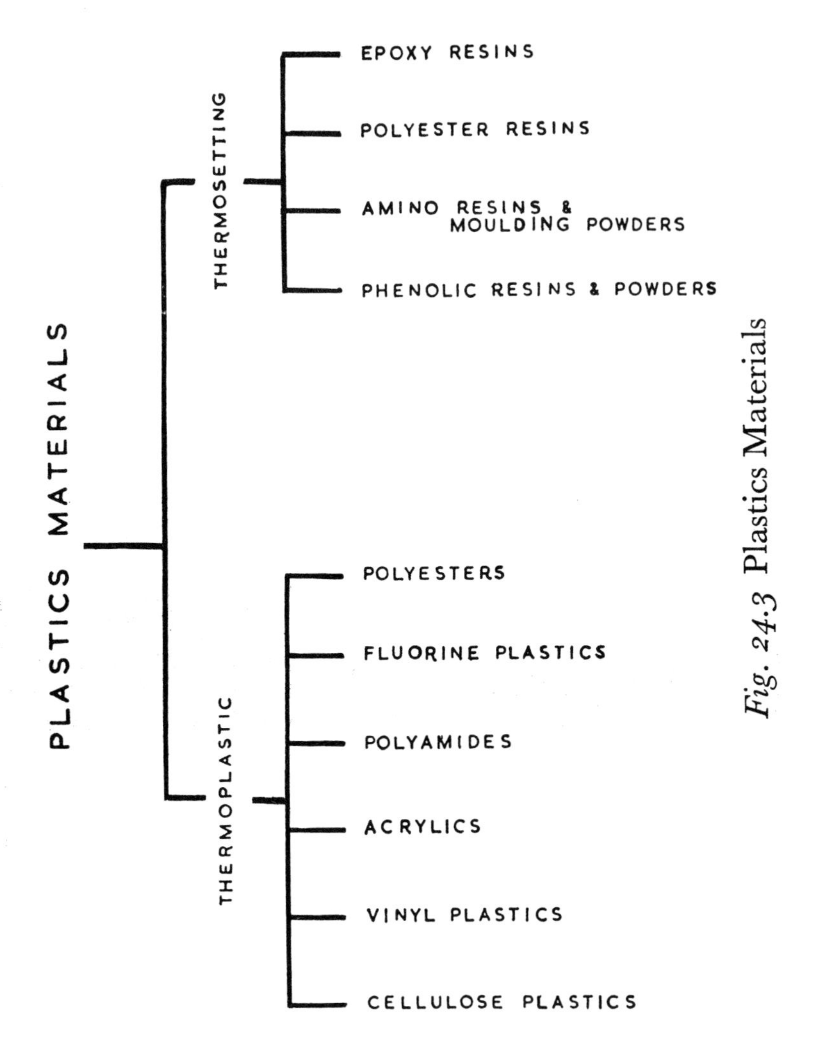

Fig. 24.3 Plastics Materials

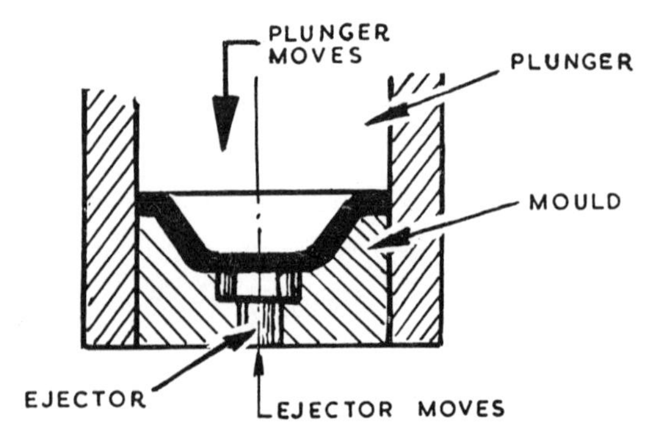

Fig. 24.4 Positive Mould

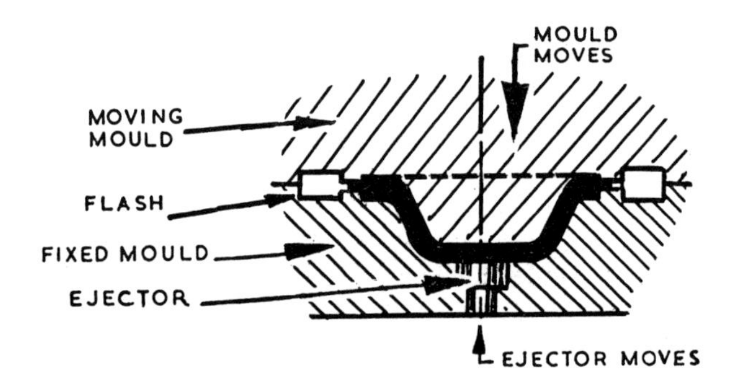

Fig. 24.5 Flash Mould

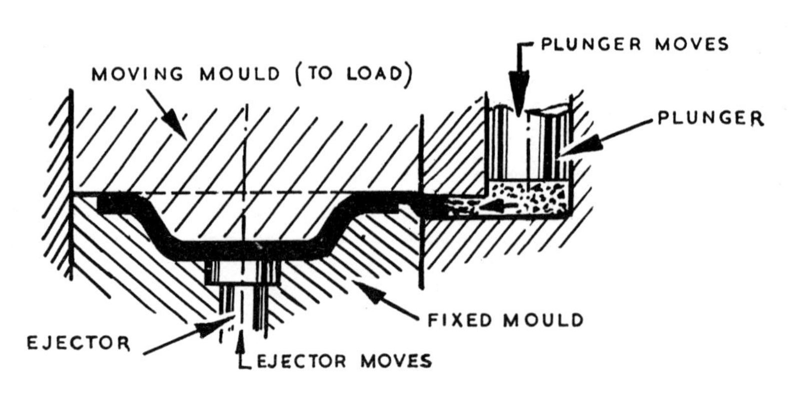

Fig. 24.6 Transfer Moulding

The **cold moulding** technique is a special variation of the compression moulding process that allows rapid production of thick-sectioned parts such as grinding wheels. In this method the material is first compressed in a cold mould, and then placed in an oven where it is baked to harden it. Cold moulding produces an inferior surface to that produced by hot moulding; parts to be made by this method must be designed with a view to preventing the warping that sometimes occurs when using this method.

24.511 *Injection Moulding*. This process is similar to the pressure die-casting process used for certain metals. The injection moulding process is the most rapid fabrication method available and can be applied to nearly all the thermoplastic materials. In order to be injection moulded, a material must be softened by heat so that it has a high viscosity and can flow when under pressure to take up the required shape.

The principle of injection moulding is illustrated in fig. 24.7. The required quantity of moulding material is introduced into the injection chamber, where it is forced by plunger through the heating zone and into the closed mould. When the mould has been filled, the material is rapidly cooled, and when it is solid, the mould is opened and the moulding ejected. This process is very similar to the pressure die-casting process, from which it was developed; in order that the process be successful, parts to be produced by this method must be carefully designed to suit the process.

24.512 *Extrusion Moulding*. This process is illustrated in fig. 24.8; it will be seen that the moulding material is fed continuously through the heating zone and through the die by means of a rotating screw. This method can be applied to all thermoplastic materials, and it differs from injection moulding in that a continuous length of material is produced instead of discontinuous mouldings. Extrusion moulding can be used to produce thin sheets; in this process a thick tube is extruded upwards, and then expanded by blowing air into it so that the required wall thickness is obtained. The tube is closed by pinch rolls, and the blown extruded film is continuously drawn off by these rolls and later cut to the required sheet size.

24.52 CASTING

Suitable plastics materials can be cast using similar techniques to those used for metals. The moulds may be of lead, rubber, or p.v.c. Casting can be used to produce plastic film by spreading the molten material on to a polished rotating drum or band, and removing it when solid using take-off rolls. The mechanical properties of the film can be modified by the speed of cooling and the amount of stretching done by the take-off rolls.

24.53 CALENDERING

In this process, the plastics material, in the form of a warm doughy mass, is passed between heated rollers so that it is thoroughly worked; about four rollers are used, and the final roller produces the required thickness. This method can be used to apply a covering to paper or fabric, and the sheet can be embossed if required.

24.54 FORMING AND PRESSING TECHNIQUES

The simplest method of forming sheet plastics material is illustrated in fig. 24.9; in this method the heated sheet material is clamped in position on the

INJECTION AND EXTRUSION MOULDING

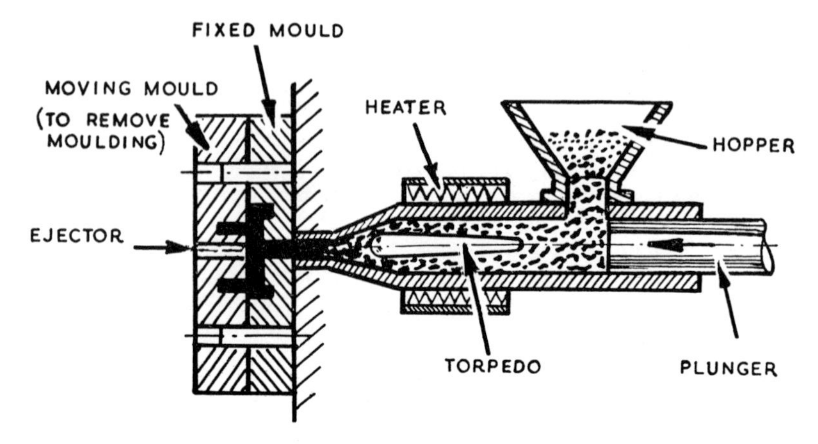

Fig. 24.7 Injection Moulding

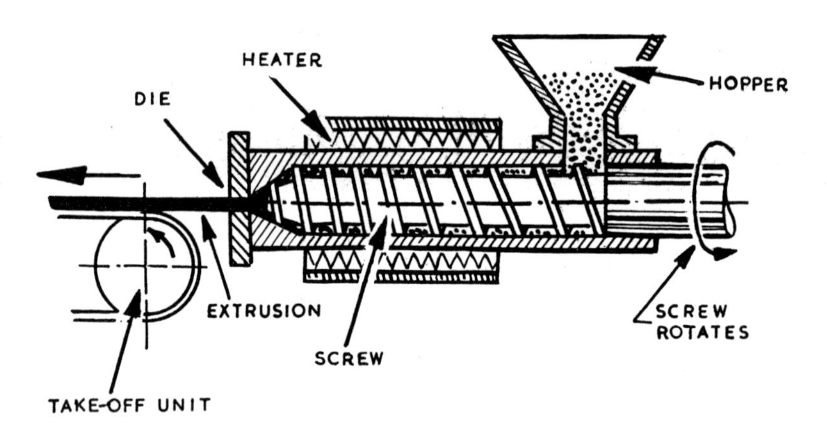

Fig. 24.8 Extrusion Moulding

die plate and then pressed into shape by the former. In the **vacuum-forming method** (fig. 24.10) the heated sheet material is clamped in position on the top of the mould and is then sucked into the mould; compressed air is used to eject the finished moulding and to accelerate the cooling. The vacuum technique causes thinning and so a non-uniform sectioned moulding is produced; it is unsuitable if uniformity of section is important.

24.541 Figure 24.11 illustrates the **vacuum-assisted pressing technique**

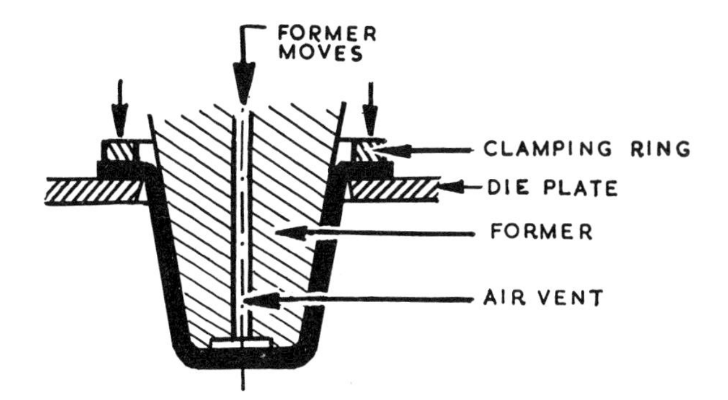

Fig. 24.9 Simple Pressing

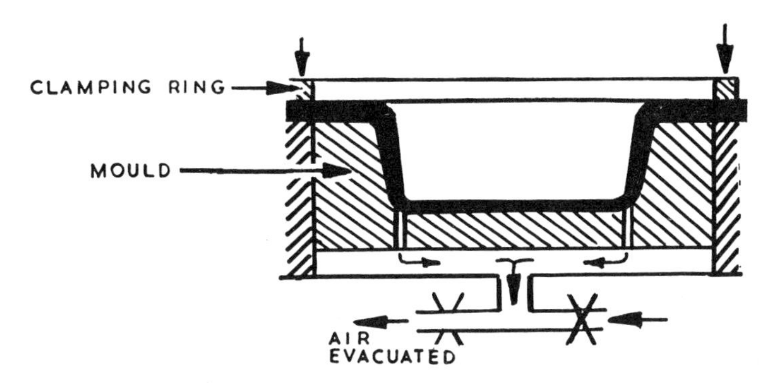

Fig. 24.10 Vacuum Forming

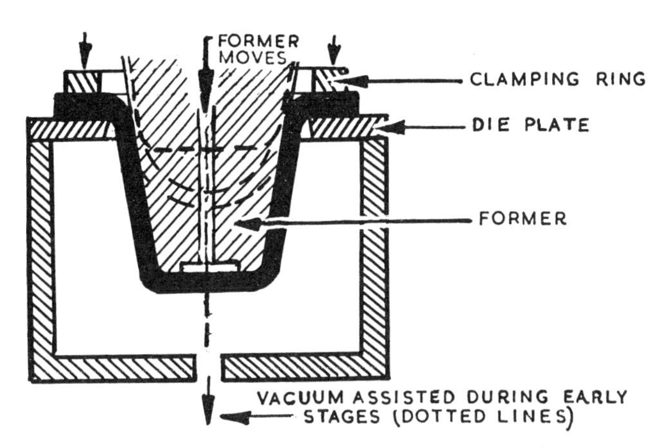

Fig. 24.11 Vacuum-assisted Pressing

in which the former is vacuum-assisted during the early stages of pressing; the **plug-assisted** method is used where a local deep draw is to be produced in an otherwise relatively flat moulding (this method is illustrated in fig. 24.12).

24.542 Part-spherical shapes can be produced by simple **blow forming** (see fig. 24.13); in this method no mould is required. When other shapes are to be produced, the sheet material can be blown into a female mould as illustrated in fig. 24.14, but there is a tendency to produce local thinning when this method is used.

24.543 **Drape forming** (see fig. 24.15) is used to produce a uniform section thickness using a vacuum; in this method the sheet material is clamped in position, and stretched by the mould as it moves into position and the final shape produced by vacuum forming over the mould.

24.544 **Bubble forming** (fig. 24.16) is a similar technique to drape forming. In this method the sheet material is clamped in position and a bubble formed by blowing compressed air through holes in the mould; the mould is then moved into position within the bubble and the shape finally produced by vacuum forming.

24.545 The **extrusion blow-moulding** technique is used to produce bottle-like shapes; a short length of tube is extruded, and its end closed by the mould; air is blown into the tube so that it expands and assumes the shape of the mould, and finally the moulding is severed from the extruded tube and the procedure repeated (see fig. 24.17).

24.55 LAMINATES

It is usual to divide lamination techniques into **high pressure** and **low pressure** techniques.

In the high pressure techniques, paper or woven fabric is impregnated with a thermosetting plastics material (called the 'resin'), dried, and then several of these impregnated sheets are heated under pressure to form the laminate. This method can be applied to tube manufacture; here the material is wound on to a mandrel, and during the winding, heat and pressure is applied by rollers. The tube is cured by further heating before removal from the mandrel; the tube can be machined if necessary.

24.551 In the low pressure technique, the laminate is built up layer by layer on to a mould made of wood, plaster, or plastics material. The reinforcement is glass fibre that has been woven into sheets using similar techniques to those used in the textile industry; each layer of reinforcement is impregnated with resin applied by brush, and which is allowed to become tacky before the next layer of reinforcement is applied. When the lay-up is completed the assembly is cured; this curing can be accelerated by gentle heating.

24.552 The weave of the reinforcement is important because it controls the strength and the 'directional' properties of the laminate, and the ability of the reinforcement material to accept the required shape. In order to prevent loss of strength caused by joins in the reinforcement sheets that are made during the lay-up operation, a weaving technique called '3-D Contour Weaving' has been developed; in this method the fabric is woven in a flatted tubular form, and the 'sock' so produced is placed on the mould for impregnation and curing.

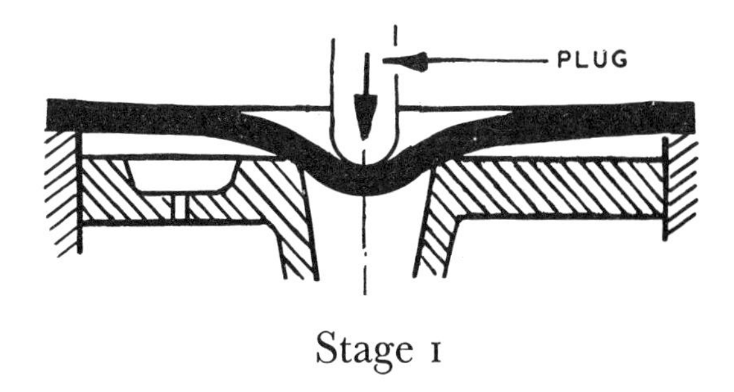

Stage 1

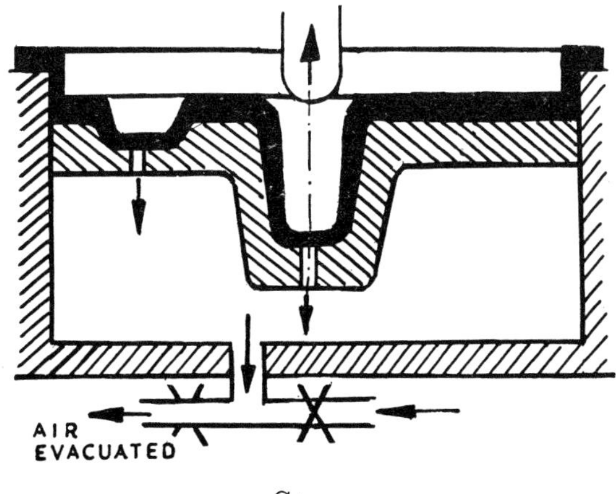

Stage 2

Fig. 24.12 Plug-assisted Vacuum Forming

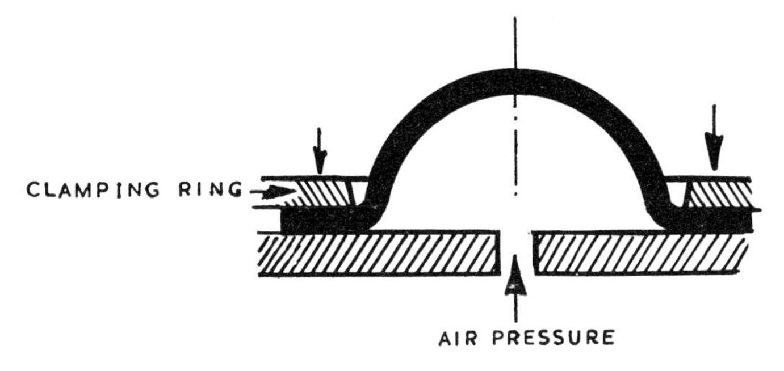

Fig. 24.13 Blow Forming

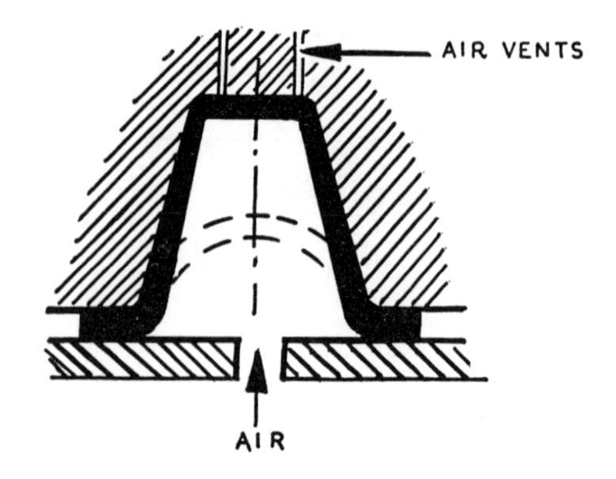

Fig. 24.14 Blowing into Female Mould

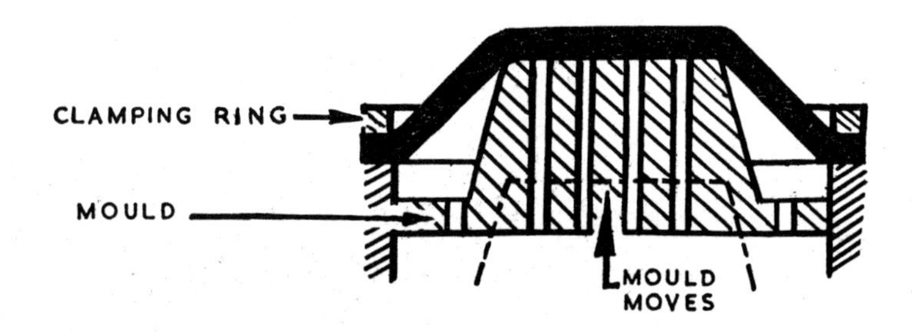

Stage 1 Mould Moves into Position and Stretches Sheet

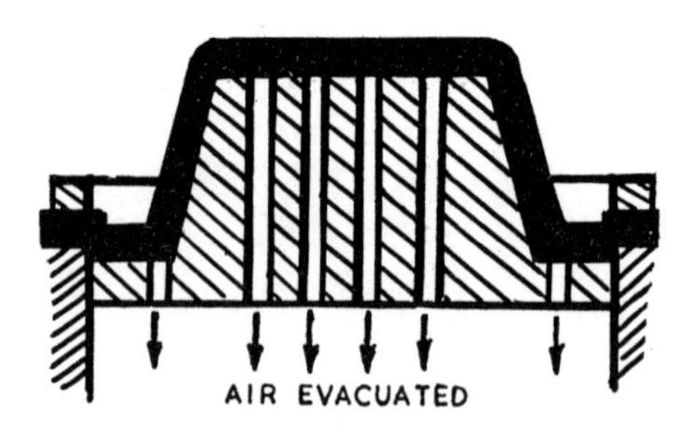

Stage 2 Vacuum Forming

Fig. 24.15 Drape Forming

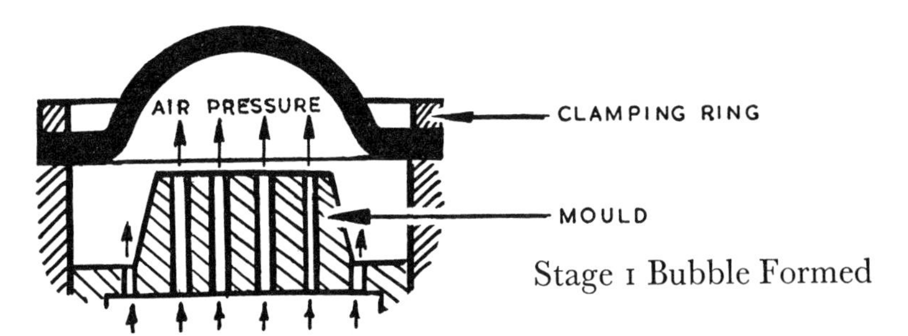

Stage 1 Bubble Formed

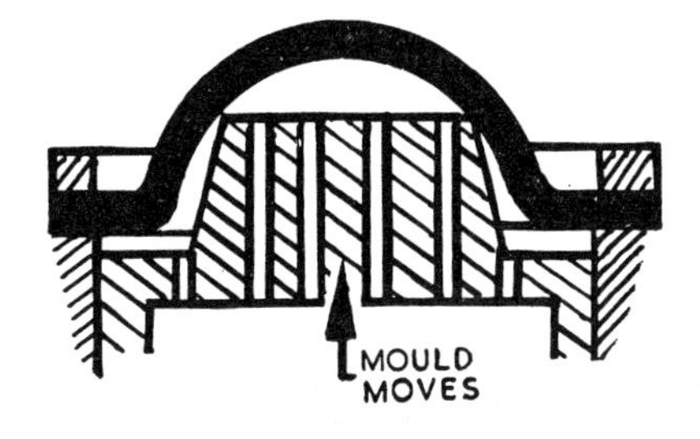

Stage 2 Mould Moves into Position

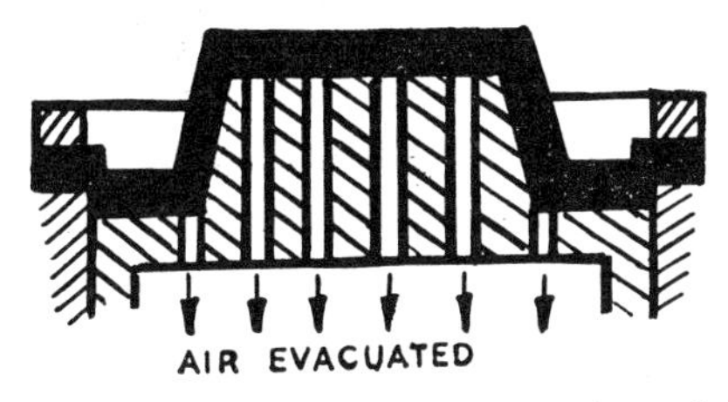

Stage 3 Vacuum Forming

Fig. 24.16 Bubble Forming

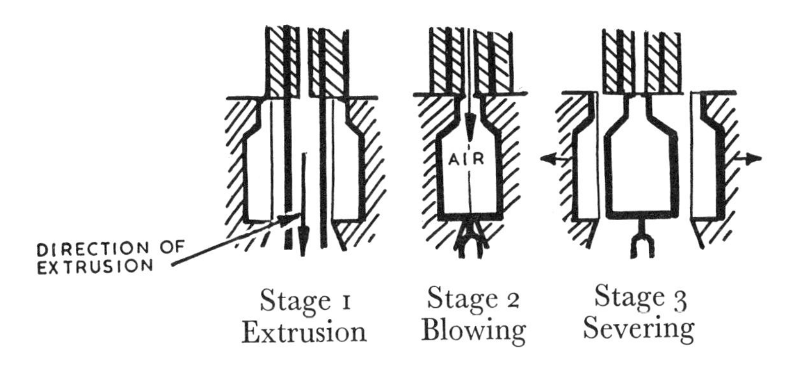

Fig. 24.17 Extrusion Blow Moulding

24.60 The Joining of Plastics Materials

Suitable plastics materials can be joined by using a solvent or cement, they can also be joined by heating or by welding. When welding is done, a filler rod is employed, and the material to be welded is heated by a stream of hot gas. Low strength joining of thin material can be done by heating and pressing two layers together along lines of up to about 3 mm width.

24.70 The Machining of Plastics Materials

Plastics materials can be machined by most of the conventional methods. It must be realised that most plastics materials have a relatively low melting point and that they will therefore soften or deform if the correct machining conditions are not maintained. These materials are very often brittle and so shock loading and vibrations must be prevented; special attention must be paid to swarf removal because many of these plastics materials produce a powdery swarf that hinders cutting action and may even cause tool breakage.

24.80 The Testing of Plastics Materials

Plastics materials are given mechanical tests that are similar to those done upon metals; they are also tested for softening temperature, and for 'thermoplasticity'. Most synthetic resins absorb water, and so a test to determine 'water vapour permeability' is usually included.

24.90 Some Applications of Plastics Materials

Plastics materials are used extensively in engineering on account of their cheapness, good electrical properties, and resistance to atmospheric corrosion. These materials are not particularly strong; polystyrene, for example, has a tensile strength of only about 48 N/mm^2. Not all plastics materials are as weak as polystyrene, and nylon, for example, has a tensile strength of about 80 N/mm^2.

Moulded plastics are used for small casings, and laminates built up by the lay-up process are used for larger casings and where greater strength is required; plastics of the 'nylon' type are used for small, lightly-loaded bearings, and laminated sheet material is machined to produce gears where silent running is required. Plastics of the 'perspex' type are used instead of glass where complicated curved shapes are required, and where the non-splintering property of perspex is an advantage over glass; polyvinyl chloride is used as an electrical insulation material as a substitute for rubber. Plastics adhesives play an important part in engineering, and metal-to-metal plastics adhesives are used in aircraft construction in place of rivets.

REFERENCES

The Fabrication of Plastics, Dr. V. E. Yarsley (Journal I.P.E.).
Plastics in Engineering, A. J. Moulam (Journal I.P.E.).
Plastics in the Service of Man, F. G. Couzens and Dr. V. E. Yarsley (Pelican).

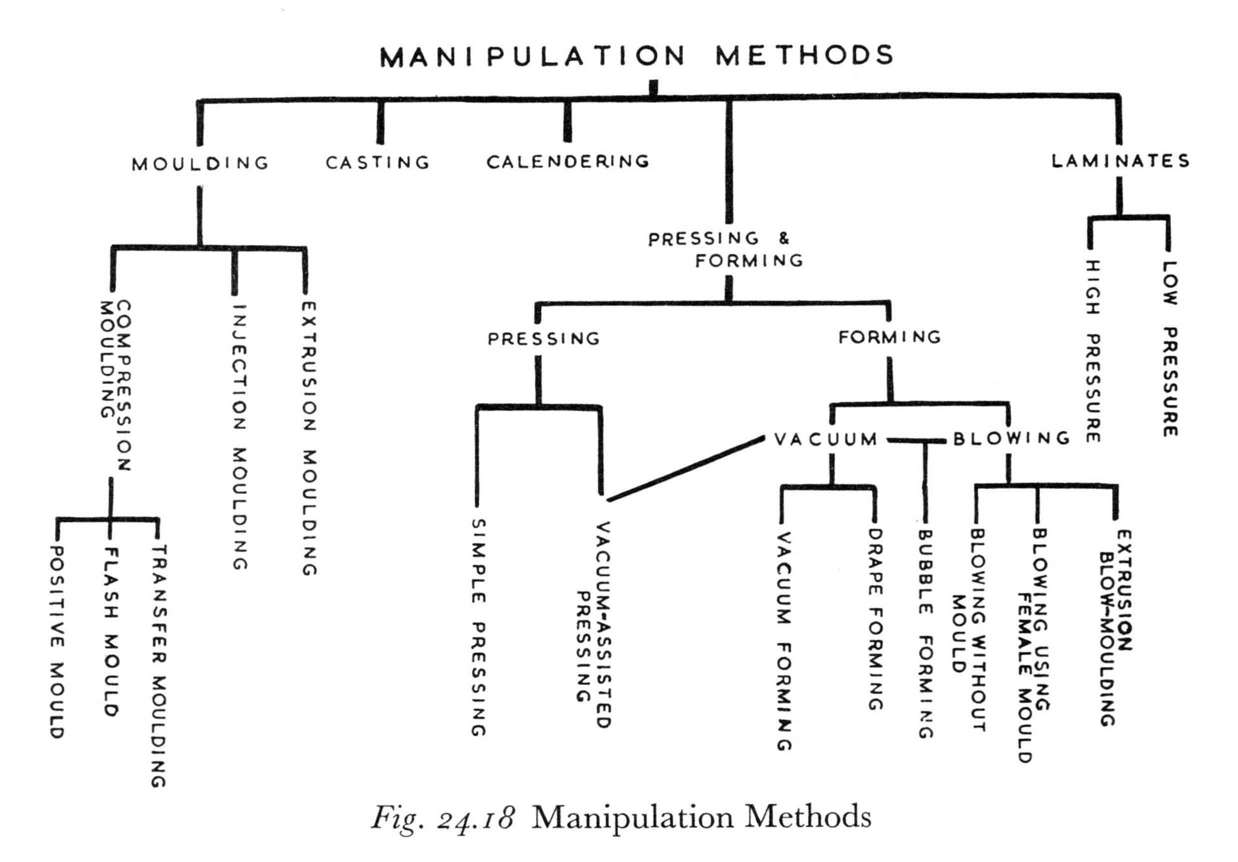

Fig. 24.18 Manipulation Methods

TABLE 24.1

SOME TYPICAL THERMOPLASTIC MATERIALS

Type	*Material*	*Characteristics*
Cellulose plastics	Nitrocellulose	Materials of the 'celluloid' type are tough and water resistant. They are available in all forms except moulding powders. They cannot be moulded because of their inflammability.
	cellulose acetate	This is much less inflammable than the above. It is used for tool handles and electrical goods.
Vinyl plastics	polythene	This is a simple material that is weak, easy to mould, and has good electrical properties. It is used for insulation and for packaging.
These plastics are so-named because their chains include the Vinyl group:	polypropylene	This is rather more complicated than polythene and has better strength.
H H | | C=C | H	polystyrene	Polystyrene is cheap, and can be easily moulded. It has a good strength but it is rigid and brittle and crazes and yellows with age.
Vinyl	polyvinyl chloride (p.v.c)	This is tough, rubbery, and practically non-inflammable. It is cheap and can be easily manipulated; it has good electrical properties.
Acrylics (made from acrylic acid)	polymethyl methacrylate	Materials of the 'perspex' type have excellent light transmission, are tough and non-splintering, and can be easily bent and shaped.
Polyamides (short carbon chains that are connected by amide groups—NHCO)	nylon	This is used as a fibre or as a wax-like moulding material. It is fluid at moulding temperature, tough, and has a low coefficient of friction.
Fluorine plastics	polytetra-fluoroethylene (p.t.f.e.)	Is a wax-like moulding material; it has an extremely low coefficient of friction. It is very expensive.
Polyesters (when an alcohol combines with an acid, an 'ester' is produced)	polyethylene terephthalate	This is available as a film or as 'Terylene'. The film is an excellent electrical insulator.

TABLE 24.2

SOME TYPICAL THERMOSETTING PLASTICS MATERIALS

Material	*Characteristics*
Phenolic resins and powders	These are used for dark-coloured parts because the basic resin tends to become discoloured. These are heat-curing materials.
Amino (containing nitrogen) resins and powders	These are colourless and can be coloured if required; they can be strengthened by using paper-pulp fillers, and used in thin sections.
Polyester resins	Polyester chains can be cross-linked by using a monomer such as styrene; these resins are used in the production of glass-fibre laminates.
Epoxy resins	These are also used in the production of glass-fibre laminates.

TABLE 24.3

SELECTED PROPERTIES OF SOME PLASTICS MATERIALS

Type	*Material*	*Specific Gravity*	*Tensile strength N/mm²*	*Initial Young's modulus N/mm²*
Cellulose plastics	Cellulose acetate: 'Bexoid'	1·32	47	1850
Vinyl plastics	Polyethylene: 'Polythene', 'Alkathene', 'Crinothene'	0·92	14	700
	Polypropylene: 'Carlona'	0·90	35	—
	Polystyrene: 'Styron', 'Bextrene'	1·06	28	2760
	Polyvinyl chloride: 'Corvic', 'Welvic', 'Cobex'	1·39	52	3100
Acrylics	Polymethyl methacrylate: 'Perspex' (sheets), 'Diakon' (powder)	1·19	62	3450
Polyamides	'Nylon'	1·14	80	2960
Fluorine plastics	Polytetra-fluoroethylene: 'Fluon', 'Teflon'	2·1	14	4000
Phenolic plastics	Mineral-filled: 'Mouldrite', 'Bakelite'	1·9	52	—
Epoxy resins	Unmodified epoxy resin: 'Lactene'	1·15	70	—

CHAPTER 25

BEARING MATERIALS

25.10 The Requirements of a Bearing Material

The basic requirements are:

1. *Wear Resistance.* The bearing should not wear away when in service, but its hardness must be relative to that of the shaft because it is equally important that the latter does not become worn or scored.

2. *Strength.* The bearing material must have a sufficiently high elastic limit in compression to support the load at working temperatures, but be tough and ductile to resist shock loading.

3. *Fairly High Melting Point.* The bearing material must not creep in service; the creep resistance increases with melting point.

4. *Thermal Conductivity.* It is desirable that the thermal conductivity of the material is such that the heat is conducted away from the bearing surface. If the bearing is to operate without lubricant the coefficient of friction of the bearing material must be low.

Bearing Materials

25.11 These can be classified as:

1. Whitemetals (these are tin-base alloys and lead-base alloys).
2. Copper-base alloys.
3. Cast iron.
4. Aluminium-base alloy.
5. Sintered metals.
6. Plastics materials.

25.20 The Whitemetals

These alloys combine hardness with ductility and toughness by having a microstructure that consists of hard intermetallic compounds of tin and antimony embedded in a soft solid solution matrix that allows the bearing to adjust itself to running conditions; during the initial running-in of the bearing the solid solution wears away slightly so that a number of reservoirs are formed to hold the lubricant and help to maintain the film of lubricant.

Whitemetal bearings are used when a low melting point alloy is required so that it can be easily cast in position.

25.21 The tin-base alloys (known as **Babbit Metals** after their originator) are the better quality whitemetals, but the less expensive lead-base alloys are suitable for medium and lower duties.

25.30 Copper-base Alloys

These include the casting plain tin-bronzes (with between about 10 and 18% tin, see page 150), and the phosphor-bronzes (with about 10% tin and about 0·05% phosphorus). They have a microstructure that consists of hard particles of an intermetallic compound of copper and tin embedded in a soft solid

TABLE 25.1

WHITE BEARING METALS

Composition %				*Applications*
Tin	*Antimony*	*Copper*	*Lead*	
93	3·5	3·5	—	Big-end bearings for motor-car engines
86	10·5	3·5	—	Main bearings for car and aero-engines
80	11	3	6	General work where heavy duty bearings are required
60	10	1·5	28·5	Bearings for internal-combustion engines and electrical machines
40	10	1·5	48·5	Medium duty
20	15	1·5	63·5	Light duty
5	15	—	80	Long bearings with medium load

TABLE 25·2

SOME BEARING BRONZES

Composition %					*Applications*
Copper	*Tin*	*Lead*	*Zinc*	*Phosphorus*	
89	10 min	—	—	0·5 min	Phosphor-bronze. Suitable for heavy loading
88	12	—	—	0·1	Hard-wearing bronze
88	10	—	2	—	Admiralty gunmetal. For general purposes; resists corrosion. Suitable for bearings when lubrication is good
76	9	15	—	0·05	Suitable when lubrication or alignment is not good enough for Admiralty gunmetal to be used
80	10	10	—	0·05	Has good anti-friction properties combined with plasticity; can be applied when lubrication is doubtful
85	5	5	5	—	Used for general castings but also for bearing shells
74	3 max	24	—	—	Has high thermal conductivity and can carry higher loads at higher speeds than whitemetals

solution matrix; this structure combines hardness with toughness and ductility.

Lead (which is almost completely insoluble in copper) is added to tin-bronzes; additions of 1% or 2% of lead improve machinability, and 5% or more reduces the dry coefficient of friction of a tin bronze. Lead-bronze with about 12% lead is very plastic but is less tough and strong than other bronzes.

25.40 Cast Iron

Grey cast iron (see page 125) is a good casting metal with excellent bearing properties. It is used extensively for machine-tool beds due to its damping characteristics.

25.50 Aluminium-base Alloy

An aluminium-base alloy containing 6·5% tin, 1·0% copper and 1·0% nickel is a useful bearing material. It is used for sand or gravity die cast bearings, and can be supplied as bars and tubes, or cast as shells; it has a low strength but a high shock resistance, and is suitable for service temperatures below 150°C.

25.60 Sintered Metals

Porous bearings that will hold oil are produced by powder metallurgy (see page 38); these bearings are useful where lubrication is difficult or where oil splashing is objectionable.

25.70 Plastics Materials

Polytetrafluoroethylene (see page 194) and the polyamide '**Nylon**' (see page 208) both have a very low coefficient of friction and are useful bearing materials. They are used where an oil is undesirable; polytetrafluoroethylene is very expensive, but nylon is inexpensive and is used for domestic equipment, motor-car accessories and similar applications.

CHAPTER 26

CUTTING-TOOL MATERIALS

26.10 INTRODUCTION

Figure 26.1 is a simplified diagram to show the principle of cutting action. The rake angle is associated with the mechanical properties of the material being cut; the clearance angle is present to prevent the tool from rubbing the workpiece, and is therefore associated with the shape of the workpiece and the tool. The location of the rake and clearance angles depends upon the direction of cutting.

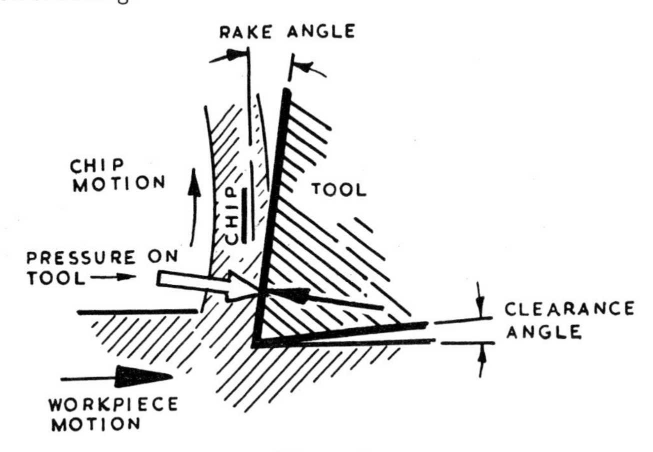

Fig. 26.1

26.20 The Requirements of Cutting-tool Materials

1. RED HARDNESS

The combination of pressure and chip movement across the face of the tool causes wear, and also generates heat; the heat increases with cutting speed. Rapid cutting demands high cutting speeds, and so the material must retain a good hardness at the high temperatures produced by the cutting action. The ability to retain hardness at these high temperatures is known as **red hardness.** Red hardness can be obtained either by using a tool material that does not soften until a high temperature is reached, or by using a tool material that has a very high initial hardness, and can suffer reduction in hardness and yet still be very hard. Hard materials are very brittle, and so tools made from these materials must be rigidly held, the workpiece must be rigidly held, and the machine tool must have high spindle speeds and be of robust design to minimise vibration.

2. COMPRESSIVE STRENGTH AND TOUGHNESS

The tool material must have a high compressive strength to prevent its deformation, and be tough to resist fracture due to shock loading.

3. RESISTANCE TO THE FORMATION OF BUILT-UP EDGE

Built-up edge is caused by the welding of the workpiece material to the tool face during cutting; it is associated with the cutting of ductile materials, and causes inferior workpiece surface and excessive tool wear. To resist the formation of built-up edge, the tool material should be chemically inert.

4. LOW COEFFICIENT OF FRICTION

If the coefficient of friction is reduced the problems due to overheating will be reduced accordingly.

Cutting-tool Materials

26.21 The principal cutting-tool materials are:

1. *Ferrous metals* (*a*) Carbon steels.
   (*b*) High-speed steels.
2. *Non-ferrous metals* (*a*) Cobalt-base alloys.
   (*b*) Cemented carbides.
3. *Non-metallic materials* (*a*) Diamond.
   (*b*) Sintered oxide.

26.30 CARBON STEELS

Carbon tool steels contain more than about 0·7% carbon, and are hardened by water quenching; a small quantity of chromium is included if an oil-quenching steel is required. Although these steels have a good hardness and toughness, they soften at temperatures over about 250°C. (see fig. 26.6) and are unsuitable for cutting at high speeds. They are used for large taps, dies, and reamers, and are also used extensively for prototype form-tools.

26.40 HIGH-SPEED STEELS

These steels contain between about 14 and 22% tungsten, and about 4% chromium; they retain their hardness at temperatures of up to about 660°C. (see fig. 26.6), and are therefore suitable for cutting at quite high speeds. If the steel is to cut a material with high abrasive characteristics, about 5% cobalt is included.

26.41 Cast high-speed steel contains complex carbides, and so forging must be done at about 1250°C. to ensure that these carbides are completely broken up, otherwise the tool will crack during hardening or when in service.

26.42 Similarly, the hardening procedure must be such that these carbides are broken up to form austenite as a result of heating, and the quenching must not produce stresses that may lead to failure when in service. The hardening procedure is as follows:

Stage 1. Slow heating to about 870°C. followed by soaking so that any carbides not transformed into austenite will be dispersed evenly throughout the austenite.

Stage 2. Rapid heating to about 1250°C (in a non-oxidising atmosphere if possible) to dissolve the remaining carbides without decarburising the surface of the tool. The tool must resist abrasion and its surface must be hard; there must not be a decarburised layer because usually the tool will have little machining done to it after hardening to expose the harder layer below the surface.

Stage 3. Quenching in oil or air, according to the composition of the steel and the shape of the tool. Very often the tool is given a modified quench such as cooling it in a salt bath at 600°C., and then quenching it in oil; this is done to reduce the temperature gradient from surface to core.

26.421 As a result of this heat treatment, the material will contain a large proportion of untransformed austenite; this can be transformed into martensite by reheating to about 600°C., or by the heat that is generated during cutting. The hardness developed by this reheating is known as 'secondary hardness'; high-speed steels are often called 'self-hardening steels' because of the hardness developed during cutting.

26.43 High-speed steels can be used for complete tools and cutters, or can be applied as tool bits, or butt welded to carbon steel shanks.

26.50 COBALT-BASE ALLOYS

Stellite is a typical cobalt-base alloy which contains cobalt, up to about 20% tungsten, 33% chromium, 3% carbon, and small amounts of iron, manganese and silicon. Stellite is produced in an electric furnace and cast into shape; it cannot be forged into shape. Although it has an excellent red hardness (see fig. 26.6) it is extremely brittle and can only be used as tips that are brazed to a medium carbon steel shank, or as blades inserted into a cast-iron milling cutter body.

26.60 CEMENTED CARBIDES

Cemented carbides are produced by powder metallurgy and consist of particles of tungsten carbide in a matrix of metal with a lower melting point; this matrix metal is usually cobalt. The metallic tungsten is mixed with carbon and heated to about 1500°C. to chemically combine the tungsten and the carbon. The tungsten carbide is mixed with cobalt metal powder by a wet-milling operation; the quantity of cobalt depends upon the grade of cemented carbide being produced. When titanium tungsten carbide is being produced, titanium carbide is introduced at this stage. The mixture is compacted in dies and given a sintering treatment at about 900°C. so that it can be cut up into suitable shapes, which are finally sintered at about 1500°C. for about 2 hours, and then slowly cooled to room temperatures.

26.61 Cemented carbides can be classified as:

1. **Tungsten carbides**, which are very hard, and used for materials, such

as irons and bronzes, that are relatively weak, but which have high abrasion characteristics.

2. **Titanium tungsten carbides**, which are less hard than tungsten carbides, and resist the tendency for chips to 'weld' to the carbide. This type of carbide is used for cutting steels.

Tungsten carbides and titanium tungsten carbides are available in a number of grades to suit workpiece material and the cutting conditions.

26.62 Cemented carbides are very brittle and must be used as tips, brazed to a carbon steel shank as shown in fig. 26.2. The seating for the tip must be carefully machined so that the tip is fully supported, and the tip must be carefully brazed to the shank.

Figure 26.3 shows the principal cutting-tool angles of a typical turning tool. It will be seen that the front-to-back angle is negative; a negative front-to-back angle directs the cutting pressure through a larger section of the tool, and also causes the point of impact to be some distance behind the cutting edge (as shown in fig. 26.4).

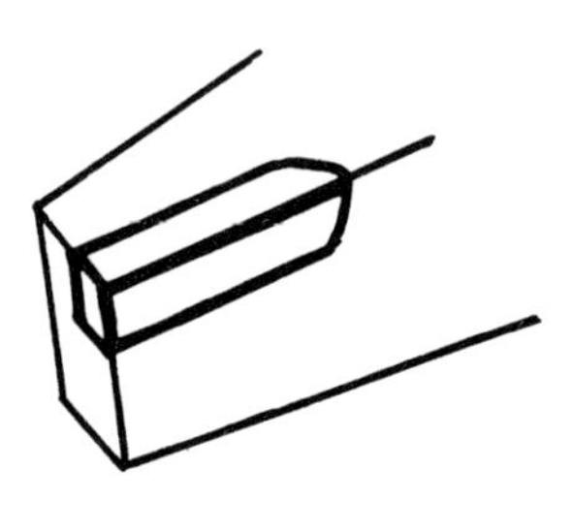

Fig. 26.2 A Tipped Tool

26.70 DIAMOND

Diamond is used to finish turn and bore non-ferrous metals and non-metallic materials, and produces an excellent surface finish. It is used at very high cutting speeds, with very fine feeds (up to 0·05 mm) and small depths of cut (up to 0·2 mm).

The diamond tip is set in a bit, which is held in a holder that is designed to allow the tool to be positioned relative to the workpiece surface.

26.71 Diamond tools are used with specially designed machine tools that do not produce vibrations; the machine spindle is belt driven to eliminate gear chatter, the spindle bearings are carefully machined to produce smooth running, and the machine is isolated from the vibration of other machines by special foundations.

26.80 SINTERED OXIDES

These ceramic cutting-tool materials consist of at least 85% aluminium oxide (Al_2O_3) with other oxides, carbides, or nitrides, to give improved strength and to exercise control during sintering.

Sintered oxides maintain a high hardness at elevated temperatures, as shown in fig. 26.6; they are also chemically inert and so 'welding' is minimised.

26.81 Sintered oxide is used as tips; the tip can be attached to the shank by metallising it and brazing it to the shank, by bonding it to the shank with epoxy resin, or by a mechanical clamp; mechanical clamping is considered to be the best method. Sintered oxides are particularly suited to the **throw-away method**; in this method the tip is clamped to a holder that produces the required negative rake angle; each cutting edge of the tip is used in turn, and when the tip is worn out it is thrown away instead of being reground. Figure 26.5 illustrates two typical holders and tips.

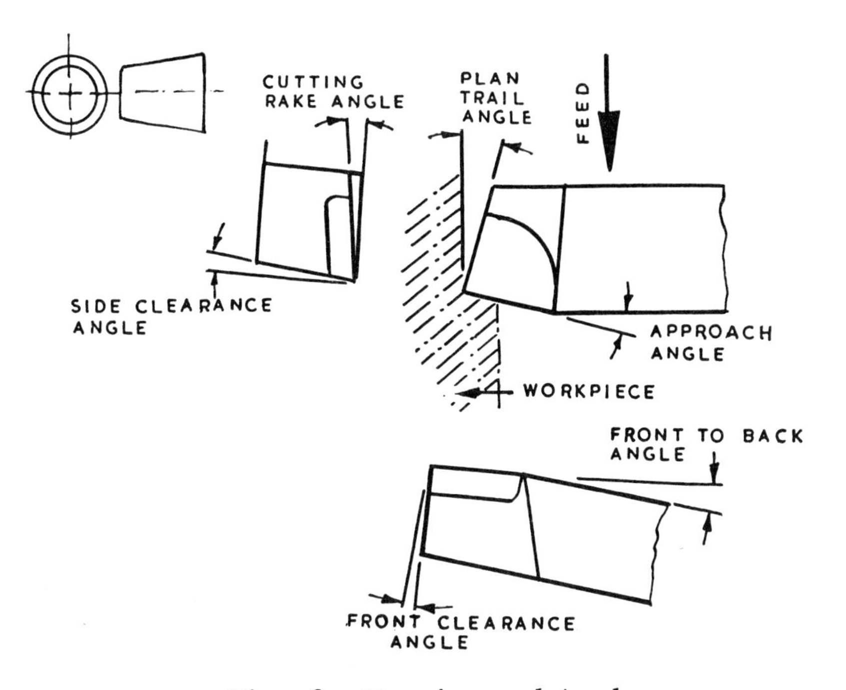

Fig. 26.3 Turning-tool Angles

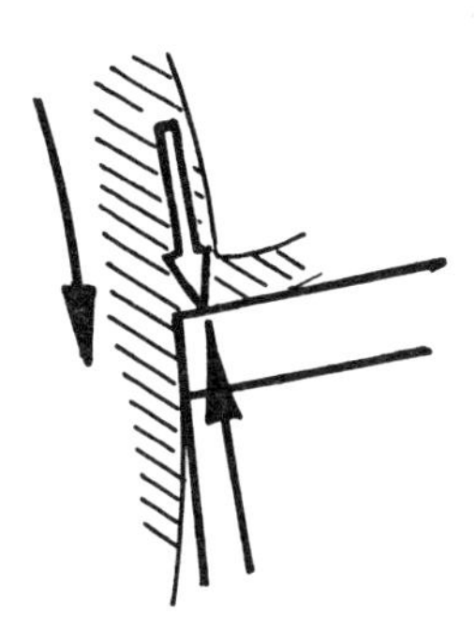

Fig. 26.4 Effect of Negative Front-to-back Angle on Direction of Pressure on the Tool

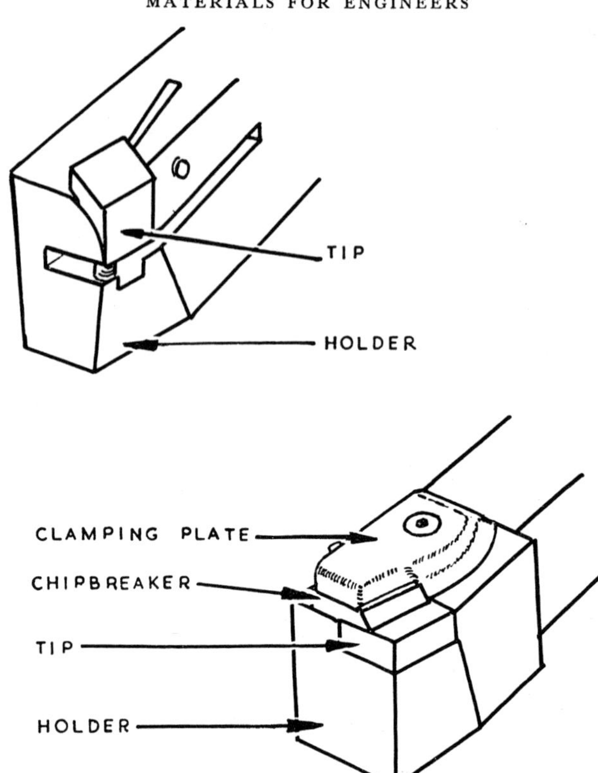

Fig. 26.5 Throw-away Tips and Holder

26.82 These materials must be used at very high cutting speeds, and are currently being used mainly for light finishing cuts at feeds of up to 0·05 mm/rev. If machine tools are to be suitable for sintered oxide cutting tools, they must be rigid, vibration free, and have high spindle speeds; the component must be rigidly clamped, and must itself be rigid.

REFERENCES

Publications issued by Messrs. A. C. Wickman and Co. Ltd.

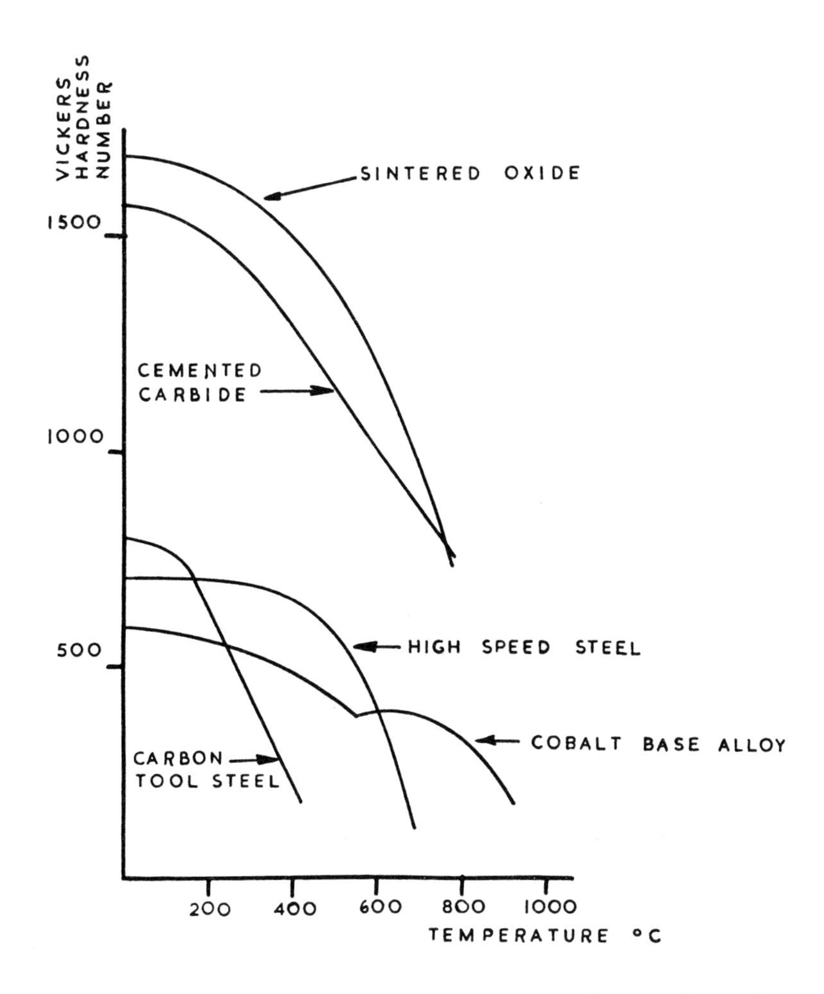

Fig. 26.6 Effect of Temperature on Hardness of Tool Materials

CHAPTER 27

METHODS OF JOINING ENGINEERING MATERIALS

A large number of methods are available for the joining of engineering materials; in this chapter the characteristics of the principal methods will be summarised, but it is not the purpose of this book to describe these methods in detail.

27.10 The Factors that Influence the Choice of Joining Method

1. The composition, mechanical properties, and physical properties of the materials to be joined.
2. The shape of the components to be joined.
3. The limiting conditions. Heat is the main limiting condition; for example, in electrical work, delicate components in the vicinity of the joint may limit the temperature that is allowed.
4. The required strength of the joint.
5. The degree of permanency of the joint.
6. The size of the components to be joined.
7. The allowable cost of the joining operation.

27.11 The Classification of Joining Methods

The many joining methods can be classified as follows:

1. Mechanical joining methods.
2. Metallurgical methods.
3. Adhesives.

27.20 MECHANICAL JOINING METHODS

These are sometimes classified as 'joining with residual stresses'; and can be subdivided into (*a*) fastening methods and (*b*) riveting.

27.21 *Fastening Methods:*

(i) Nut and bolt fastening, in which both parts to be joined are drilled to a suitable clearance size. The method requires that there is ample space around the parts to be joined so that the bolt can be assembled in the holes, and also that there is room for the spanners used to tighten and release the parts.

(ii) Set-screw and screwed part fastening. In this method one part is drilled to a suitable clearance size, and the other part is screwed to accept the set-screw that is used to join them; only one spanner is necessary to tighten or release the joint. This method is useful where there is no room for a nut, or when two spanners would be awkward to apply.

(iii) Stud and nut fastening. Here the stud is either screwed into the larger component, or attached to it during casting or moulding of that component; the smaller component is fastened to the larger by a nut at the end of the stud. In this method only one spanner is required to make and release the joint, but like the set-screw method, care must be taken not to damage the thread in the screwed part.

In these methods, use is made of washers, and locking devices such as spring washers, tabwashers, locking plates, and lock-nuts.

(iv) Pipe fittings. In these methods, a nipple (or an olive) is attached to the pipe, and tightened on to the seating in the union by means of the union nut. This method is used to connect water, petrol, and oil pipes.

The foregoing methods are used when the parts are to be separated easily for maintenance or repair, without damage to the parts or to the fastening components (the exception being the tabwashers and locking plate, which are usually replaced upon reassembly).

27.22 *Riveting*. In this method, the plates to be joined are drilled to accept the rivets, which, before riveting, are headed only at one end, and with a shank that is longer than the combined thickness of the plates to be joined. The joint is made by forming a second head using special equipment, so that the rivet shank fills the holes and the plates are compressed between the rivet heads. The rivet size and the spacing of the rivets is designed with due regard to the various ways in which the joint can fail; generally the rivet is designed to fail at a slightly lower stress than the plates being joined because rivets can be more easily replaced at low cost.

Various combinations of plate and rivet positioning are employed to suit conditions; the plates may be lap joined (that is, overlapped and riveted together), or be butt joined (that is, in the same plane) and held together by rivets that attach the plates to cover plates. A cover plate is a plate that extends along the length of the joint and covers both plates to be joined; its width depends upon the number of rows of rivets to be employed.

In heavy engineering, steel rivets are employed and used hot so that they are in a plastic condition, and stressed upon contraction to draw the plates together. In light engineering suitable aluminium alloy rivets are used that have been solution treated to make them soft, and which become harder and stronger due to precipitation after joining is done.

27.30 METALLURGICAL JOINING METHODS

These methods are sometimes classified as 'joining without residual stresses'; they involve local casting, alloying, or crystal growth across the joint line.

27.31 *Soldering*. In this method a joining agent is used that is different from either of the materials being joined, but which alloys locally with the materials. A number of solders are available to suit the materials to be joined and the conditions of joining.

Tinman's solder contains about 62% tin and 38% lead; this is the eutectic for the tin-lead system (see fig. 27.1) and solidifies at about 183°C.

Plumber's solder contains 33% tin and 67% lead; this solder solidifies over a temperature range of between about 260°C. to about 183°C. and allows the plumber to make his 'wiped joint' (see fig. 27.1).

Solders for joining copper alloys contain about 2·5% silver and about

97·5% lead; the silver is used instead of tin because tin, and copper would combine to produce a brittle constituent that would weaken the joint

The parts to be joined must be clean and free from surface oxides; a flux is used to slag away these oxides. The most common flux is hydrochloric acid ('spirits of salts'), but this flux leaves behind a highly corrosive residue; if the joint cannot be washed (as in radio work) rosin-base flux which is almost completely non-corrosive, is usually used, but this is only effective on copper, and tin-plate.

27·32 *Brazing.* This is a form of soldering that is done at a higher temperature, using brass as the joining agent (hence the name 'brazing'); brazing produces

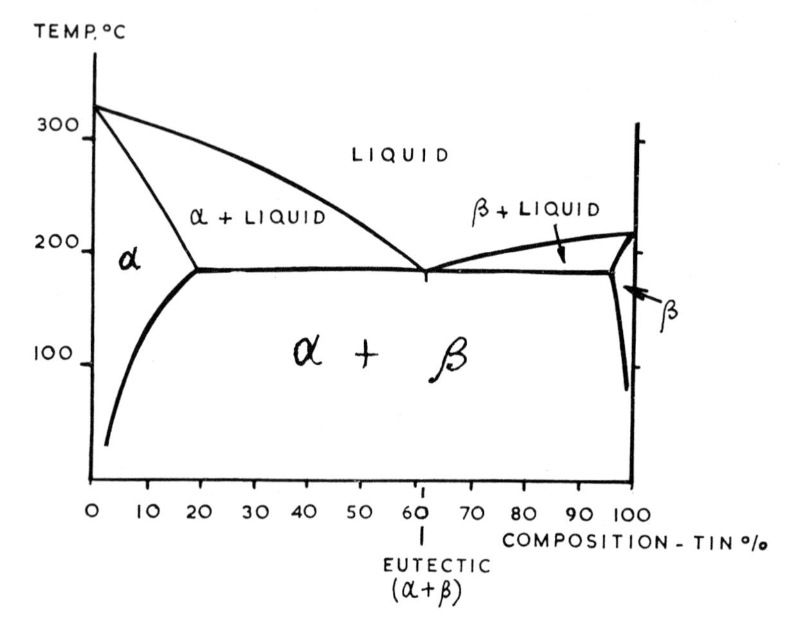

Fig. 27.1 The Lead-tin Equilibrium Diagram
α Solid Solution of Tin in Lead
β Solid Solution of Lead in Tin

a stronger joint than does soldering. A borax-type of flux is usually used, but a fluoride-type of flux is used for high-grade silver soldering. For general work a brazing solder that contains about 50% copper and 50% zinc, with a melting point of about 870°C., is used. Silver solders contain from 10 to 80% silver, with copper and zinc according to requirements; these silver solders have melting points from 625 to 870°C., according to their composition. All these brazing solders have a 'solidification range'.

27·33 *Welding Processes.* These processes can be classified as (i) fusion welding and (ii) pressure welding.

27·331 *Fusion Welding* is similar to soldering and brazing in that a joining agent is used, but in this case the 'filler', as it is called. is similar to the material being joined. There are three types of fusion welding; these are gas welding, arc welding, and thermit welding.

Gas welding uses a gas flame to locally melt the filler rod and the material to be joined. The gas can be oxy-hydrogen (for low temperature work on lead), oxy-acetylene (produces a temperature of up to about 3000°C. and good heat concentration), and atomic hydrogen (producing temperatures of up to about 4000°C.).

Arc welding. In the carbon arc process the arc is struck between a carbon electrode and the work, and a separate filler rod is used. In the metallic arc process a filler rod is used as one electrode and is melted during welding to fill the joint; this process is used mainly for welding steel.

Thermit welding. This process is used for the repair of iron and steel castings. A mould is made around the area to be repaired and powdered iron ore mixed with powdered aluminium is placed in a container near the mould. The casting is heated, and the powder fired; as a result of the firing the oxygen from the iron oxide combines with the aluminium, freeing the iron, which runs into the mould to weld the material as required.

27.332 *Pressure Welding* can be classified as forge welding and resistance welding.

(i) Forge welding. In this method hammer blows and heat are combined to produce a crystal growth across the joint line.

(ii) Resistance welding. In this method local heating is produced due to the resistance of the metal being joined, to the passage of an electrical current; there are a number of variations of resistance welding. Spot welding is used to produce a lap joint by gripping the sheets to be joined between two heavy electrodes of small diameter, the resistance causes local melting between the sheets; seam welding is similar to spot welding except that two rollers, or one roller and a plate, are used as the electrode system to produce a continuous joint line. Butt welding is usually used to join lengths of wire and rod by pressing their ends together and passing an electrical current through the pieces, to cause heat to be generated at the contact faces; flash welding is similar except that heat is applied before the pieces are pressed together.

In the projection welding method, a number of projections are punched in the thinner of the plates to be joined at the spots at which the plates are to be joined; the welding process is similar to spot welding except that localisation of the joint is obtained by the projections rather than by using small-diameter electrodes. The projections are removed by the welding, but the heights of the projections must be within 0·01 mm of each other if the process is to be a success.

27.34 *Casting Techniques.* In one version of this technique the smaller parts of an assembly are machined, then positioned in the mould, and the larger component cast around them; this technique is associated very largely with the die-casting process. In the other version of joining by casting, the smaller component is cast into the larger component and then machined if necessary; the production of whitemetal bearings is a typical example of this technique.

27.35 *Moulding Techniques.* Studs and similar components can be introduced into the mould before the injection moulding of plastics materials; this technique is similar to the 'casting around' technique already described.

27.36 *Joining by Rolling.* Laminated sheets can be produced by rolling thin

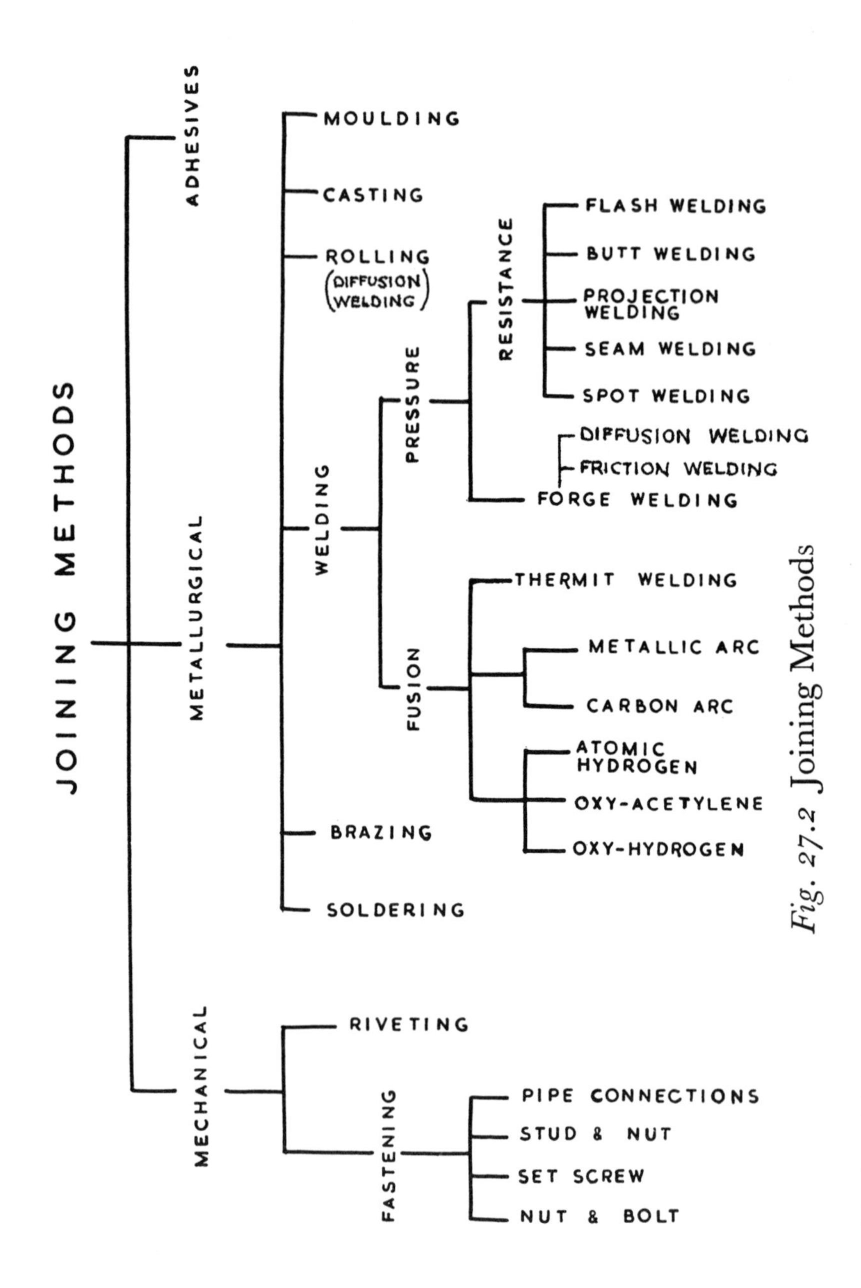

Fig. 27.2 Joining Methods

sheets together, this method is an extension of welding. Aluminium alloy clad with commercially pure aluminium to combined strength with good corrosion resistance at the surface is a typical example of this technique.

27.40 ADHESIVES

Synthetic adhesives of the 'impact' type, and adhesives of the thermoharden-ing type, which require a combination of pressure and heat to 'cure' them, are used to join both non-metals and metals. The 'Redux' process used to fabricate parts of aircraft is an example of the latter method.

CHAPTER 28

THE SURFACE TREATMENT OF METALS

28.10 Metal is given surface treatment to protect it against corrosion, to improve its appearance, or to produce special surface properties such as hardness.

The most important reason for surface treatment is to give protection against atmospheric corrosion. Atmospheric corrosion requires both moisture and oxygen; mechanical protection can be obtained by painting the surface to exclude air and moisture. A more expensive treatment, such as plating, must be done if a more efficient protection is required.

A number of factors must be considered when selecting the surface treatment method to be employed; these factors include:

1. The reason for the treatment, i.e. corrosion protection, appearance, or special surface properties.
2. The metal to be treated.
3. The size and shape of the part to be treated.
4. The dimensional accuracy of the treated part.
5. The permissible cost of the treatment.

The main surface treatment methods are reviewed in this chapter.

Surface Treatment Methods

28.11 Surface treatment methods can be classified as follows:

1. Coating with metal.
2. Chemical treatment.
3. Oxide coating.
4. Painting.

28.20 Coating with Metal

The protection given by a metal coating can be **direct** or **sacrificial**. Direct protection is obtained by using a relatively noble coating metal, complete protection is obtained only if the coating completely covers the surface, and will continue only as long as it remains intact. Sacrificial protection is obtained by using a coating metal that is less noble than that being protected, and corrodes instead of it; protection by this method does not depend upon a complete coverage of the surface, and continues even if the coating becomes broken.

28.21 ELECTROPLATING

This is done in a plating bath, in which the part to be plated is the cathode, and the plating metal is introduced either into the electrolyte or as a reactive anode that is consumed during the process.

28.211 *Nickel-chromium plating* is used extensively on brass, steel, and zinc alloys to give corrosion resistance and improved appearance. The nickel deposit is between 0·01 and 0·03 mm thick, and the chromium deposit on it is only about 0·0002 mm thick; when steel is nickel plated, a thin 'flash' of copper is applied first. Each layer is polished before the next layer is applied, but **bright nickel plating** does not require polishing; this bright nickel plating is obtained by the addition of agents to the plating bath.

28.212 *Hard-chromium plating* with about 0·002 mm thick deposit of chromium, which is polished, gives a very hard non-porous coating.

28.213 *Cadmium plating* is ductile and can be applied to parts that are to be formed after plating; its low coefficient of friction is an advantage when screws are to be given corrosion resistance treatment. Cadmium plating is used on radio chassis parts, motor car electrical equipment, etc.; it has a poor resistance to acids and must not be allowed to come into contact with foodstuffs because of the toxicity of its compounds.

28.214 *Zinc plating* is much cheaper than cadmium plating and gives a thinner deposit than galvanising (also a zinc coating method) and is therefore better than that process for the protection of screw threads because accuracy is less affected. Zinc plating is used extensively for lock mechanisms and for car-window winding gears.

Zinc plating and cadmium plating are sacrificial protection methods, and so complete coverage of the surface is less critical than when plating with more noble metals (for example, nickel and chromium).

28.22 HOT-DIPPING

In these methods the metal is passed through a bath of molten coating metal.

Hot-dip Tinning. In this method steel (about 0·25 mm thick) is pickled to remove scale, passed through a molten flux bath, and then into the tin bath. The final coating thickness is controlled by a squeegee system. Tin plate is used for food containers and kitchen equipment because of the non-toxicity of tin; tinplate can be easily joined by soldering.

28.221 *Hot-dip Galvanising.* Before galvanising, steel is cleaned by polishing or by shot blasting, and then washed. It is then passed through a flux bath so that a layer of flux is formed on its surface; this later is oven-dried to protect the surface from further oxidation until immersion in the zinc bath, where it peels away from the surface. Galvanising is used for corrugated iron, buckets, and window frames.

28.23 ELECTRO-GALVANISING AND ELECTRO-TINNING

These are similar processes in which steel is passed continuously through cleaning and plating cells; the zinc or tin is introduced into the plating cell as a reactive anode. Electro-galvanising produces a thin zinc coating (about 0·002 mm thick) and is used for products that are later to be formed, joined by spot-welding or soldering, and then painted or enamelled; typical electro-galvanised products are steel kitchen cabinets, office furniture, refrigerator parts, and car components such as petrol tanks. Electro-tinning is a rapid method of producing tinplate; it is particularly useful because it can produce a thicker deposit on one side of the sheet than on the other.

28.24 CLADDING

A thin sheet of a corrosion-resisting metal can be rolled on to each side of the metal to be protected. **Alclad** (pure aluminium cladding on aluminium alloy) and **Niclad** (nickel cladding on steel) are typical examples of cladding.

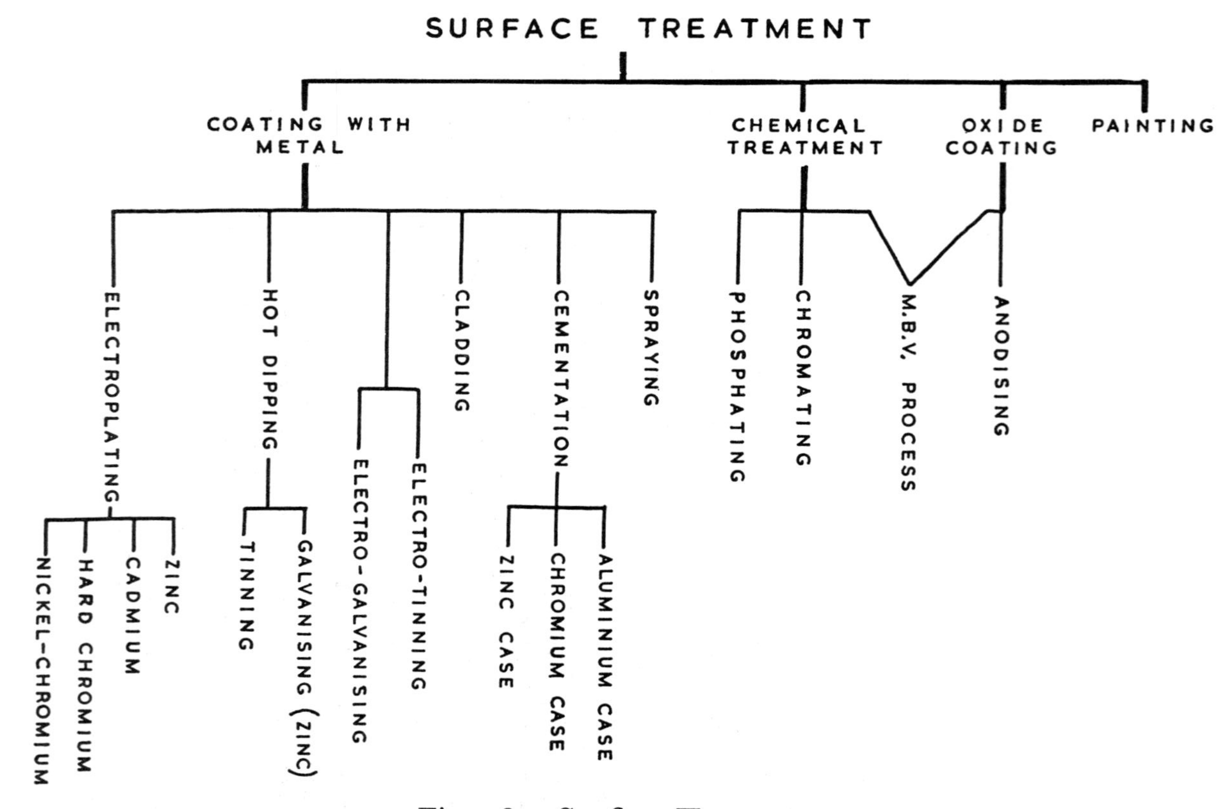

Fig. 28.1 Surface Treatment

28.25 CEMENTATION

This is a similar process to the carburising process used to surface harden steel (see page 105, section 13.31); the metal to be treated is surrounded by the protecting metal in powder form, and then heated to a temperature that is lower than the melting point of both the metals involved; the protecting metal enters the surface of that to be protected to produce a 'case'. Typical cementation processes are **Sherardising** (zinc case), **Chromising** (chromium case), and **Calorising** (aluminium case).

28.26 SPRAYING

Typical examples of spray-coating are zinc spraying and aluminium spraying. The metal to be used as the coating is in powder or wire form, and is fed into a pistol which melts it and projects it as tiny particles on to the surface to be protected. The **Schoop** process is a zinc-spraying process that uses an electrically heated pistol to spray the surface with zinc.

28.30 Chemical Treatment

Phosphating. This process is applied to steel and to zinc-base alloys; it involves heating the metal in a solution of acid phosphates to produce a coating that forms the base for the painting, varnishing, oiling, or lacquering that must follow; **Bonderising**, **Granodising**, and **Parkerising** are proprietary variations of this process. **Coslettising** is a phosphating process that is applied to iron and steel, and involves heating the part in a solution of phosphoric acid and iron filings.

28.31 *Chromating* is used extensively on magnesium alloys, and also on zinc base alloys; in this process the part is immersed in a bath containing potassium bichromate and additives.

28.32 *M.B.V. Process* (Modified Bauer-Vogel process). This aims at thickening the oxide film that forms naturally on aluminium surfaces; the parts are immersed in an acqueous solution of sodium carbonate and sodium or potassium chromate for about 5 minutes. The film so produced can be made harder and more corrosion resistant by immersion in a sodium solution for about 45 minutes; the film can be coloured by additions to the bath.

28.40 Oxide Coating

Anodising is applied to aluminium and its alloys, and aims at thickening the oxide film that forms naturally on the surface. This process is done in a cell in which the aluminium is the anode and the cathode is lead or stainless steel; it takes about 30 minutes. The oxide film produced can be dyed if necessary.

28.50 Painting

As already stated, a mechanical protection can be obtained by cleaning the surface and then painting it to exclude air and moisture. It is important that all traces of corrosion are removed before painting, otherwise corrosion will continue under the paint. Corrosion can be inhibited by priming the cleaned surface with zinc or lead oxide.

CHAPTER 29

HEAT-TREATMENT FURNACES AND TEMPERATURE-MEASUREMENT METHODS

Furnaces

29.10 GAS-FIRED FURNACES

The most common fuel used in these furnaces is town's gas (refined coal gas) and air. The burner is of the Bunsen type, and the flow of primary air is controlled by means of a valve.

The atmosphere inside the furnace is important because of the high temperature at which heat treatment is done. If the atmosphere is **oxidising** (**or decarburising**) a scale will be formed on the surface of the metal being treated so that it is of poor quality, and also insulated against the full effect of quenching; it is important that the decarburisation of steel is minimised because loss of carbon will alter its surface properties. If the furnace atmosphere is **reducing** (**or carburising**) scaling is reduced, but when applied to steel it alters the surface properties due to the addition of carbon. An oxidising atmosphere is produced by introducing more air than is necessary for complete combustion, and a reducing atmosphere is produced by introducing less air than is necessary for complete combustion; a neutral atmosphere is difficult to produce by mixture control. If a neutral atmosphere is essential, as when bright annealing, a muffle furnace (see fig. 29.2) is used; the muffle atmosphere can be air, or be a controlled atmosphere. A controlled atmosphere can be produced by burning coal gas in a separate chamber with a restricted amount of air; the products of combustion are passed through a condenser to remove the water content, and finally unburned coal gas is added to obtain the required atmosphere.

29.11 Sometimes, as when hardening high-speed steel (see page 215, section 26.42) the material must be slowly heated to a certain temperature to ensure uniform heating, and then rapidly heated to the final temperature to prevent grain growth and scaling. In these cases a two-chamber furnace is used in which the lower chamber is heated by forced air and gas so that it is at a high temperature, and the top chamber is heated only the by hot gases that reach it from the lower chamber so that it is at a lower temperature.

29.12 The furnaces so far described are batch furnaces; if large numbers of parts are to be gradually heated, soaked, and then cooled, a continuous furnace is used. The continuous furnace is long, and the workpieces conveyed along its length; the temperature is kept low at the entrance end, and the heating and cooling rate is adjusted by the temperature 'zones' along the furnace and the rate at which the parts are conveyed along the length of the furnace.

29.20 ELECTRIC FURNACES

The **resistance furnace** uses heating elements placed around the heating chamber; the atmosphere is usually air, but a controlled atmosphere can be

HEAT-TREATMENT FURNACES

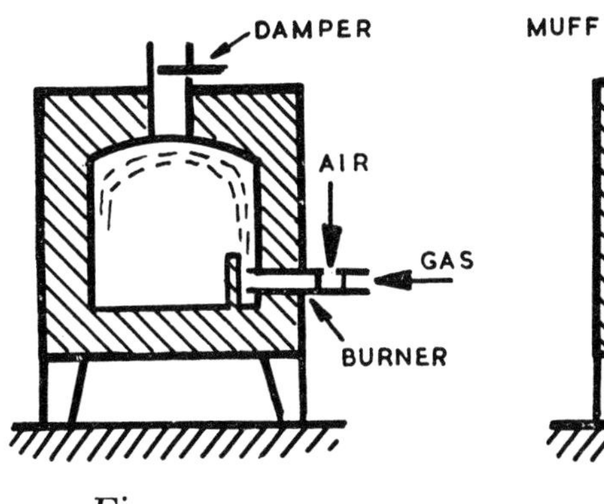

Fig. 29.1
Simple Gas-fired Furnace

Fig. 29.2
Muffle Furnace

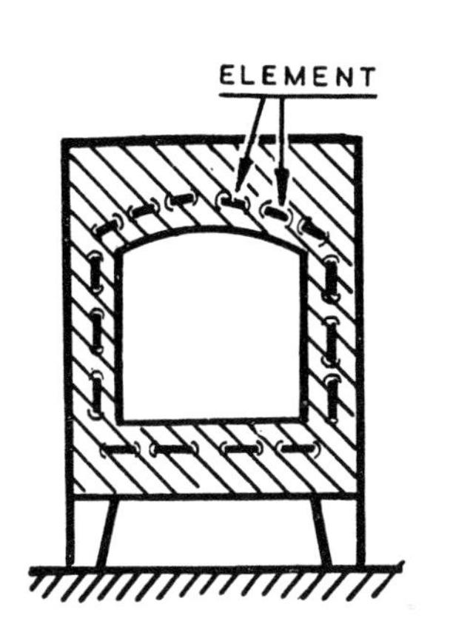

Fig. 29.3
Resistance Furnace

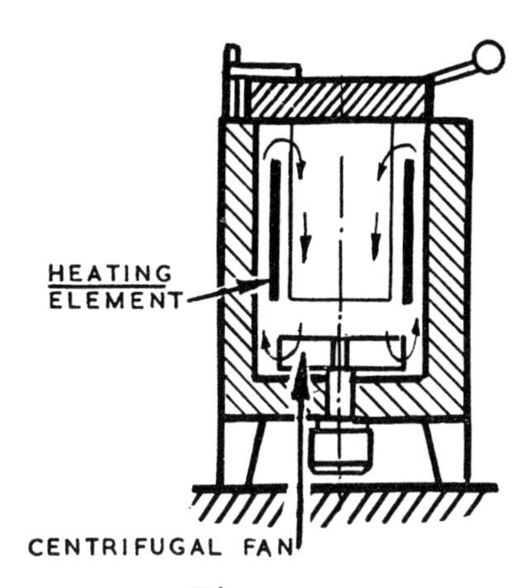

Fig. 29.4
Forced Air-circulation Furnace

introduced if required. This type of furnace enables very accurate temperature control to be exercised. The **forced air-circulation electric furnace** (see fig. 29.4) is used for low temperature heat treatment where the heat transfer is by convection; the air circulation is increased by the action of a fan. The **high frequency induction furnace** (see pp. 81 and 112) is used for surface hardening.

29.30 SALT-BATH FURNACES

Material can be heated by immersion in liquid salts. The salts can be held in a container that is externally heated, or in a container where the salts are heated due to their resistance to the passage of electricity through them between two pure iron electrodes that are also in the container. Neutral salts are used for heating and for delayed quenching, and carburising salts are used for surface hardening.

Salt-bath furnaces produce an even and a rapid heating, and no oxidising takes place because air is excluded from the surface of the workpiece. The part to be heated must be warmed before immersion in the salts, and cleaned after the heat treatment to remove any salt deposit.

Temperature-measurement Methods

29.40 Temperature-measurement methods can be classified as:

1. *Contact methods.* In which some part of the instrument is in contact with the hot body.
2. *Non-contact methods.* Which use light or heat radiation.

29.41 CONTACT METHODS

Liquid Expansion Thermometer. The most common examples of this type are the mercury-in-glass thermometer, which can be used at up to 500°C., and the mercury-in-steel type that can be used at up to 600°C. The mercury-in-steel type is used in conjunction with a fine flexible steel capillary tube and a Bourdon-type pressure gauge; this system is more satisfactory for industrial use because the gauge can be up to 30 m away from the thermometer bulb.

29.411 *Vapour Pressure Thermometers.* These are similar to the mercury-in-steel type, but use a volatile liquid; they can be used to measure temperatures of up to 800°C. and the gauge can be placed up to about 60 m from the bulb.

29.412 *Indicating Cones* (Seger cones). These are cones of about 12 mm diameter and 25 mm high that are made from a suitable salt mixture so that they melt at the required temperature; the composition of the salt is adjusted so that as the temperature being indicated is approached the cone bends over from its apex and touches the base upon which it stands when the temperature being indicated is reached. These cones are used to indicate temperatures between 600 and 2000°C., and the temperature that is indicated is marked on each cone. Cones that cover the desired range are placed within the furnace, and they indicate that at a certain time the temperature within the furnace was between certain limits.

29.413 *Indicating Paints and Crayons.* These are applied to the component being heated, and change colour or appearance according to the temperature reached at the point where they are applied. These methods are often used to indicate the temperatures at which gas turbine parts operate.

29.414 *Electrical Resistance Pyrometer.* The temperature of metal wire affects its electrical resistance; the variation in resistance is measured using a circuit of the Wheatstone Bridge type, and is converted into temperature variation using a calibration chart. Instruments that operate on this principle are bulky and are usually used to calibrate other types of pyrometer.

29.415 *Thermo-electric Pyrometer.* When two dissimilar metals are joined together as shown in fig. 29.5(*a*), and heat is applied to one end, called the

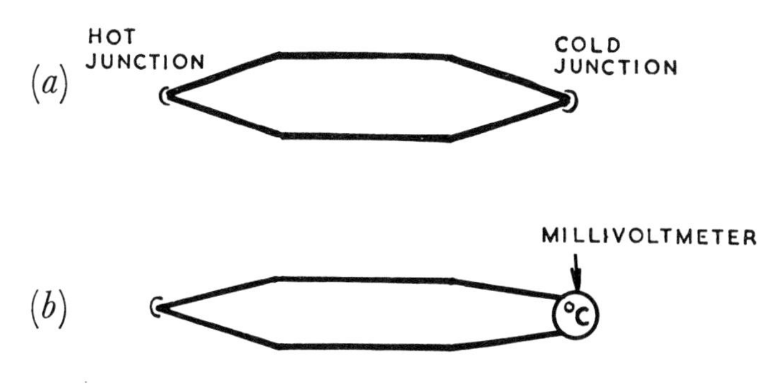

Fig. 29.5 Thermo-electric Pyrometer

hot junction, an electromotive force (e.m.f.) is set up in the circuit, causing current to flow; this is called a thermocouple. The electromotive force is related to the difference between the temperature at the hot junction and the temperature at the cold junction. If an electrical measuring instrument is introduced at the cold junction (fig. 29.5(*b*)), the e.m.f. can be measured; the measuring instrument can be calibrated to indicate the temperature directly. The materials used for the thermocouple depend upon the temperature range to be measured.

Typical thermocouple materials are:
- Copper and constantan (constantan is an alloy of 60% copper and 40% nickel).
- Platinum and platinum-rhodium alloy.

29.42 NON-CONTACT METHODS

Radiation Pyrometer. This type of pyrometer measures the intensity of the heat radiated by the hot body by concentrating the heat energy on the hot junction of a very sensitive thermocouple. The Féry Total Radiation Pyrometer (see fig. 29.6) is a well-known example of this type of pyrometer. The energy is

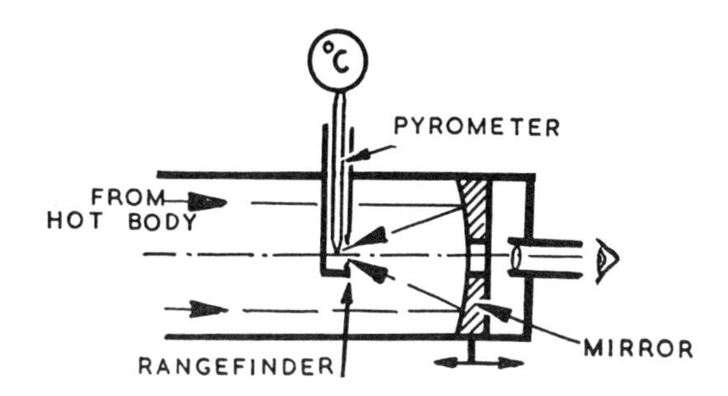

Fig. 29.6 Féry Total Radiation Pyrometer

concentrated on the hot junction by a concave mirror, which is positioned by using a split type of rangefinder to focus the heat rays on the hot junction. Most radiation pyrometers are calibrated over the range 700–2000°C.

29.421 *Optical Pyrometer.* This type of pyrometer measures the intensity of light radiation emitted by the hot body by comparing it with the radiation of

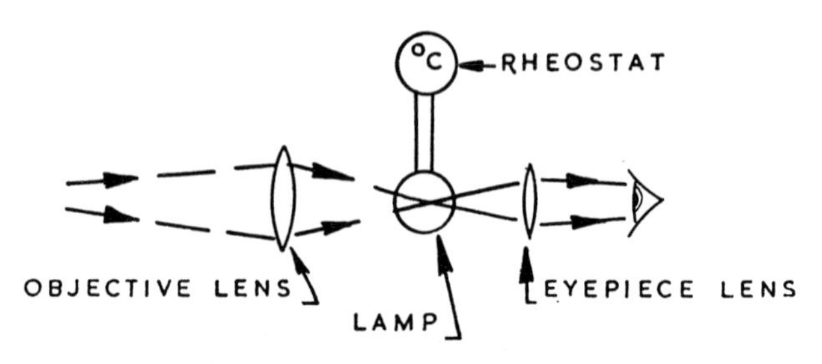

Fig. 29.7 Principle of the Disappearing Filament Optical Pyrometer

another source of known value. The Disappearing-filament Pyrometer is a typical pyrometer of this type; the eyepiece is adjusted so that a sharp image of the hot body is formed in the same plane as the lamp filament. The brightness of the filament is adjusted by means of a rheostat until it matches that of the hot body, and the temperature is indicated directly by an ammeter. This type of pyrometer can be used to measure temperatures over the range 700–1800°C.

QUESTIONS

1. (*a*) Discuss the considerations that must be made when selecting the material from which to make an engineering component.
   (*b*) What are the desired and acceptable characteristics of a material for the following applications?
   (i) Motor-car body.
   (ii) Lathe bed.
   (iii) Gas turbine blade.
   (iv) Food processing equipment.
   (v) Motor-car carburettor body.
   (vi) Brake lining.
2. Discuss the circumstances in which the following methods of metallic ore refining are used:
   (i) Fire refining.
   (ii) Electrolytic refining.
3. (*a*) For what reasons are (i) commercially pure metals and (ii) alloys used in engineering?
   (*b*) The melting point of aluminium is 660°C., and the melting point of silicon is 1414°C. The aluminium silicon eutectic contains 11·6% silicon and it melts at 577°C. The solid solubility of silicon in aluminium rises from 0 to 1·6% when the temperature is increased from room temperature to 577°C.; the solid solubility of aluminium in silicon rises from 1 to 4% when the temperature is increased from room temperature to 577°C. From this information sketch the aluminium-silicon thermal-equilibrium diagram (assume it to be composed of straight lines). Using your diagram, suggest a suitable casting aluminium-silicon alloy and describe the structural changes that take place when it cools from the liquid state to room temperature.
4. Discuss the main difference between (i) sand casting, (ii) die casting, and (iii) investment casting.
5. Distinguish between a cast product and a wrought product; discuss the factors that must be taken into account when selecting the method by which the raw material for a particular component is to be produced.
6. (*a*) Explain the meaning of the term 'grain flow'.
   (*b*) Describe the forging processes (i) upsetting and (ii) drawing down.
7. Produce simple diagrams to illustrate the difference between (i) direct extrusion and (ii) indirect extrusion.
8. (*a*) Compare the characteristics of (i) a cold worked metal and (ii) a hot worked metal.
   (*b*) Explain the meaning of the terms (i) recrystallisation and (ii) grain growth.
9. Discuss the methods whereby the mechanical properties of a metal can be altered.
10. (*a*) Define (i) a mechanical property and (ii) a physical property.

(*b*) Explain why it is necessary to standardise test piece dimensions.

11. (*a*) Define 'proof stress' and state the circumstances in which it is used.
(*b*) The following results were obtained as the results of a tensile test upon an aluminium alloy:

Force in kN	10	12	14	16	18	20	22	24
Extension in mm	0	0·018	0·034	0·053	0·068	0·083	0·098	0·114
Force in kN	26	28	30	32	34	36	38	40
Extension in mm	0·131	0·143	0·165	0·180	0·202	0·225	0·255	0·360

Diameter of test piece before test, 11·3 mm; diameter of test piece at waist after test, 9 mm. Gauge length, 56·5 mm; length after test, 73 mm. Determine (i) The 0·2% proof stress for the material, (ii) its percentage elongation, (iii) its percentage reduction in area, and (iv) its Modulus of Elasticity.

12. Two materials specifications are handed to you and include the following information:

	A	*B*
Yield point (N/mm^2)	240	530
Tensile strength (N/mm^2)	500	920
Elongation % on $5{\cdot}65\sqrt{S_0}$	21	10

Sketch the force-extension diagram for these two materials, assuming that they have the same Modulus of Elasticity.

13. You are given a piece of brass sheet 50 mm long, 12 mm wide, and 1 mm thick. Suggest a method of testing its ductility.

14. Three samples of steel have the properties listed below:

Sample	*Tens. str.* N/mm^2	*El.% on* $5{\cdot}65\sqrt{S_0}$	*Izod Number*	*HB*
A	370	24	30	105
B	1250	7	10	650
C	780	30	42	280

What are their relative merits with respect to shock resistance, resistance to abrasion, ductility, and strength?

15. Outline the various tests which indicate the ductility of a material, and state the circumstances in which each would be used.

16. Sketch typical load-extension curves as obtained from a tensile test on (i) a low carbon steel specimen, and (ii) an aluminium alloy specimen. Compare and indicate the important parts of the curves, and relate them to the behaviour of the metal under test.

17. What information would you expect to find in a British Standard Specification for steel sheet?

18. Briefly outline the actual property tested by most commercial hardness testing machines, and explain why this particular property is tested.

19. Draw a diagram to illustrate the essentials of a creep-testing machine. Sketch a typical curve indicating the behaviour of steel under such a test and explain why the extrapolation of short-time creep test results to assess the life of a material is considered to be dangerous.

20. Briefly describe one method of fatigue testing. Sketch a curve to indicate

the results of a series of fatigue tests on a material; indicate 'fatigue limit' on your curve.

21. (*a*) What is implied by (i) creep and (ii) fatigue?
(*b*) Under what conditions of service are the above important?

22. Suggest a method of examining a small forging to assess the suitability of its grain flow.

23. Trace and describe the various processes involved in the production of low carbon steel sheet. Start with the origin as iron ore, and end with the steel in sheet form. Indicate the principles involved at each stage of the production.

24. Some steels are produced by refining in an electric furnace; what type of steel would be produced in this way, and why is an electric furnace employed?

25. Iron ore can be classified as (i) high phosphorus and (ii) low phosphorus. What is the connection between this classification and the refining used to produce steel from pig iron?

26. Explain why steelmaking using a converter was unpopular in Britain for many years, and why its popularity has increased during recent years.

27. Produce curves to indicate the effect of carbon upon the mechanical properties of steel. Name the impurities that are usually associated with steel and indicate the effect of each upon the mechanical properties.

28. Explain why a steel forging is normalised. Describe the procedure when normalising a 0·4% C steel forging, and state the temperature to which it is heated and the structural changes that take place during the operation.

29. Four small identical specimens of 0·6% C plain carbon steel are given the following heat treatments after heating together to just above the upper critical point for the metal:

Specimen A is quenched in water.
Specimen B is quenched in water, reheated to 250°C. and cooled in air.
Specimen C is quenched in water, reheated to 500°C. and cooled in air.
Specimen D is cooled very slowly from the upper critical temperature.

(i) Sketch the final microstructure of each specimen and indicate the microconstituents.
(ii) Compare the mechanical properties of the four specimens after the heat treatment.
(iii) Suggest typical applications of each of the treatments.

30. What is implied by 'critical cooling rate' of a steel?

31. Make sketches to indicate the microstructure of the following plain carbon steels before heat treatment: 0·2% C, 0·4% C, 0·9% C, and 1·2% C.

32. Distinguish between (i) full annealing, (ii) sub-critical annealing and (iii) normalising as applied to the heat treatment of plain carbon steels, with respect to the object of each and the procedure in each case.

33. A steel gear wheel is to withstand high stresses and is to operate at reasonably low temperatures. Specify the carbon content of the steel from which to manufacture this gear, and outline the heat-treatment procedure. Indicate, with the aid of suitable diagrams, the effect of the treatment upon the microstructure of the steel.

34. Describe the nitriding process; indicate the advantages and also the limitations of this process.

35. (*a*) State four problems associated with the use of plain carbon steels, and indicate how these are overcome by the alloying elements used in alloy steels.
(*b*) The following are alloy steels; state a typical use to which each would be put, and also indicate the effect of the elements introduced into each:
    (i) 18% Cr, 8·5% Ni, 0·1% C, 0·8% Mn.
    (ii) 12% Mn, 1·2% C.
    (iii) 0·12% C, 3·0% Ni, 0·45% Mn.
    (iv) 22% W, 5·0% Cr, 0·8% C.
36. What is meant by 'mass effect' with respect to the heat treatment of steels?
37. (*a*) What are the special requirements of a heat-resisting steel?
(*b*) Heat-resisting steels are classified into three main groups; what is the significance of this classification?
38. Nickel is sometimes included in a casehardening steel. What is the object of the addition of nickel, and how will it affect the heat treatment procedure?
39. (*a*) Nickel and chromium are two common alloying elements used in steels. List the effects, both good and bad, of using them singly, and then state the effects of combining them.
(*b*) The addition of a high percentage of nickel to steel produces an austenitic structure at room temperature. What other alloying element has this effect, and what is the characteristic of the alloy steel so produced?
40. (*a*) Produce flow diagrams to illustrate the processes involved in the production of (i) wrought iron and (ii) cast iron; outline the object of each stage in the manufacture of each of these metals.
(*b*) Sketch the microstructure of (i) wrought iron and (ii) cast iron, and relate these to the manufacturing method and the characteristics of each.
41. Make a list of the advantages and also the disadvantages of cast iron as an engineering material. Explain how the effect of some of these disadvantages can be removed.
42. (*a*) Explain the purpose of the malleabilising heat treatment applied to cast iron castings.
(*b*) What are differences between the Blackheart and the Whiteheart Malleabilising processes? Illustrate your comparison between the products of these processes by producing sketches of the following microstructures: (i) Blackheart cast iron, (ii) surface layers of Whiteheart cast iron, (iii) core of Whiteheart cast iron.
43. (*a*) State the forms in which carbon may be found in cast iron, and discuss briefly the influence of carbon upon the properties of cast iron.
(*b*) Explain the effects of other constituents in the metal, and of the casting cooling rates, in determining the forms in which the carbon may appear in the structure. Illustrate your explanation with the iron-carbon-equilibrium diagram and with sketches of typical microstructures.
44. Write an essay on 'High Duty Cast Irons'; discuss the methods of producing these cast irons and comment upon their characteristics.
45. (*a*) What are the general characteristics of copper alloys?
(*b*) Why is it necessary to have a range of brasses?
(*c*) A small brass bearing housing in a pump was found to be cracked

shortly after the pump was installed. Suggest a possible cause of the cracking.

46. Write an essay on 'New Metals in Engineering' in which you outline the circumstances that demand these metals, and discuss the properties associated with them, and the problems associated with their manipulation.
47. 'The fabrication characteristics of an alloy are often affected considerably by the proportions of the constituents.' Support this statement by taking brass as an example, and explaining the connection between the composition of some typical brasses and their fabrication characteristics.
48. (*a*) Aluminium alloys are classified as (i) wrought alloys and (ii) cast alloys; each group is subdivided into 'heat-treatable' and 'not heat-treatable' alloys. Explain the implications of this classification.
49. Sketch the relevant part of the aluminium-copper equilibrium diagram to explain the effect of (i) solution treatment and (ii) precipitation treatment. What other alloying additions will produce a heat-treatable aluminium alloy?
50. Write an essay on 'Magnesium and its Alloys'. In your essay, outline the extraction method used to obtain magnesium from its ore, the characteristics of magnesium, and the reasons for the use of magnesium alloys, and review the principle types of magnesium alloys.
51. Specify suitable non-ferrous alloys for the following applications and give the reasons for your choice:
    - (i) Domestic water tap body.
    - (ii) Domestic draught excluder material.
    - (iii) Sheet metal for laundry machinery.
    - (iv) Valve seating for motor-cycle engine.
    - (v) Non-sparking tool.
    - (vi) Springy electric contact.
    - (vii) Domestic food-mixer body.
52. Discuss the problems associated with the use of materials at high temperatures, and explain how these problems are met by non-ferrous alloys.
53. List some non-metallic materials that are used in engineering, and give typical applications of those you list.
54. (*a*) Explain the implications of the terms (i) thermoplastic and (ii) thermosetting plastics materials.
    (*b*) Give some typical examples of the use of plastics materials in engineering and indicate the advantages that these have over metals.
    (*c*) Review the manipulation methods used upon plastics materials, and indicate how the component must be designed to suit the manipulation method.
55. (*a*) What are the requirements of a cutting tool material?
    (*b*) List the cutting tool materials now available to the engineer, and indicate their behaviour at high temperatures, and hence the cutting speeds at which they can be employed.
    (*c*) Indicate which of the above materials are heat treated and which demand special consideration regarding holding, etc.
56. Review the joining methods used in engineering, and indicate the circumstances in which each would be used.
57. Explain why metals are given surface treatment, and review the more common surface treatment methods in current use.

APPENDIX I

A Selection of British Standard Specifications

Materials

Aluminium alloys	Wrought	BS 1470–1475
	Cast	BS 1490
Brass	Muntz metal (hot rolled)	BS 1541
	(rods and sections)	BS 1949
	(die cast)	BS 1400–B4–C
	Cartridge brass	BS 267, 378, 885
	Basis brass	BS 265
	Naval brass	BS 251 and 252
	(die cast)	BS 1400–B5–C
Bronze	Admiralty gunmetal	BS 1400–G1–C
	Leaded gunmetal	BS 1400–LG2–C
	Phosphor bronze	BS 1400–PB3–C
Cast irons	Grey iron castings	BS 1452
	Whiteheart malleable iron castings	BS 309
	Blackheart malleable iron castings	BS 310
	Pearlitic malleable iron castings	BS 3333
	Spheroidal or nodular graphite	BS 2789
	Austenitic cast iron	BS 3468
Magnesium alloys	Wrought	BS 3370, 3372, 3373
	Cast	BS 2970
Nickel silvers	Wrought	BS 1824
Steel	Wrought	BS 970
	Cast	BS 3100
Zinc and zinc alloys	For die casting	BS 1004

Testing

Handbook—Mechanical tests for metals	BS Handbook No. 13
Tensile testing of metals	BS 18
Brinell hardness testing	BS 240
Diamond pyramid hardness numbers	BS 427
Direct reading hardness testing—Rockwell Principle	BS 891
Impact test—test pieces	BS 131
Ductility tests—simple bend	BS 1639
Creep tests	BS 3500
Fatigue tests	BS 3518

APPENDIX II

PROPERTIES OF SOME METALS

(These are approximate because many properties depend upon past treatment)

Metal	*Melting Point °C.*	*Specific Gravity*	*Specific Heat (0–100°C.) J/kg°C.*	*Coefficient of Linear Expansion*	*Relative Thermal Conductivity at 20°C.* *	*Relative Electrical Conductivity* *	*Young's Modulus 'E'*† *N/mm²*	*Tensile Strength N/mm²*	*Modulus of Rigidity N/mm²*	*Poisson's Ratio*
Aluminium	660	2·7	980	24×10^{-6}	61	64	70×10^3	60	26×10^3	0·35
Copper	1083	8·9	390	$16{\cdot}6 \times 10^{-6}$	100	100	125×10^3	160	48×10^3	0·34
Iron (pure)	1535	7·9	450	$11{\cdot}9 \times 10^{-6}$	15	17	206×10^3	270	82×10^3	0·29
Lead	327	11·4	130	$29{\cdot}1 \times 10^{-6}$	9	8	16×10^3	15	5×10^3	0·44
Magnesium	651	1·74	1030	$26{\cdot}1 \times 10^{-6}$	39	39	45×10^3	100	17×10^3	0·30
Nickel	1458	8·9	450	$12{\cdot}8 \times 10^{-6}$	17	25	200×10^3	370	78×10^3	0·28
Tin	232	7·3	220	$21{\cdot}4 \times 10^{-6}$	16	15	40×10^3	13	19×10^3	0·33
Titanium	1660	4·5	450	9×10^{-6}	4	3	114×10^3	460	43×10^3	0·32
Tungsten (wire)	3410	19·3	140	$4{\cdot}5 \times 10^{-6}$	39	34	400×10^3	4500	140×10^3	0·34
Zinc	419	7·1	380	33×10^{-6}	27	29	90×10^3	155	35×10^3	0·25

* Copper (100) is high.
† See Section 6.24.

INDEX